Physics & Everyday Thinking

Fred Goldberg

Steve Robinson

Valerie Otero

IT's ABOUT TIME ®

HERFF JONES EDUCATION DIVISION

Armonk, NY 10504
www.its-about-time.com

IT's ABOUT TIME®

HERFF JONES EDUCATION DIVISION

84 Business Park Drive
Armonk, NY 10504
Phone (914) 273-2233
Fax (914) 273-2227
www.ITS-ABOUT-TIME.com

President
Tom Laster

Director of Product Development
Barbara Zahm, Ph.D.

Creative Director
John Nordland

Creative Artwork
Dennis Falcon

Editorial Coordinators
Todd Fishlin
Lauren Harmonay
Anthony F. Battle

Additional Technical Art
Michael Hortens

Production
Howard P. Johnson,
Howard Communigrafix, Inc.

Production/Studio Manager
Robert Schwalb

The PET project is supported, in part, by Grant #0096856 from the National Science Foundation.
Additional support provided by San Diego State University,
Tennessee Technological University and the University of Colorado at Boulder.

PET Acknowledgements

PROJECT DIRECTORS

Fred Goldberg – San Diego State University
Steve Robinson – Tennessee Technological University
Valerie Otero – University of Colorado at Boulder

OTHER DEVELOPERS

Danielle Harlow
Michael McKean
Ben Williams

GRAPHICS AND ILLUSTRATIONS

Carlos Lopez

VIDEO

Scott Cahill
Derya Cobanoglu
Cynthia D'Angelo
Mary Kidd
Michael Noon
Luc Robinson
Marc Robinson
Derick Stevens

ELEMENTARY TEACHERS

Anna Harber
Helen Douglas
Gail Becker
Stephanie Wendt
Linda Fox
Alicia Schumaker

FACULTY COLLABORATORS

Timothy Ewers
David Henry
Andy Johnson
Jim Stewart
Michael Svec

EDITOR

Judith Leggett

To the Student

Welcome to *Physics and Everyday Thinking (PET)*. The PET approach may be very different from other science courses you've done. Here's a short discussion of some of these different features and how you, as a PET student, can take full advantage of them.

Why is this course different?

Physics is not a collection of static facts and equations to be absorbed and remembered. Rather, it's a set of changing ideas about how the world works, together with the dynamic process by which such ideas are developed. This process involves a lot of creative thinking, along with experimentation, observation and logical reasoning. Research shows overwhelmingly that the most effective way for people to *learn* physics is by *doing* physics.

In the PET course you will be part of a microcosm of the scientific community. You'll make predictions based on *your own* ideas, perform experiments and record your observations, and draw *your own* conclusions based on the evidence you gather. Some activities will focus on the process by which you are learning and about the way in which science knowledge is developed.

You'll find that this book doesn't look like a familiar, traditional science textbook. Instead it's a workbook where you record *your own* ideas and observations. You'll work in collaboration with your classmates, discussing your thoughts and ideas at each stage, initially in small groups and finally trying to come to consensus as a whole class. ***Don't expect your instructor to give you the 'right' answers!*** Instead, your instructor and the course materials will serve as a guide to help you formulate your own responses to questions. From time to time, you'll compare your ideas with those developed by scientists; it's likely that they'll be quite similar.

PET is activity-based and discussion-oriented, with three major goals:

(1) To help you develop a deep understanding of physics ideas that can be used to explain everyday phenomena

(2) To help you become more aware of how your own ideas about physics change and develop over time, and how the structure of the classroom and curriculum facilitate these changes.

(3) To help you practice and develop an understanding of how knowledge is developed within a scientific community and the nature of that knowledge itself.

The aim of the PET format is for you to take charge of your own learning, so there's very little formal lecturing in the PET course. During class you'll spend most of your time performing experiments, working with computers, and discussing ideas. You'll also continue your learning outside class, often using the Web.

What is expected of you?

Attend and Participate: In the PET course, you're primarily responsible for your own learning, and you contribute to the learning of your classmates, so it's important that you come to class and participate actively.

Respect Classroom Norms: The learning process works best if everyone has the same expectations. The PET course is probably different from most other classes you've taken, so it's worth emphasizing some of the behaviors expected of you:

- Always consider if your ideas are truly consistent with the evidence you've gathered. Always offer evidence to support your ideas.

- Listen carefully as other students explain their thinking.

- Pay respectful attention to other students as they explain their ideas, and ask questions as appropriate. It's often a good idea to note others' ideas in your workbook, next to your own.

- An idea is 'good' if it makes sense and is consistent with all the available evidence. A PET class is intended to function as a scientific community, so it is the responsibility of the class itself to develop good ideas.

A Note to Prospective and Practicing Teachers

The physics topics covered in the PET course are closely aligned with those for elementary grades in the Benchmarks for Science Literacy (AAAS, 1993), National Science Education Standards (NRC, 1996), and the science education standards for most states.

The benchmarks and standards mentioned above call for science instruction at **all** levels to be inquiry based. Research clearly shows that this is the most effective way to learn science concepts. Having experienced the approach in a PET class you'll be better prepared to implement it in your own classroom. Also, the activities that focus on the thinking of young children should give you insights you can use in your own classes.

The PET project has developed many activities for use in elementary classes, and compiled them into a booklet, *Elementary Science and Everyday Thinking* (ESET). For copies, please contact the publishers.

A Note to General Education Students

You may feel at first that the videos of children discussing physics concepts and the activities associated with the videos are not relevant to you. However, as you pay attention to the videos, you will probably find that they clarify your own ideas, and help you develop your metacognitive skills (your ability to reflect and think about the process of thinking).

Table of Contents

†These activities and homework exercises focus on Learning about Learning issues (nature of science, elementary students' ideas, or PET students' learning), and may include readings, video transcripts, and students' drawings.

Interactions and Energy

Activity 1–Measuring Speed
Developing Ideas

Purpose

In the first few chapters of the *PET* course you will think about how the motion of an object is related to how it interacts with the rest of the world. To gather evidence and test your ideas, you will need a reliable method to determine a particularly important aspect of the motion of an object – its speed. For example, it may be important to know if the object is moving at a constant speed or if its speed is changing. If the speed is changing it may also be important to know how quickly it is changing.

In many activities your group will use a Motion Sensor, a device connected to a computer, to gather evidence. In this first activity you will find out

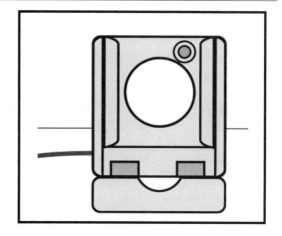

how to use the Motion Sensor, and the computer program that runs it. You will also begin to consider how the Motion Sensor informs you about what is happening to the speed of an object during short periods of time.

 How can you represent motion involving speeding up, slowing down and constant speed?

Initial Ideas

Imagine taking a short trip in your car. When you first start out, you push on the gas pedal; the car starts moving and then picks up speed as you pull away. Once you reach a reasonable speed you set your cruise control. Your speed remains constant for a while. As you approach your destination, you use the brakes to slow the car down and make it stop.

How could you represent the motion of your car in a way that shows how it is different in these three situations (speeding up, constant speed, and slowing down)? Think about the question on the next page by yourself.

You will have a chance to share your ideas with your group, and the whole class, a little later.

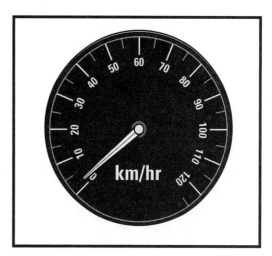

On your own, try to think of two different ways to represent the motion of the car. Show how its speed is behaving during the three segments of the short trip described on the previous page. (You might want to use pictures, math symbols, charts, diagrams, graphs, equations, arrows etc.). Sketch your representations below.

Now share your ideas with your group members. Listen to everyone's ideas and try to agree on the two representations that are most informative about what is happening to the speed of the car during each part of the trip. Illustrate these representations on a large presentation board.

 Your instructor will now lead a short, whole-class discussion about each group's ideas. Be prepared to explain your group's representations and make a note of any useful ideas that are different from those of your group.

Collecting and Interpreting Evidence

 EXPERIMENT #1: Can you create speed-time graphs representing speeding up, slowing down, and constant speed?

YOU WILL NEED:

- Copy of *How to Use the Motion Sensor* (located in Appendix)
- Access to a Motion Sensor connected to a computer
- Color pencils
- Large board
- Meter ruler

STEP 1: Examine the Motion Sensor. There are several different models of sensors and yours may look different from the one shown here. However, for all sensor models the part that does the measuring is inside a circular opening, covered by a grille. (Note that most sensor models allow you to adjust the 'tilt' of the sensor mechanism in some way.)

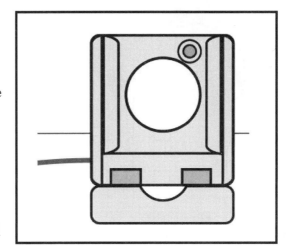

The sensor works by emitting short pulses of high-frequency sound (beyond the range of human hearing) that reflect back to the sensor from any object in front of it (within a limited range). The sensor then sends information about these pulses to the computer, which uses it to determine the speed of the object.

There may also be a switch on the sensor that can be used to select either short or long range, depending on how far away the object of interest is likely to move. For now you should set the switch on the 'long' range setting. (On some sensor models, a small picture of a person may indicate this setting. If you cannot identify the right setting, ask your instructor for help.)

STEP 2: On your computer, open the data collection file for this experiment. (Your instructor will tell you how to open files and operate the data collection program on the computers in your classroom.) When the file opens you will see a blank speed-time graph.

As shown on the graph on the next page, the program is set to measure speeds between 0 and 120 centimeters per second (cm/s) for a period of three seconds.

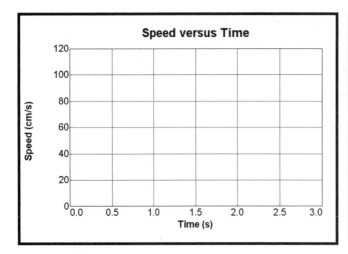

Instructions for how to operate the most common computer programs used with motion sensors are given in the Appendices of this book. You should tear those pages out now and have them handy until you get used to how to operate the particular program you are using.

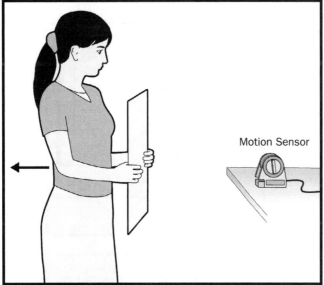

Motion Sensor

Since the motion sensor works by reflecting high-frequency sound from the object in front of it, it is best if that object has a hard, flat, surface facing the sensor. Therefore, when performing the following experiments, it is a good idea for the moving person to hold a large board up in front of them as they move.

Place the motion sensor on the edge of the table and make sure there are a few yards of clear path across the floor in the direction the sensor is aimed.

Your group's task will be to produce speed-time graphs by having your group members stand in front of the sensor and then move away from it in different ways.

One of your group members should now stand (with a board, as shown) about 1 meter from the sensor, and slowly move towards and away from it while you collect data. (Refer to the instructions again.) Watch the graph being drawn on the computer as your group member moves to and fro. The data collection will stop on its own after three seconds.

Repeat this procedure so that each member of your group has a chance to move in front of the sensor and a chance to operate the computer program you are using to collect data.

> If you have large bumps or 'spikes' in your speed-time graph, this is usually an indication that something is interfering with the sensor. If this happens often you should ask your instructor for some tips as to how to produce smoother data.

STEP 3: Repeat the experiment, only this time your group member should not move, but stand still about 1 meter from the sensor while the computer records the data.

 How does the speed-time graph look when person is not moving?

 Does this make sense to you? Briefly explain why the speed-time graph looks as it does.

STEP 4: Your task is now to generate three speed-time graphs showing three different types of motion. (Speeding up, constant speed, and slowing down.)

First, have one of your group members start about 50 cm from the sensor and practice moving away from the sensor, gradually speeding up as they do so. Use the motion sensor to check whether their speed is really increasing the whole time.

> It takes about a second for the computer to start recording data after you click on the relevant button (or hit the 'Enter' key). To make sure you see the start of the person's motion on the graph it is a good idea for them to watch the computer screen and only start moving when they see the start of the graph appear on the screen.
>
> If your group member's speed increases beyond the maximum shown by the graph you may need to increase the maximum value for the display on the speed axis. See the instructions for your particular program to find out how to do this.

 When you are satisfied that you have good data, use a colored pencil to sketch the speed-time graph below and label it "Speeding up."

MEASURED SPEED-TIME GRAPH

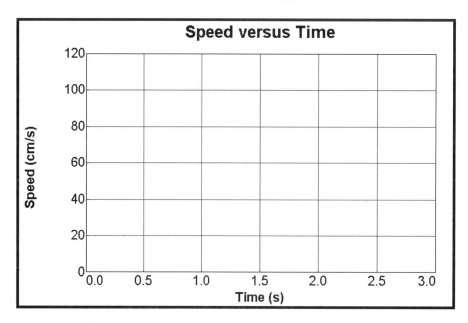

Now have a different group member try to move away from the motion sensor at a constant speed. As before, use the motion sensor to check whether their speed remains approximately constant or not.

 When you are satisfied that you have good data that represents motion at a constant speed, use a different color to sketch the speed-time graph on the same set of axes above and label it "Constant speed."

Finally, have yet another group member start moving away from the motion sensor quickly, but gradually slow down and stop.

 Again, when you are satisfied that you have good data, use a third color to sketch the speed-time graph on the same set of axes and label it "Slowing down."

STEP 5: Your next task is to have a group member move in such a way as to imitate the motion of the car in the journey first described in the Initial Ideas section of this activity. Produce a speed-time graph that has the same general shape as the car's motion would produce.

 Suppose one of your group were to start at rest, start to move away from the sensor and speed up as they do so, then move at constant speed for a while, and finally slow down and stop. Below, sketch what you think the speed-time graph for this complete journey would look like. (Note: No values or units are shown on the speed and time axes, as only the general shape of the graph is important.)

 MAKING PREDICTIONS

At many points in this course you will be asked to make a <u>prediction</u>; that is to think about, and write down, what you think will happen before you perform an experiment. (Such questions will usually ask you to "Imagine..." or "Suppose...") Note that a prediction in science is <u>not</u> just a guess, but is supported by reasons drawn either from your prior experience or from your general ideas about how the world works. (Scientists call such a set of general ideas a "model.") When you are asked to make a prediction it is <u>very</u> important that you take the time to explain the reasoning behind your response <u>before</u> you perform the experiment. Whenever you are being asked to make a prediction in this class you will see this icon,, in front of the question.

PREDICTED SPEED-TIME GRAPH

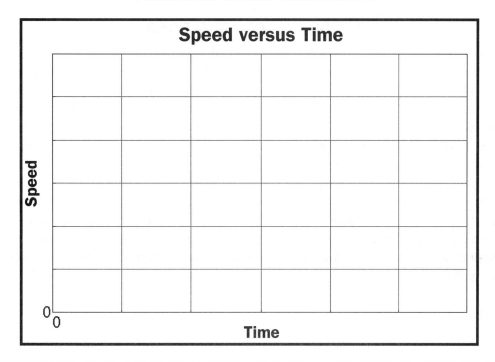

Briefly explain why you drew your predicted graph as you did.

Now have one of your group start about 50 cm from the motion sensor and try to match the shape of your predicted graph as closely as possible as they move away from the sensor.

> **You may need to extend the measuring time to be able to include all three aspects of the motion. See the instructions for your particular program to find out how to do this.**

 RECORDING OBSERVATIONS

During this course you will be performing lots of experiments and using computer simulations. You will usually be asked to record what you <u>observe</u>. For example, you may be asked to write down what you see happening, or sketch a graph that you have recorded. It is important that you read carefully what it is you are supposed to record, as sometimes it may be only a small part of everything that actually happens. It is also important to be as precise as possible, such as not just recording that an object is moving, but also whether its speed is increasing, decreasing or staying approximately constant. Also, although it is difficult sometimes, try not to be influenced by what you think will happen and just record what you actually see. Also, be sure to discuss your observations with your group before you record them, as people sometimes see things differently. Whenever you are being asked to record your observations in this class you will see this icon, , in front of the instruction or question.

Sketch the speed-time graph for the motion of your group member below.

MEASURED SPEED-TIME GRAPH

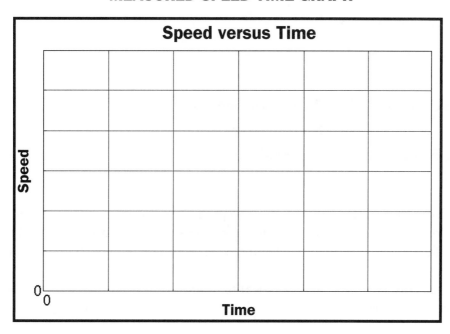

Speed versus Time

Speed

0

0 **Time**

 MAKING INFERENCES

After you have performed an experiment, you will often be asked to make some <u>inferences</u>; that is, try to make sense of what is happening, based on your ideas and the evidence provided by your observations. These inferences could be as simple as interpreting a speed-time graph to determine what the motion of an object was like in a small part of one experiment, or you could be asked to make a general statement about the way the world works, based on evidence from several activities. You should be certain that any inferences you make are indeed supported by evidence, and you will often be asked to definitively explain how this is so. Whenever you are being asked to make an inference you will see this icon,, in front of the question.

 Is your measured speed-time graph **exactly** the same as your predicted graph? If not, describe any differences and explain briefly what you think caused them.

EXPERIMENT #2: How can you make a low-friction cart on a track speed up, slow down, and move at a constant speed?

YOU WILL NEED:

- Low-friction cart
- Track
- Wood blocks of various thickness (or similar)
- Copy of *How to Use the Motion Sensor*
- Access to a Motion Sensor connected to a computer
- Color pencils

STEP 1: Your task in this experiment is to produce speed-time graphs for the low-friction cart as it moves along the track. You should produce three separate graphs that show it speeding up, slowing down, and moving at a constant speed.

You can use any means at your disposal to produce these graphs. However, before you start any experiments, discuss with your group what strategies you will use to try and produce these graphs.

Describe how you will try to produce the speed-time graphs of the cart.

Speeding up:

Slowing down:

Constant speed:

STEP 2: You can now check your ideas using the Motion Sensor. Slot the sensor on to the end of the track and set it to short range. (On some sensor models this setting may be indicated by a small picture of a cart, like the one you will be using.)

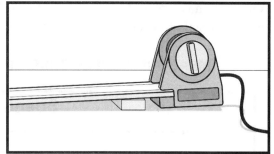

On the computer, open the data collection file for this experiment. Now use the Motion Sensor to record speed-time graphs while you test your strategies.

> **The Motion Sensor will not make accurate measurements if the cart is too close. When you are performing any experiments with a cart, start with the rear of the cart at least 20 cm away from the sensor and have it move *away* from the sensor.**

The sensor will detect the nearest object that lies within its beam of high-frequency sound. If your graphs have large spikes, bumps, or sharp dips in them it is likely that some other object is interfering. You might try some of the following to reduce these effects.

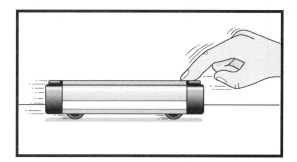

> **If you are using your hand to push the cart, it is possible that the sensor is picking up the motion of your hand instead of that of the cart. Try pulling on the front lip of the cart instead of pushing it from the rear.**
>
> **If the graph starts out looking as you expect, but then suddenly changes as the cart gets further away, it is possible that the sensor is detecting some other object once the cart passes it. Try removing objects that are close to the track, such as books, bags, etc.**

When you have good data for each of the three types of motion, use different colored pencils to sketch the graphs below and label them appropriately.

MEASURED SPEED-TIME GRAPHS FOR CART ON TRACK

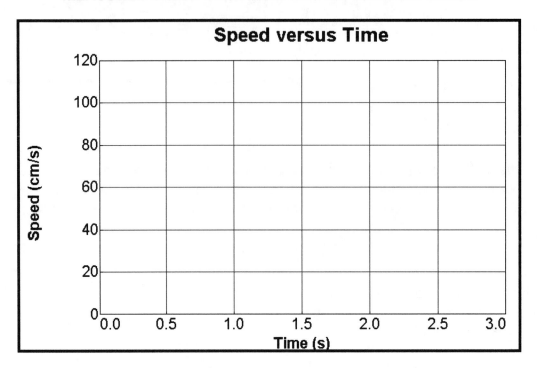

 Did the strategies your group decided on at the beginning of this experiment produce the types of speed-time graphs you thought they would? If not, describe what strategies you **did** use to produce these graphs.

Summarizing Questions

 Discuss these questions with your group and note your ideas. Leave space to add any different ideas that may emerge when the whole class discusses their thinking.

S1: With which method you used in this activity was it easier to produce smooth graphs, having people move in front of the sensor, or using the cart moving along the track? Why do you think this is?

S2: In the Initial Ideas section at the beginning of this activity you considered a short car journey. Suppose the car had failed to start and had not moved at all. Below, sketch what you think the speed-time graph would look like in this case, and explain why you drew the graph as you did.

S3: Shown below is a speed-time graph for a car during part of journey.

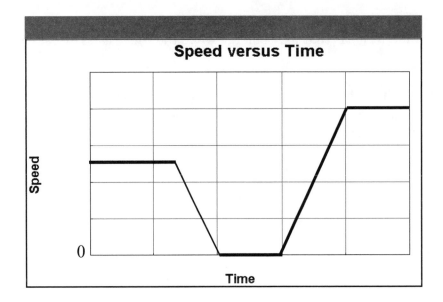

Describe the motion of the car and write a short 'story-line' about a journey that could produce a speed-time graph like this.

Activity 1 Homework—Ideas about Learning Science
Learning about Learning

Name:_____ Date:_____ Group: _____

This activity has two parts. In Part 1, you will write your ideas about how you learn science. In Part 2, you will write your ideas about how scientists create scientific knowledge. We will revisit this assignment later in the semester.

Your instructor will hand back each part of this assignment separately, so please put your name on both parts. Part 2 will be returned during Chapter 4 and Part 1 will be returned during Chapter 6.

PART 1: **Your Ideas about Learning Science**

Fill out the table below by circling whether you agree or disagree with the statement on the left. In the column on the right, explain why you agree or disagree.

Learning Science	Agree/ Disagree	Explain your reasoning
Before I learn a science topic, I usually try to think about what I already know about the topic.	Agree Disagree	
My own science ideas are useful in learning science, even if they turn out to be different from scientists' ideas.	Agree Disagree	
If my own science ideas turn out to be quite different from the science ideas I am supposed to learn, I find it hard to abandon my own ideas.	Agree Disagree	
When I am trying to learn a science concept, I usually either fully understand it or I don't get it at all.	Agree Disagree	

Learning Science	Agree/ Disagree	Explain your reasoning
When trying to learn a science topic, confusion can actually be quite useful.	Agree Disagree	
In order for me to learn science topics, I need to spend a reasonable amount of time describing my current thinking out loud to other students.	Agree Disagree	
In order for me to learn science topics, I need to spend a reasonable amount of time listening to the thinking of other students.	Agree Disagree	
I am a science person.	Agree Disagree	

Name:_____ Date:_____ Group: _____

PART 2: **Your Ideas about Science Knowledge**

Fill out the table below by circling whether you agree or disagree with the statement on the left. In the column on the right, explain why you agree or disagree.

Science Knowledge	Agree/ Disagree	Explain your reasoning
As long as experiments are done correctly, they will be able to prove a theory to be correct.	Agree Disagree	
Developing new science knowledge involves following careful procedures, rather than being creative.	Agree Disagree	
A hypothesis is an educated guess.	Agree Disagree	
Once accepted by the scientific community, scientific ideas are considered fact.	Agree Disagree	
Scientists are particularly objective. They are not influenced by their personal experiences or beliefs when they do science.	Agree Disagree	

Science Knowledge	Agree/ Disagree	Explain your reasoning
If a new idea is supported by scientific evidence, other scientists usually accept it with little resistance.	Agree Disagree	
Science ideas are usually generated by a scientist working alone, with little collaboration with other people.	Agree Disagree	

Purpose

We use the idea of energy in many ways in everyday life. For example, there is sometimes talk of an 'energy crisis' when fuel supplies run low, people eat 'energy bars' to keep them going, and we say small children have 'lots of energy' when they run around. So it is probably no surprise to you that scientists associate a form of energy with the motion of an object – they call it **kinetic energy**. The faster an object is moving, the more kinetic energy it possesses. (Of course, an object at rest possesses no kinetic energy.) Thus, as the speed of an object changes, the amount of kinetic energy it has also changes.

In many sports, such as soccer, the speed of the ball (and, hence, its kinetic energy) changes often. Do you think something has to happen to cause a change in kinetic energy of the ball, or can it just happen on its own?

 What is needed (if anything) to change the kinetic energy of an object?

Initial Ideas

Think about watching an ice hockey game. Under what circumstances does the kinetic energy of the puck change during the game? Do these changes just happen on their own, or is an outside influence responsible in every case?

Discuss your ideas with your group and then, in the space below, describe some of the changes you might see in the puck's motion. What, if anything, do you think causes each change?

 Participate in a brief class discussion to share your ideas. Make a note of any ideas that are different from those of your group.

Collecting and Interpreting Evidence

 EXPERIMENT #1: How do pushes and pulls affect speed?

YOU WILL NEED:

- Low-friction cart
- Track
- Meter stick
- Colored pencils
- Copy of *How to Use the Motion Sensor*
- Access to a Motion Sensor connected to a computer

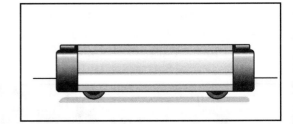

STEP 1: Place your cart at rest on the track. Now one of your group should give it a quick hand push. Let the cart move over a distance of about 1 meter and then another member of your group should grab the cart to stop it. (Do not use the Motion Sensor yet.)

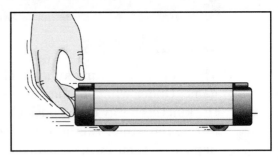

 What happens to the cart when your group member pushes it?

What happens to the cart when the second person grabs it?

STEP 2: Return the cart to the starting point and now start it moving with a quick pull on the lip at the front of the cart.

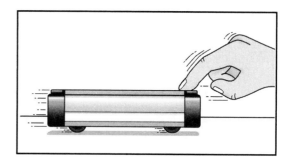

 Does the cart behave in approximately the same way when it is pulled as when it was pushed? Does it behave very differently?

 Does this behavior suggest that pushes and pulls have the same effect on the cart, or very different effects?

> **When using the Motion Sensor, a pull is often a better choice than a push, since your hand will not interfere with the sensor.**

STEP 3: Return the cart to the starting point and start it moving with a **gentle** push (or pull). This time, when the cart reaches about halfway along the track, give it another quick push (or pull), in the **same direction** as its motion. Stop the cart when it reaches the end of the track.

 What effect does the second push have on the motion of the cart?

STEP 4: Again, return the cart to the starting point and start it moving with a quick push (or pull). As the cart passes the halfway point along the track, tap it in the direction opposite its motion **very gently** with your finger.

> **This may take some practice – the tap should not be strong enough to reverse the direction of the cart, not to stop the cart completely!**

 What does this gentle tap do to the motion of the cart?

STEP 5: Finally, return the cart to the starting point and again start it moving with a quick push (or pull). As the cart passes the halfway point along the track, tap it in the direction opposite its motion with your finger so that it returns to the starting point at about the same speed as it was moving before your tap.

 What effect does this harder tap have on the motion of the cart?

STEP 6: In all the situations you looked at above, it is evident that the speed, or direction, of the cart changed when someone's hand did something to it. Do you think such changes happen instantaneously, or is there a gradual change (over a short period of time) from one value to another?

Consider this conversation between two students, who were discussing their ideas of how the speed of the cart changed when it was given a quick tap in the direction it was already moving, and its speed increased from 20 cm/s to 40 cm/s.

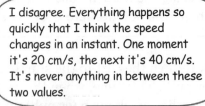

I think the speed changes gradually over a short period of time. At different points in time during this period the speed of the cart passes through all the values between 20 cm/s and 40 cm/s.

I disagree. Everything happens so quickly that I think the speed changes in an instant. One moment it's 20 cm/s, the next it's 40 cm/s. It's never anything in between these two values.

Kristen

Amara

Do you agree with Kristen or Amara (or neither of them)? Explain your thinking.

STEP 7: You can use the Motion Sensor to check your ideas. Open the Motion Sensor data collection file for this activity on your computer. Record speed-time data while you repeat the experiments from STEPS 1, 3, 4, and 5. Start the cart about 20 – 30 cm in front of the Motion Sensor each time.

 Sketch the speed-time graphs produced by the Motion Sensor from STEPS 1, 3, 4, and 5 below.

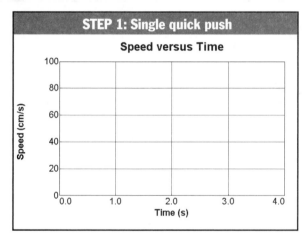

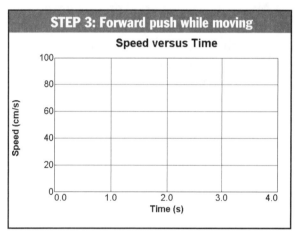

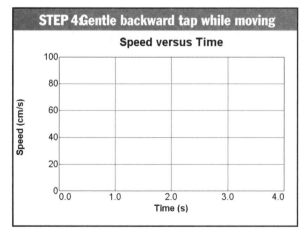

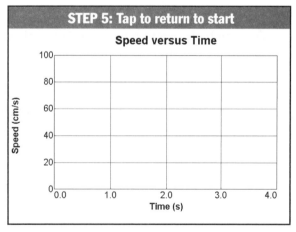

 Look at all of the graphs you drew above. In each case, when someone's hand was doing something to the cart, did its kinetic energy change in some way, or did it stay about the same? What evidence from the speed-time graphs supports your idea?

Did the changes in speed in each graph happen over a period of time (however short) or did they happen instantaneously (jump from one value to another in an instant)? How do the graphs tell you this?

STEP 8: How do you think the changes in speed of the cart are related to the contact between it and the hand? To help you think about this question, consider the speed-time graph shown here. This graph shows a cart that was given a quick shove and then moved along the track (as in STEP 1).

 Mark the whole period on this graph where you think the hand was in contact with the cart. Mark an 'X' at the end of this period to show the point where you think the hand lost contact with the cart. Explain your reasoning.

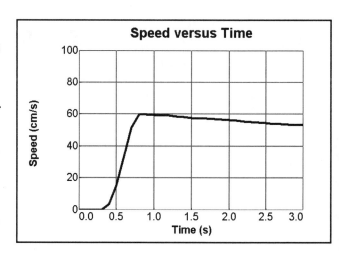

Your instructor will now show you a slow-motion video of a hand giving a quick shove to a cart to start it moving. The video also shows speed-time data being recorded for the motion of the cart.

 What does the video show about the relationship between the time the hand is in contact with the cart and the time the speed of the cart is increasing?

 Does this evidence agree with your indicated period on the graph above? If not, mark a new period (and the point at which contact is lost) on the graph and label it appropriately.

Now return to the speed-time graphs you drew in STEP 7. Use a different colored pencil to shade in the periods of each graph during which you think the hand was in contact with the cart. Briefly explain below why you chose those particular sections.

 EXPERIMENT #2: Is it only people that can change the kinetic energy of objects?

YOU WILL NEED:

■ Two low-friction carts (work with another group if necessary)

■ Track

■ Meter stick

■ Colored pencils

STEP 1: In Experiment #1 you saw how the speed of a cart changes while someone is pushing or pulling it. Is it only people that can do this or could it be done another way?

Working with another group if necessary, place two carts on the track, about 20 – 30 cm apart. Make sure of the following:

● The two ends of the carts facing each other will **not** stick together with any Velcro™ pads there may be on them.

● There are **no** magnetic effects between the ends of the carts that face each other.

● There is **no** spring-loaded plunger in either of the ends of the carts that face each other.

Now, give one of the carts (we will call this the *launched cart*) a **gentle** shove with your hand so that it collides with the other cart (we will call this the *target cart*). Watch carefully what happens to the motion of the two carts during the collision between them.

 Describe what happens during the collision.

Does the kinetic energy of the *launched cart* change during the collision? How do you know?

 Does the kinetic energy of the *target cart* change during the collision? How do you know?

 What, if anything, do you think caused the kinetic energy of each cart to change?

Interactions and Energy

When scientists study the natural world they focus their attention on different types of interactions between objects. When two objects interact they *act on* or *influence* each other in some way. In this course you will be studying many different types of interactions. In each case you will study what evidence you would look for to identify the occurrence of each interaction and will learn how to describe these interactions in different ways.

We will call an interaction in which two objects in contact push or pull on each other a **contact interaction**. If this is the only interaction influencing the two objects then during the interaction there will be a change in speed (or direction) for at least one of them[1].

In this activity you have already examined contact interactions between two stiff (or rigid) objects, like that between the two carts. (In the next two activities you will be considering other types of contact interaction.)

In this activity you have already examined contact interactions between two stiff (or rigid) objects, like that between the two carts. (In the next two activities you will be considering other types of contact interaction.)

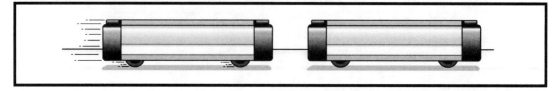

---

[1]If an object is involved in more than one contact interaction at the same time, then it is possible that the tendency of one interaction to change the speed of the object may cancel the effect of another interaction out, and the speed of the object may not change at all. For example, if two people were to try to push the cart along the track in opposite directions (with the same strength push), then the cart would not move at all, even though it is simultaneously involved in two interactions.

Energy Diagrams

In terms of energy, the action or influence during an interaction changes some form of energy associated with the objects involved. Scientists sometimes use energy diagrams to describe interactions, and we will also do this throughout much of the course. Before the collision between the two carts, the launched cart had some kinetic energy and the target cart had none. After the collision, the target cart was moving, and hence had more kinetic energy than before. However, the launched cart stopped (or was moving more slowly) so it had less kinetic energy than before. We can represent these 'before and after' situations, in terms of energy, using diagrams like these:

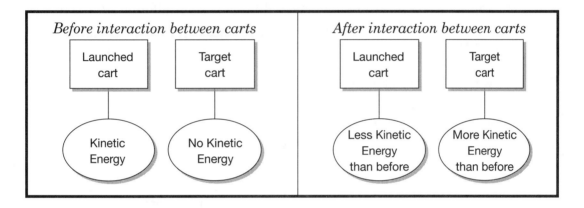

These energy changes suggest that during an interaction there is a *transfer of energy* between the objects involved. When there is such an energy transfer, one object must be the provider of the energy. This object is called the **energy source** because it supplies the energy that is transferred. The other object gains the energy transferred to it, so it is called the **energy receiver**. So, during the short period of time the two carts were in contact, they interacted with each other and there was a transfer of energy from the launched cart to the target cart.

While this transfer was occurring during the interaction, the kinetic energy of the launched cart was decreasing and the kinetic energy of the target cart was increasing. All this information can be included in an energy diagram, as shown here.

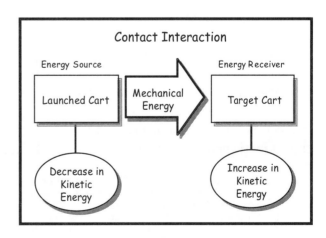

In this case we label the energy being transferred as **mechanical energy**, to identify it as an energy transfer that causes the speed of an object to be affected is some way. We can use the following definition to recognize when mechanical energy is being transferred between objects during an interaction.

> **When the objects in an interaction push or pull on each other and at least one of them changes its speed, this is evidence for a transfer of Mechanical Energy.**

As you move through this course you will encounter other types of energy transfer that will be labeled differently, depending on the evidence used to identify them. For example, the nature of the energy transfer in an electric circuit, in which a battery transfers energy to a bulb to make it light, is very different from the mechanical energy transfers[2] you have seen in this activity.

We can now put all three of our energy diagrams together to 'tell the story' of the collision between the two carts in terms of energy.

For simplicity, in most cases from now on we will only draw the energy diagram for the period of time during which the interaction is actually occurring, since it is only then that the energies associated with objects change, and there is an energy transfer between them. We will call this type of a diagram a Source/Receiver (S/R) energy diagram.

In the example of the collision between the two carts the energy changes in the source and receiver involve the same type of energy – kinetic energy. However, this does not have to be the case. When other objects participate in a contact interaction it may not be their kinetic energy that changes.

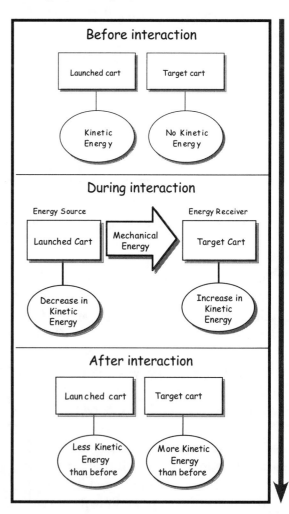

---

[2]Although we have introduced the idea of a **transfer of mechanical energy** in the context of contact interactions, it is important to note that the evidence for a transfer of mechanical energy during an interaction does **NOT** require that the interacting objects be in contact, only that there is a change in speed of at least one of them. This distinction will become important in later chapters when we will examine interactions in which objects do not touch each other, but do change their speeds as a result of the interaction between them.

Chemical Potential Energy

Think about how you use the idea of energy to describe how you feel sometimes. After a good night's sleep you might get up and feel 'full of energy'. But after a long day you might say you feel 'drained of energy'. This seems to suggest that people can store energy internally and that it can increase or decrease. This is indeed true. The food we eat is treated by our bodies (in a complex chemical process) and as a result, energy is stored in chemicals in our bodies.

We will call this **chemical potential energy** and it may change when we use our muscles to perform tasks. (The word 'potential' is used by scientists for certain types of energy to signify that they have the *potential* to produce changes in other types of energy, such as a change in kinetic energy in the case of the cart. You will encounter other types of potential energy later in the *PET* course.)

> When a person uses their muscles to increase the speed of an object during a contact interaction their chemical potential energy decreases[3].

With these ideas we can also draw a S/R energy diagram for the situation where you gave the cart a quick shove with your hand to get it moving:

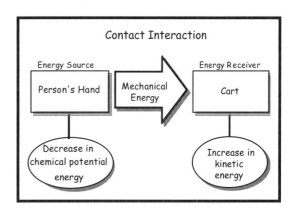

Describing Interactions

So, the basic description of an interaction in energy terms is:

> When any two objects interact, the energy source object transfers energy to the energy receiver object. There is a decrease of some type of energy in the energy source, and an increase of some type of energy in the energy receiver.

---

[3]However, when a person uses their muscles to slow or stop an object during a contact interaction their chemical energy does not increase. Instead, some other energy changes take place that we will not go into here.

To describe *any* interaction in terms of energy, you should now ask yourself *five* questions.

- ■ **Energy source:** which object supplied energy during this interaction?
- ■ **Energy decrease:** what type(s) of energy changed in the source?
- ■ **Energy transfer:** what type of energy transfer took place?
- ■ **Energy receiver:** which object gained energy during this interaction?
- ■ **Energy increase:** what type(s) of energy changed in the receiver?

As you progress through other *PET* activities you will describe many more types of interaction in this way.

Summarizing Questions

 Discuss these questions with your group and note your ideas. Leave space to add any different ideas that may emerge when the whole class discusses their thinking.

S1: What evidence would you look for that would tell you that a stationary object is involved in a contact interaction? What if the object is already moving?

S2: Another example of a contact interaction is when a soccer player uses his or her muscles to kick a stationary soccer ball. Complete the S/R energy diagram below for what happens during this interaction.

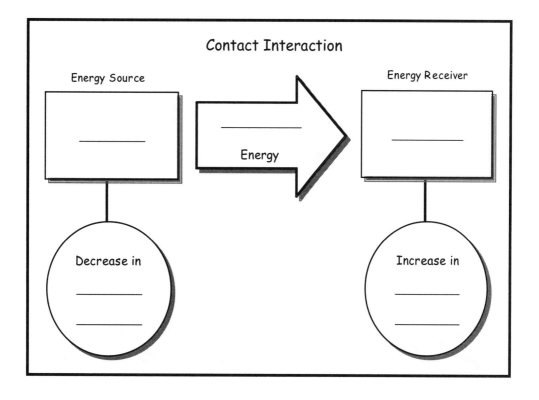

S3: Shown to the right are speed-time graphs for two carts that were involved in a collision similar to what you observed in Experiment #2 of this activity. (To remind you, you gave the 'launched cart' a quick push and it then collided with a stationary 'target cart'.) In this case students used two Motion Sensors and recorded the speed of both carts over the *same period of time.*

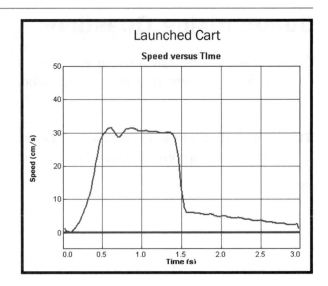

On the graphs use a colored pencil to indicate:

a) The period over which you think the hand was in contact with the launched cart.

b) The period on **both** graphs over which you think the two carts were in contact with each other.

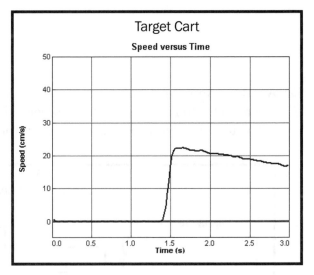

Explain below why you chose these particular periods.

 Participate in a class discussion about these summarizing questions.

Explanations in Science

There are many different types of explanations in science. However, they all have the same general structure in that they make a "claim," and then support that claim with reasons, using a logical argument. The claim might be some new idea you have about how the world works, that you support with experimental evidence. (For example, an idea about changes in speed during contact interactions that you support with evidence from some speed-time graphs.) The claim might also be a prediction you make about the outcome of an experiment before you actually do it. In that case, you might support the claim with some of your ideas about how the world works. (Note that you have already been engaging in these types of explanation in the first two activities in this chapter.)

A third type of explanation is when you use scientific ideas to construct a logical argument as to why a real-world event that has already taken place happened as it did. This type of explanation is generally what people understand when they refer to a **scientific explanation** and we will also use that terminology.

In many activities throughout *PET*, after you have developed some ideas in class about how the world works you will be asked to either write (or evaluate) a scientific explanation in terms of those ideas. In doing so, it is important that you formulate and write a well-crafted explanation. In the following sections we provide some suggestions for how such scientific explanations could be structured.

I. Describe the Situation using a Diagram

Most phenomena or events that you will need to "explain" involve situations where there are one or more interactions. In this chapter you are learning to describe interactions in terms of energy, so it will usually be appropriate to start your explanation by drawing an energy diagram.

II. Write the Explanation Narrative

Use the diagram to guide the written part of the explanation; that is, translate the various parts of the diagram into words. If your explanation involves some claims about how some observable aspect of an object changes, make sure you connect this aspect to some change in energy. (For example, connect any changes in speed to changes in kinetic energy.) Somewhere within your written narrative (often the last sentence) you should also make a specific connection to the actual event being explained. That connection helps make your written explanation logically consistent. Also, be sure that your explanation focuses on the interactions being asked about, and not on other interactions that happened before, or after.

As you write the explanation narrative, keep the following three criteria in mind:

■ Your explanation should be **accurate**; all included ideas correspond to ideas agreed upon by the class

■ Your explanation should be **complete**; all the ideas needed to make your case are included

■ Your reasoning should be **logical and clear**; your narrative should explicitly connect the included ideas to the phenomenon or event you are explaining, and it should be well written and easy to follow.

These criteria of accuracy, completeness, logical reasoning and clarity should also be used to evaluate the energy diagrams and explanations written by others. If all the criteria are met, the explanation should be considered "good." If at least one of the criteria is not met, then the explanation should be considered "poor" and in need of revision.

Earlier in this activity you pushed a low-friction cart so that it collided with a stationary cart. The following should be considered as an example of a good explanation, using ideas about energy, as to why the stationary cart started to move as a result of the collision.

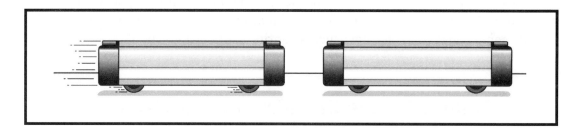

 EXPLANATION #1: Why did the target cart start to move when the launched cart collided with it?

> Note that this is a question about the collision between the two carts. Therefore, the explanation should focus on the contact interaction between the two carts and not on the interaction between the hand and the launched cart that started that cart moving.

Describe the situation using a diagram:
(You have already seen this energy diagram earlier in the activity.)

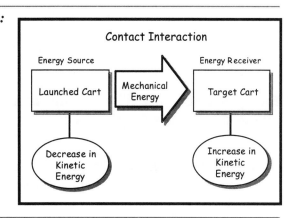

Write the narrative:

> The launched cart is moving toward the target cart and when they collide there is a contact interaction between them. The energy source during this interaction is the launched cart, and mechanical energy is transferred from it to the target cart, which is the energy receiver. Because of this energy transfer, the kinetic energy of the launched cart decreases while the kinetic energy of the target cart increases. Because the target cart was initially at rest, this increase in its kinetic energy means that it starts to move.

This explanation was intended to be "good." You should now consider how the three criteria introduced earlier are addressed in both the diagram and narrative.

 Completeness: (All ideas needed are included.) Does the explanation identify the interaction responsible for starting the target cart moving and include all the energy transfers and changes necessary to account for why it starts moving?

 Accuracy: (All ideas included correspond to established ideas.) Do the ideas about interactions, energy transfer and energy changes correspond to ideas the class has discussed and agreed upon?

 Logical Reasoning and Clarity: (Narrative is well written and connects ideas to the phenomenon) Is the narrative well written? Does it make sense to you? Circle the sentence in the narrative that connects the scientific ideas about interactions and energy changes to why the cart starts moving.

Now consider what happens to the launched cart during the same collision. Use the explanation on the previous page to help guide you in writing a scientific explanation for why the launched cart slows down during the collision.

 EXPLANATION #2: Why did the launched cart slow down when it collided with the target cart?

Describe the situation using a diagram:
(Draw an energy diagram for the interaction responsible for slowing the launched cart.)

Write the narrative: (Use the example above as a guide.)

 Participate in a class discussion about these scientific explanations.

Activity 2 Homework—More on Scientific Explanations
Developing Ideas

Name:_____ Date:_____ Group: _____

At the end of Activity 2 you read about a recommended procedure for constructing a scientific explanation that uses established ideas to construct a logical argument as to why a real-world event happened as it did. You also saw a model of a good explanation and then practiced constructing one of your own.

As a reminder, it is useful to first represent the situation using a diagram that accurately represents the relevant interaction, followed by a written narrative that connects the relevant scientific ideas together to each other, and to the event. As you construct or evaluate both these parts of an explanation you should keep the following three criteria in mind:

- **Accuracy:** All the ideas used in the diagram and/or narrative correspond to ideas established and agreed on by the class. (No ideas are used that have not been previously established and agreed on.)
- **Completeness:** All the established ideas necessary to explain the event are included in the diagram and/or narrative. (No relevant ideas are missing.)
- **Logical Reasoning and Clarity:** The narrative is well written so that it flows logically and is easy to follow. It also explicitly connects the relevant ideas to the event being explained.

In this homework assignment you will be presented with three alternative explanations for the same event. All three of these explanations are intended to be poor because they do not satisfy one of the criteria above. Your task will be to identify which of the three criteria is not satisfied in each case, and explain why you think so. After this you will be given an opportunity to construct your own explanation for the same event.

The event these explanations are addressing is why a stationary cart starts to move along the track when someone uses their muscles to give it a quick shove with their hand.

EXPLANATION: Why did the cart start to move when it was given a push by somebody's hand?

Version #1

Describe the situation using a diagram:

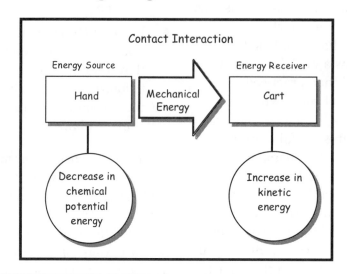

Write the narrative:

When the hand shoves the cart there is a contact interaction between them. During this interaction the kinetic energy of the cart increases, which means that it starts to move.

 Which criterion (accuracy, completeness, clarity or logical reasoning) is not satisfied by this explanation? Briefly explain why you think so.

Version #2

Describe the situation using a diagram:

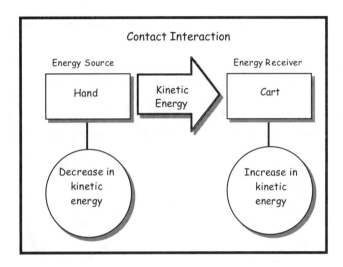

Write the narrative:

During the contact interaction between the hand and the cart kinetic energy is transferred between them. The type of energy that changes in the two interacting objects is always the same as the type of energy that is transferred. So, this means that the kinetic energy of the hand decreases while the kinetic energy of the cart increases. Since the cart was at rest to start with, this increase of kinetic energy means that it starts to move.

 Which criterion (accuracy, completeness, clarity or logical reasoning) is not satisfied by this explanation? Briefly explain why you think so.

Version #3

Describe the situation using a diagram:

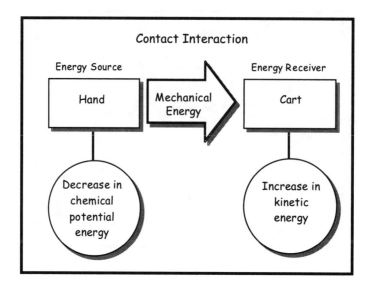

Write the narrative:

When the hand shoves the cart, mechanical energy is transferred between the hand and the cart. So, the hand decreases in chemical potential energy and the kinetic energy of the cart increases.

 Which criterion (accuracy, completeness, clarity or logical reasoning) is not satisfied by this explanation? Briefly explain why you think so.

Now it's your turn. Construct your own explanation for why the cart starts to move, making sure all three criteria are satisfied.

Version #4

Describe the situation using a diagram:

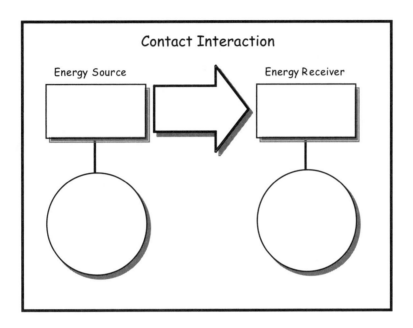

Write the narrative:

Activity 3–Another Contact Interaction
Developing Ideas

Purpose

In Activity 2, you examined contact interactions between rigid bodies. In one example energy was transferred to a launched cart from a person's hand. Another type of contact interaction occurs when at least one of the bodies involved is stretchy or springy, like a spring, a rubber band, or a piece of elastic.

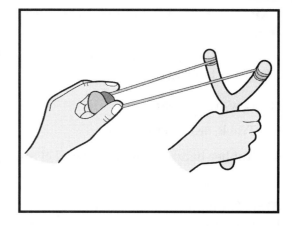

When springy or stretchy bodies are involved in a contact interaction they get stretched (or released) or deformed in some way, but what energy changes take place during such an interaction? For example, what energy transfers and changes occur when a child launches an arrow from a toy bow, or a small stone from an elastic slingshot?

 What energy changes take place in elastic objects when they are involved in a contact interaction?

Initial Ideas

 While a small stone is being launched from an elastic slingshot, is the stone an energy source in an interaction, an energy receiver, or neither? How do you know? What about the elastic in the slingshot?

Collecting and Interpreting Evidence

 EXPERIMENT #1: Where else can a launched cart get its energy from?

YOU WILL NEED:

- Low-friction cart
- Track, or level tabletop
- Rubber-band cart launcher and clamp
- Meter stick

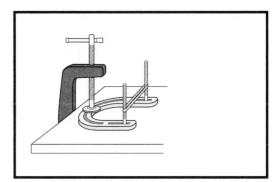

STEP 1: Fix your rubber-band cart launcher to the end of the track (or table). Place one end of the cart against the rubber band and push the cart back, so that the band is stretched about 1 cm back from its starting position. Let the cart go and watch its motion carefully. Stop the cart after it has moved about 50 cm.

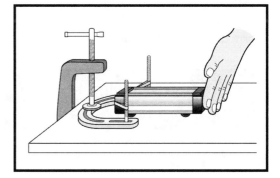

 Describe what happens to the cart **after** you let go.

 During the short period of time that the rubber band is actually pushing on the cart (after you release it), how do you think the cart is moving? Is it speeding up, slowing down, or moving at a reasonably constant speed? Why do you think so?

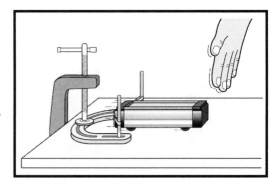

Do you think that the cart was involved in a contact interaction of some sort while it was being launched by the rubber band? If so, what evidence supports your answer? What object do you think was the energy source for the interaction? If not, why not?

STEP 2: Now, repeat the experiment from STEP 1, but this time make sure the rubber band is stretched back 3 cm before you release the cart.

 What is different about the speed of the cart after launching when the rubber band is stretched back further?

 Do you think there is a relationship between how far back the rubber band was stretched and the amount of increase in the cart's kinetic energy? How do you know?

 EXPERIMENT #2: What happens when a cart hits a rubber band?

YOU WILL NEED:

- Low-friction cart
- Track, or smooth tabletop
- Rubber-band cart launcher and clamp
- Colored pencils
- Copy of *How to Use the Motion Sensor*
- Access to a Motion Sensor connected to a computer

STEP 1: Mount the rubber-band cart launcher on the end of the track or table (if it is not already). Place the cart at rest about 20-30 cm away from the launcher and give it a **gentle** push toward the rubber band.

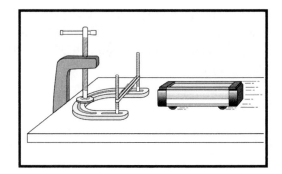

Observe the interaction between the rubber band and the cart carefully. Stop the cart when it gets back to the starting point.

 Describe what happens to the rubber band *and* the cart during the interaction between them.

 When the cart reverses direction, do you think it does so in an instant or do you think the change takes place gradually, over a short period of time? In other words, do you think that the speed of the cart remains the same and only its direction changes at some moment in time or do you think the cart actually slows down, stops, and speeds up again? Briefly explain your thinking.

STEP 2: Repeat the experiment, but push a little harder, so that the cart is going faster when it hits the rubber band.

 What is different about the way the rubber band behaves during this interaction?

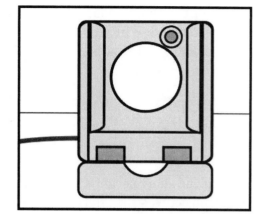

STEP 3: You can use the Motion Sensor to determine how the cart behaves during its interaction with the rubber band. Place the sensor on the track (or table), about 40-50 cm from the launcher and facing toward it.

 Open the Motion Sensor data collection file for this activity. Repeat the experiment from STEP 1 and sketch the speed-time graph for the interaction below.

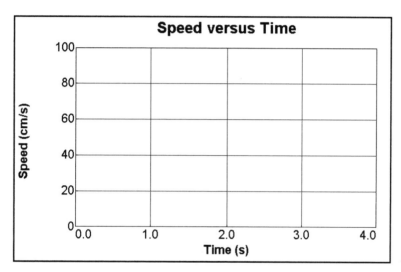

 Briefly describe the behavior of the speed of the cart while it was reversing direction.

 Using a colored pencil, indicate on the graph at what moment in time, or over what short period of time, do you think the cart was interacting with the rubber band. How do you know?

Consider the short period while the cart was **slowing down** and the band was being stretched. Which object was the energy source and which was the energy receiver during this period of time? How do you know?

 During the short period while the rubber band was pushing the cart away again, which object was the energy source and which was the energy receiver? How do you know?

Elastic Potential Energy

By now you have probably deduced that stretchy or springy objects can store energy in them when they are stretched (or compressed) from their normal state. We will call this energy **elastic potential energy**.

 From your observations in this activity does it seem that there is a relationship between the amount a rubber band is stretched and the amount of elastic potential energy it has? What evidence do you have?

As you probably deduced, such a relationship does exist:

> **When a springy or stretchy object becomes more stretched (or more compressed) its elastic potential energy increases.**
>
> **When a springy or stretchy object becomes less stretched (or less compressed) its elastic potential energy decreases.**

Summarizing Questions

 Discuss these questions with your team and note your ideas. Leave space to add any different ideas that may emerge when the whole class discusses their thinking.

S1: What are some similarities and differences between contact interactions that involve elastic objects (like those in this activity) and those that involve only rigid objects (like those in Activity 2)?

S2: In the contact interactions you examined in this activity, what **two** types of energy changed **in the objects themselves**? What is the evidence for these energy changes?

S3: When a contact interaction involving elastic objects occurs, what type of energy is **transferred between the two objects**? What evidence supports this idea? (You may want to look back to Activity 2 to answer this question.)

S4: Complete the following S/R energy diagram for the contact interaction in which the cart **slowed down** as it ran into the rubber band.

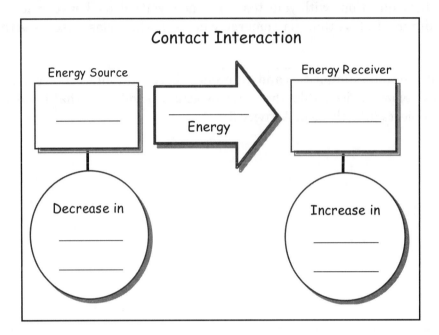

S5: In Experiment #1 of this activity you held a cart against a rubber band, as shown here, before letting go to launch it. Do you think there was a contact interaction between the cart and the rubber band even while you were holding the cart? If so, why did the speed of the cart not change until after you let go? If not, why not?

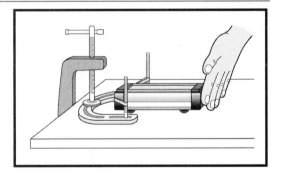

Evaluating a Scientific Explanation

In many walks of life people make claims that they support with "scientific reasoning." For example, such claims could vary from saying that eating certain foods causes certain illnesses, to a claim that aliens are living on a distant planet. In this course you and your classmates will also be making claims and supporting them with scientific ideas and logical reasoning. One way to help judge whether such claims are valid is to examine the reasoning behind them and whether this reasoning constitutes a good scientific explanation. Therefore, it is important that you develop the skill of evaluating scientific explanations to determine if they are good or poor. This will also help you when you construct your own scientific explanations, either verbally or in writing.

In the Initial Ideas section of this activity you were asked some questions about launching a stone from an elastic slingshot. Below is a scientific explanation for why the stone starts to move in this case, written by a group in another class.

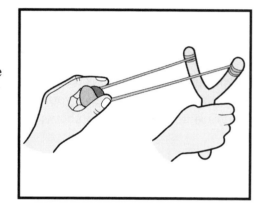

 EXPLANATION: Why did the stone start to move after the elastic was released?

Describe the situation using a diagram:

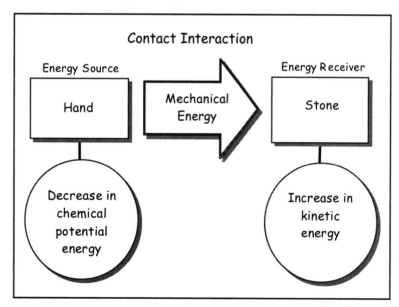

Write the narrative:

> Before the elastic was released there was chemical energy in the child's hand. When the elastic was released this energy was transferred to the stone and became kinetic energy.

Decide whether this explanation is "good" or "poor" by reviewing each of the following criteria.

Present	Criterion
YES/NO	Complete: All ideas needed are included
YES/NO	Accurate: All ideas included correspond to established ideas
YES/NO	Logical Reasoning and Clarity: Narrative is well written and connects ideas to the phenomenon to be explained.

If you find this to be a good explanation, state your reasons below. If you find it to be a poor explanation, give your reasoning below and correct what is wrong in the diagram and explanation above, or write a new explanation below.

 Participate in a class discussion about the summarizing questions and your evaluation of the explanation above.

Activity 4–Slowing and Stopping
Developing Ideas

Purpose

When examining contact interactions in the previous activities you saw that the speed (and perhaps direction) of at least one of the objects involved changed significantly during the interactions. For example, to make a hockey puck slow down and stop quickly, a player could let it hit his stick. Its kinetic energy will decrease during that interaction between them. If it didn't hit the stick, or anything else, do you think that the puck would ever stop?

In the world around us, nearly all moving objects, if left alone, seem to eventually slow down and stop. Do you think this is due to an interaction or is it just their natural tendency?

Why do moving objects tend to slow down and stop? Where does the energy go?

Initial Ideas

A popular summer game for young children is to run and launch themselves onto a long sheet of plastic, covered with water. They slide along the sheet without stopping, or even seeming to slow down, until they reach the end of the sheet.

Why do you think this is? Would the game be as much fun if there were no water on the plastic sheet? Briefly explain your thinking.

If the plastic sheet were made much, much longer, do you think a 'slider' could still reach the end without seeming to slow down? Again, explain your thinking.

 Participate in a brief class discussion to share your ideas.

Collecting and Interpreting Evidence

 EXPERIMENT #1: What happens when objects rub together?

YOU WILL NEED:

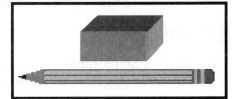

- Small block of wood
- Pencil, with a rubber eraser on the end

STEP 1: Rub the palms of your hands together **vigorously** for about 10 seconds, then quickly hold them against your cheeks.

 What do you notice about how warm your hands feel?

 Does it matter whether both hands are moving while you rub them together, or only one? (Check if you are not sure.)

STEP 2: Now touch the pencil eraser to your lip and note how cold (or warm) it feels. Rub the eraser **vigorously** on the palm of your hand for about 10 seconds. Then quickly touch the eraser to your lip again.

 Does the eraser feel cooler or warmer than it did before? Does it feel the same? What about the part of your hand you were rubbing the eraser on?

 When two objects rub together what seems to happen to **both** of them?

STEP 3: Place the wood block on the table and give it a quick push.

 Why do you think the block slows down and stops **after** the push?

 What evidence supports the idea that **after your initial push** the block was involved in some sort of contact interaction while it was sliding across the table? What other object do you think the block was interacting with?

 You have seen that the block lost kinetic energy as it moved across the table. Do you think any objects gained energy in this process? If so, what objects were they and what type of energy do you think they gained?

Contact Interactions Involving Friction and Thermal Energy

You are no doubt familiar with the idea of friction and its effects in slowing down and stopping moving objects. In fact, whenever two objects (or surfaces) rub together they interact with each other in friction-type contact interaction.

Such interactions occur everywhere in the world around us. Sometimes they are useful, such as when you use your brakes to stop your car. At other times we try to minimize their effects, such as when you put oil in your car's engine to prevent excessive wear on the moving parts that rub together.

As you have now also observed, when two objects rub together they **both** warm up – that is, their temperature increases. As you might expect, we can associate this warming up with an increase in a form of energy we will call simply **thermal energy**.

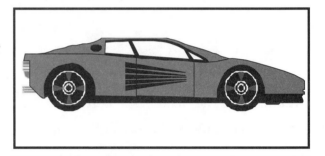

Note that the increase in temperature in a friction-type contact interaction is sometimes very small and difficult to detect without special equipment (as with the block sliding across the table).

When the temperature of an object increases, its thermal energy increases.

When the temperature of an object decreases, its thermal energy decreases.

Using this information, complete the following S/R energy diagram for the friction-type contact interaction that made the wood block slow down as it slid across the table **after the initial push**.

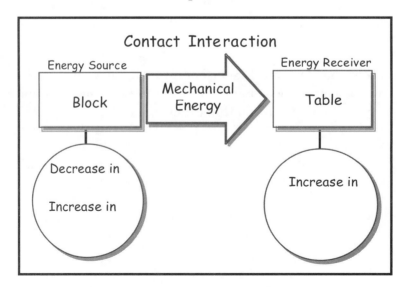

Contact Interaction

Energy Source

Block

Mechanical Energy

Energy Receiver

Table

Decrease in

Increase in

Increase in

Notice that in this case, while there is a **decrease** in the kinetic energy of the block, there is also an **increase** in its thermal energy. You may be wondering how it is possible for both these changes to take place and the object still be an energy source in the interaction. However, this is possible, if the kinetic energy and thermal energy change by different amounts.

 In order for the block to be the **energy source** in this friction-type contact interaction, which would have to be larger: the amount by which its kinetic energy decreases or the amount by which its thermal energy increases? Explain your reasoning.

 EXPERIMENT #2: What if there were no friction?

YOU WILL NEED:

■ Cart with friction pad attachment

■ Track

■ Access to a Motion Sensor connected to a computer

■ Colored pencils

■ Copy of *How to Use the PET Simulators* (an Appendix to this book)

■ Access to the *I&M computer simulator*

STEP 1: Examine the cart and note the friction attachment that, when lowered, allows a felt pad to touch whatever surface the cart is placed on. Place the cart on the track and lower the friction pad so that it is **firmly** in contact with the track. However, do not lower the pad so much that the wheels of the cart are no longer touching the track.

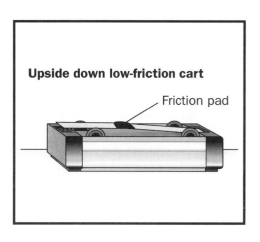

Upside down low-friction cart

Friction pad

STEP 2: Open the Motion Sensor data collection file for this experiment. Place the cart about 20-30 cm in front of the Motion Sensor and give it a quick shove away from the sensor. Record Motion Sensor data while you do this.

 Sketch the speed-time graph of the cart below.

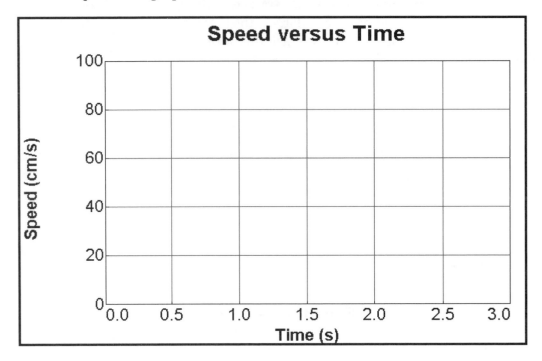

Speed versus Time

 Describe the motion of the cart **after** the initial shove. Is an interaction responsible for this behavior? If so, what type of interaction do you think it is, and what two objects are interacting?

STEP 3: Now raise the friction pad slightly, so that it only rubs very lightly on the track, and repeat the experiment.

 Using a different color pencil, sketch the speed-time graph on the same axes above. (Label the two lines FIRM PAD and LIGHT PAD.)

Does the cart still slow down after the initial push? What interaction do you think is responsible for this behavior?

 Does the cart slow down as quickly as it did before? Why do you think this is so?

STEP 4: Finally, raise the friction pad completely, so that it does not rub on the track at all, and repeat the experiment.

 Using a different color pencil sketch the speed-time graph on the same axes above. (Label this line NO PAD.)

 What is the motion of the cart like now, after the initial push? Does it still slow down (however slightly) or does it move in a different way?

 Why do you think the cart behaved in this way, even though the pad is not rubbing on the track?

Suppose you could remove the effects of friction **completely**, and then repeat the experiment.

 What do you think the cart's motion would be like now, after the initial shove? Explain your reasoning.

STEP 5: *Simulator Exploration.* You can check your idea using a special computer program, called the *I&M Simulator.* See "*How to Use the PET Simulators*" for instructions on how to access this program.

A NOTE ON SIMULATORS

You will use several different simulators throughout the *PET* course. These simulators are special computer programs written to give a visual representation of scientists' models of how the world works. When you run these simulators the behavior of objects in them is determined by the ideas and mathematical equations developed by scientists. These ideas and equations were developed in the same way as you are developing your ideas; that is, after collecting and interpreting evidence from real-world experiments.

Thus, simulations are scientists' models that represent real world phenomena. They are not the same thing as the phenomena themselves. When you work with the simulations in *PET*, you are not performing an "experiment" as you would with real apparatus. Instead, you are exploring and testing your ideas in comparison with a model developed by scientists.

When you open the setup file for this simulator exploration you will see a picture of a cart on a track. Also shown is a speed-time graph for the cart.

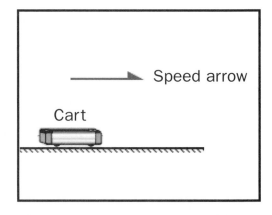

When you run the simulation, the cart is given a very quick initial push and then moves along the track. The speed-time graph of the cart (after the initial push) is plotted automatically for you and the simulation stops on its own after 10 seconds. While the simulation is running, a red 'speed-arrow' appears above the cart.

In addition, the influence of friction on the motion of the cart can be controlled. Currently the surface of the track is set to be 'Rough.'

 Run the simulation and watch the behavior of the speed-arrow. How does this arrow change to represent the slowing down of the cart?

Sketch the speed-time graph below. Label the line 'Rough'. (Note that the speed-time graph shows only the motion **after** the initial push and does not show the quick speeding up during the push.)

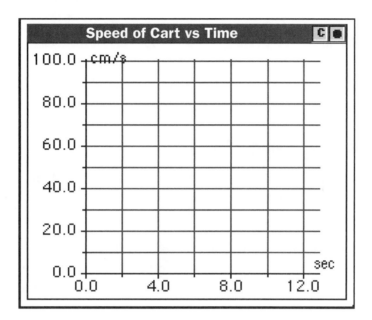

STEP 6: To change the influence of friction, first rewind the simulator, and then click on the selection tool. Next, double click on the picture of the cart, to bring up its 'properties' box.

In the properties box change the surface from 'Rough' to 'Smooth', then click on the 'OK' button.

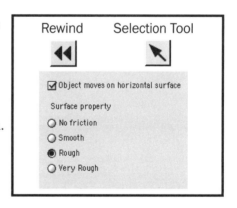

 Now run the simulation again and, using a different color pencil, sketch the speed-time graph above. Label this line 'Smooth.'

Finally, rewind the simulator, set the surface to 'No friction' and re-run the simulation.

 Again, sketch the speed-time graph above and label it 'No friction.'

 With the influence of friction completely removed, how is the motion of the cart in the simulator model different now, **after** the initial push? How does this compare with your prediction at the end of STEP 4?

Why do you think the speed of the cart does not change now?

Summarizing Questions

 Discuss these questions with your team and note your ideas. Leave space to add any different ideas that may emerge when the whole class discusses their thinking.

S1: In everyday situations, moving objects tend to slow and stop eventually. Do you think this behavior is due to an interaction, or does it just happen naturally? Does the kinetic energy just disappear, or does something else happen to it?

S2: What are some similarities and differences between friction-type contact interactions and the other types of contact interaction you examined in previous activities?

S3: Complete the S/R energy diagram below for the interaction in which the cart (with friction pad lowered and rubbing on the track) slows down gradually as it moves along the track. (Consider the pad to part of the cart.)

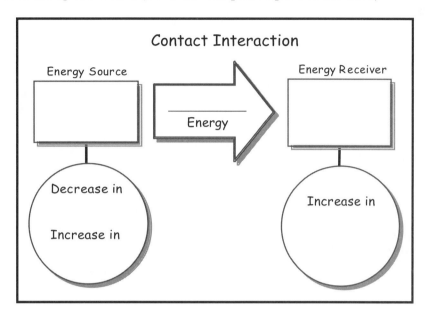

S4: In Experiment #2 of this activity you investigated what the motion of a cart would be like with no friction. Why do you think you used the simulator model in the final stages of this experiment, rather than the real cart and track?

S5: In the last three activities you have seen examples of three different types of contact interactions. While watching a moving object, what evidence would you look for to tell you that it is currently involved in a contact interaction of any type?

S6: When an object is involved in a contact interaction, does the interaction seem to last over a period of time (however long or short) or does it only happen at a single instant in time? Support your answer with evidence from the activities in this chapter.

S7: Suppose it were possible for you to start an object moving by giving it a quick push, and then arrange for it to be free of the influence of **any** contact interactions. After the initial push, do you think it would speed up, slow down, or keep moving at a constant speed? Explain your reasoning.

S8: Two students were discussing their ideas about how the speeds of objects change when they are involved in a contact interaction.

I think the speed of an object only changes while the interaction is actually happening. As soon as contact with the other object in the interaction is lost, the speed stops changing. When we launched the cart with a rubber band, as soon as contact was lost between them the cart stopped speeding up.

I agree that the speed changes because of the interaction between the objects, but I think the interaction only starts the speed changing. The change continues after contact is lost. I think that after the cart lost contact with the rubber band it continued to speed up, at least for a short period of time.

Daryl

Luisa

Do you agree with Daryl or Luisa, or neither? What evidence supports your thinking?

Explaining "Rug Burn"

In the Initial Ideas section of this activity you considered a game in which children launch themselves onto a water-covered plastic sheet. As you probably discussed, this game would not be such fun if there were not water on the sheet. In fact, the child would slow and stop very quickly and probably also suffer what is sometimes known as a 'rug burn' on the places where their skin rubbed directly on the plastic. Fill in the blanks in the S/R energy diagram and narrative below to complete the scientific explanation for why the 'rug burn' occurs as the child slides quickly to a stop on the dry plastic.

EXPLANATION: Why does a 'rug burn' occur when a child slides on a dry plastic sheet?

Describe the situation using a diagram.

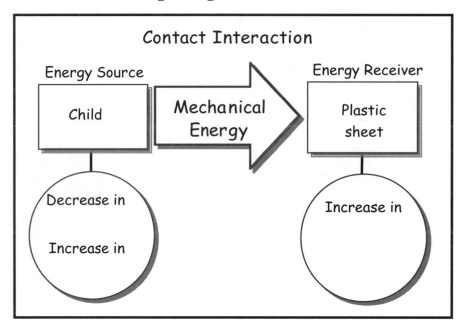

Write the narrative:

While the child is sliding across the plastic sheet there is a _____

- type _____ interaction between them. During this interaction, the

_____ energy of the child decreases while the _____

energy of the area of their skin that is rubbing on the plastic increases. (At the

same time mechanical energy is transferred to the plastic sheet, which also causes

its _____ energy to increase.) This increase in the _____

energy of the child's skin means that the _____ of this area increases

and so causes it to burn.

 Participate in a class discussion about the summarizing questions and the explanation above.

Name:_____ Date:_____ Group: _____

Summary of Energy Types

You have now seen different types of contact interaction, in which **mechanical energy** is transferred from a source object to a receiver object. (Remember, the evidence for this mechanical energy transfer is that the speed, or direction, of at least one of the objects changed in some way.) You have also been introduced to several different types of energy that can be associated with various aspects of the interacting objects themselves. These are:

- **Kinetic Energy**: Related to how fast an object is moving.

- **Chemical Potential Energy**: Associated with chemical processes in people's bodies.

- **Elastic Potential Energy**: Related to how stretched or compressed an elastic object is.

- **Thermal Energy**: Related to the temperature of an object.

You have also seen how the ideas of energy transfer and energy changes during contact interactions can be used to construct scientific explanations for real-world events. In this homework activity you will have more practice using these ideas.

Practice with Energy Diagrams

At the beginning of Activity 2 you were asked to think about the circumstances under which the motion of the puck during an ice hockey game might change. Look back at your ideas from that activity and think about how you might describe them in terms of interactions and energy.

To practice using your energy ideas, complete the S/R energy diagrams on the next page for some interactions in an ice hockey game. In each case, read the description of the interaction and then complete the energy diagram.

(Some of the information has been completed for you.)

Interaction #1:

A player uses his muscles to swing his stick, ready to hit the puck. (Note: This is an interaction between the player and the stick. The puck is not involved – yet!)

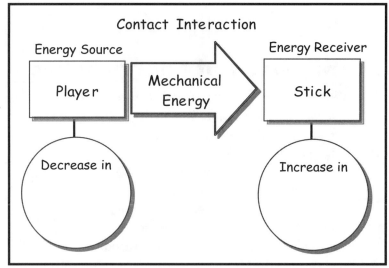

Interaction #2:

After being hit, the puck slides across the ice, slowing down slightly as it moves.

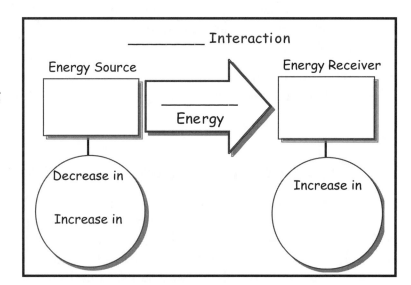

Interaction #3:

The puck hits the goal net. The net stretches as the puck slows down.

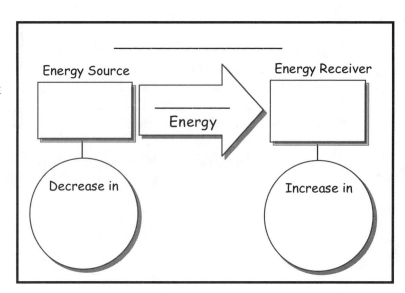

Interaction #4:

A player from the red team is skating across the ice when he collides with a player from the blue team, who was stationary before the collision. As a result the red player stops and the blue player is sent sliding across the ice. (Neither of the players use their muscles to push each other – they just collide.)

> **Draw your own S/R energy diagram for the collision between the two players.**

Explaining 'Brake Fade'

When you apply the brakes on a bicycle, pads of rubber are pushed against the metal rims of the wheels to slow them down in a **friction-type contact interaction** between the pads and wheels.

One of the problems that can occur with bicycle brakes is that of 'brake fade,' which is the loss of the brake's ability to stop the bicycle. (This usually happens with prolonged, heavy use of the brakes, such as when descending a steep hill.)

One reason this can occur is that the rubber brake pads can get so hot they begin to melt, causing a reduction in their ability to grip the wheel. How could the brake pads get so hot that this happens? Try to write a scientific explanation for the circumstances that lead to brake fade using your ideas about friction-type contact interactions.

EXPLANATION: How does 'brake fade' occur?

Describe the situation using a diagram:

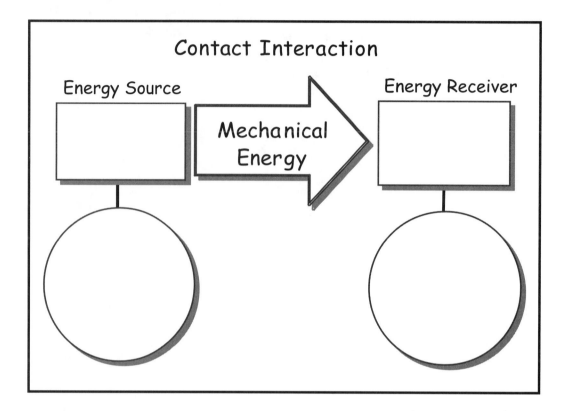

Write the narrative: (Remember to make a connection between the scientific ideas you use and the fact that the brakes do not work as efficiently.)

Activity 5—Warming and Cooling
Developing Ideas

Purpose

In the previous activity, you saw that whenever objects rub together in a friction-type contact interaction, the thermal energy of both of them increases. Thus, such interactions always cause the temperature of **both** interacting objects to increase, so that they are warmer than their surroundings.

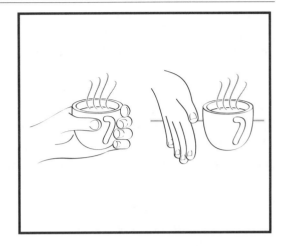

From your everyday experiences, you are probably aware of other situations in which the thermal energies of objects increase. For example, if you hold a hot cup of coffee, your hand becomes warmer. In fact, even if you don't touch the cup, but just hold your hand nearby, your hand still becomes warmer. In each case your hand is increasing in thermal energy. Is this increase in thermal energy due to a different type of interaction? If so, is mechanical energy being transferred between the interacting objects, or is another type of energy being transferred in these cases?

From your everyday experiences, you also know that warm objects eventually cool back down. For example, your

hands warmed up considerably while you were rubbing them together, but they soon cooled back down after you stopped rubbing them. Was an interaction responsible for your hands cooling down, or did this just happen on its own?

You know that friction-type contact interactions result in an increase in thermal energy. The purpose of this activity is to explore whether any other types of interaction can change the thermal energy of objects and, if so, what the characteristics of these interactions are.

Can other types of interactions change the thermal energy of objects?

EXPLORATION #1: Do warm and cool objects interact when they are touching?

STEP 1: Last year a group of students performed an experiment to determine what happens when a warmer object is touching a cooler object. They poured hot water into a flask. Then they poured cold water into a beaker and inserted the hot water flask into the middle of the cold water beaker. They put thermometers in both the hot water flask and the cold water beaker, and recorded the temperatures every 30 seconds for 6 minutes

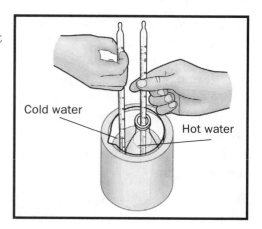

Below is a graph of their results.

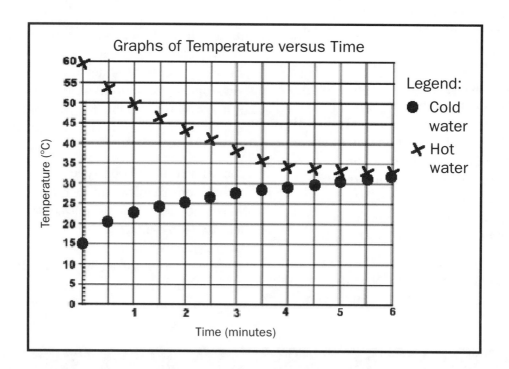

 Draw smooth lines through each of the two sets of data points (the crosses and the circles).

STEP 2: Now answer the following questions about what you think was happening during this six-minute period.

 Do you think the hot and cold water were interacting with each other? What evidence supports your thinking?

 What happened to the thermal energy of the hot water during the six minutes? How do you know?

 What happened to the thermal energy of the cold water during the six minutes? Again, how do you know?

 What appears to be happening at about six minutes? Why do you think this is happening?

The interaction between the hot water and the cold water is called a **heat-conduction interaction**. Such interactions take place whenever two objects with **different** temperatures are touching each other[1].

---

[1]While the condition of touching objects is common between heat-conduction and contact interactions, note that they also have conditions that are different. A contact interaction requires that the objects push or pull on each other with no regard to their temperatures, while a heat-conduction interaction requires the touching objects to have different temperatures, with no regard to pushes or pulls. (If a hot object were to push or pull on a cold object we would actually have both types of interactions occurring simultaneously!)

STEP 3: In all the contact interactions you examined in the preceding activities mechanical energy was transferred between the interacting objects.

Do you think mechanical energy is being transferred between the interacting objects in a heat-conduction interaction? Briefly explain your reasoning.

The type of energy that is transferred during a heat-conduction interaction is called **heat energy**. Heat energy is **always** transferred from the warmer object to the cooler object. We can use the following definition to recognize when heat energy is being transferred between objects during an interaction.

> **When the objects in an interaction change their temperature such that one of them becomes warmer while the other becomes cooler, this is evidence for a transfer of Heat Energy.**

Fill in the S/R energy diagram below to describe the interaction between the hot water and the cold water.

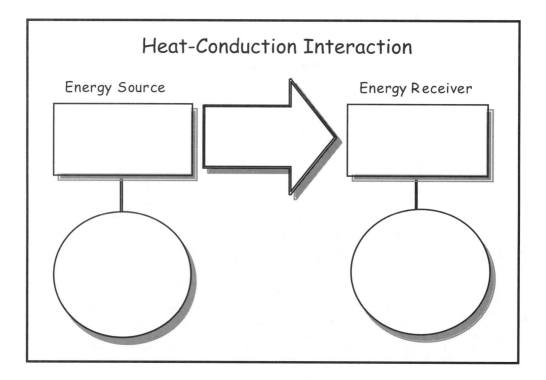

Suppose you are holding a cup of hot coffee in your hand. Draw an S/R energy diagram to describe the interaction between your hand and the cup of hot coffee.

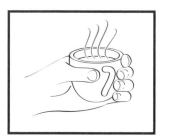

Check your energy diagrams with another group, and resolve differences, if there are any.

EXPLORATION #2: Do warm and cool objects interact when they are near each other, but not touching?

STEP 1: In a heat-conduction interaction, the interacting objects are actually touching each other. However, do objects with different temperatures have to touch for them to interact in a way that changes their thermal energy?

Do you think two objects that have different temperatures can interact with each other when they are near (but not touching) so that heat energy is transferred between them? Give an example to illustrate your thinking.

Think about standing by a fire. You feel the warmth of the fire, yet you are not touching it. This is because your skin is absorbing the infrared radiation (IR) being emitted by the fire. The emission of IR by a warm object, and its absorption by a cooler object, is a different way that heat energy can be transferred between objects. Moreover, since IR can travel across space, the two interacting objects do not have to be in contact for this transfer of heat energy to take place!

Later in the *PET* course, you will learn about visible light, which is itself a form of radiation. All light sources you can see, such as a light bulb or the sun, emit *visible* light radiation. However, objects can also emit other forms of radiation, such as infrared, that are not visible to people. In fact, it turns out that **all** objects emit infrared radiation from their surfaces. The amount of IR emitted depends on the temperature of the object. ***The warmer the object, the more infrared radiation it emits.*** Although our eyes are not sensitive to infrared radiation, other objects, like our skin, can absorb infrared radiation, causing the absorbing object to become warmer. This is why you feel warm when you turn your face toward the sun on a bright summer's day.

This type of interaction is called an **infrared interaction** and, just like heat-conduction interactions, happens only between objects of *different* temperatures.

For example, in the picture shown here, there is an infrared interaction between a hot cup of coffee (the energy source) and the cooler hand (the energy receiver). During this infrared interaction, ***heat energy*** is transferred from the cup to the hand.

 Complete the following S/R energy diagram to describe the infrared interaction between the cup of coffee and the hand.

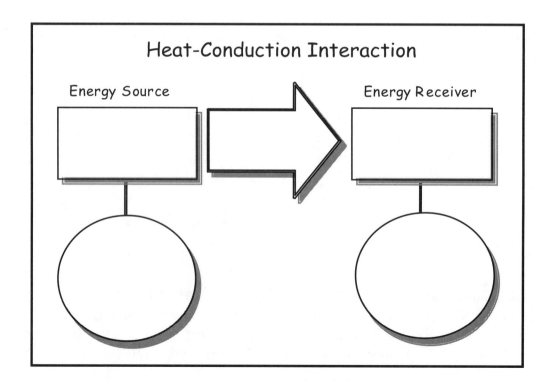

Note that when any two objects interact because they have a temperature difference, whether they are touching (heat-conduction interaction), or not touching (infrared interaction), the type of energy transferred is always **heat energy**.

STEP 3: Although our eyes cannot see infrared radiation, special infrared cameras can detect infrared radiation. These cameras usually produce images that are shades of a single color, such as gray. *The greater the amount of infrared radiation emitted by the source, the brighter the image in the camera.* The brightest images in an infrared camera are the warmest objects.

Your instructor will show you videos of examples from everyday life taken with both an infrared video camera and a regular video camera. You will be able to see how objects appear both in visible and infrared radiation.

 As each section of the video is shown, the class will stop and discuss the S/R energy diagrams and associated questions.

Rubbing Hands Together

 The skin of the hands glows brightly after the hands are rubbed together. Complete the energy diagram to describe what happens. (You can assume the IR camera absorbs the IR radiation and warms up somewhat.)

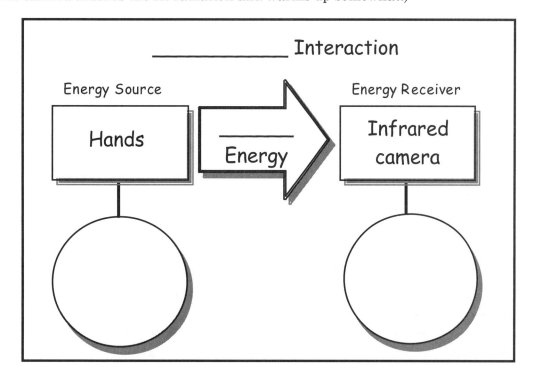

Pouring Hot Water Into a Glass

 Complete the two S/R energy diagrams below describing the interactions involved in the video after the hot water has been poured into the glass and the glass is glowing brightly, as seen by the IR camera.

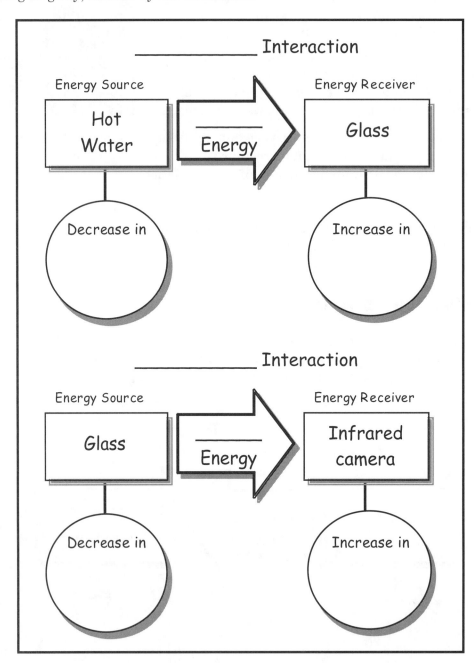

Notice that in this example the glass is involved in two interactions at the same time. Further, in one of these interactions (with the hot water) it is the energy receiver, and in the other interaction (with the infrared camera) it is the energy source. In the next section you will consider this situation further.

Chains of Interactions

As already noted, it is possible for an object to be involved in more than one interaction at the same time. When such an object is the energy receiver in one interaction and the energy source in another we can include it in an S/R diagram showing these interactions in a 'chain.' (The energy change for the glass has deliberately been left blank for now.)

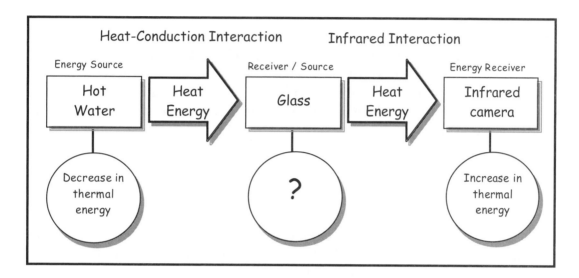

From the S/R energy diagrams you completed for the two interactions separately you can see the two interactions are tending to have opposite effects on the thermal energy (and hence temperature) of the glass. What will actually happen will depend on which of these effects is strongest.

 Suppose the tendency of the heat-conduction interaction to increase the thermal energy of the glass were stronger than the tendency of the infrared interaction to reduce its thermal energy. What would actually happen to the thermal energy and temperature of the glass?

 When in the video is the glass likely to be in this situation? Just after the hot water has been poured into it, or after the hot water has been in the glass for a long time. Explain your reasoning.

Now, suppose the tendency to increase the thermal energy of the glass were weaker than the tendency to reduce its thermal energy. What would happen to the thermal energy and temperature of the glass now, and when in the video would this most likely be happening? Again, explain your reasoning.

In both of the situations you considered above, the thermal energy of the glass was changing. Whenever **any** type of energy associated with an object (such as thermal, kinetic, chemical potential, elastic potential, and others yet to be introduced) is changing we say the object is in a **transient state**. However, when no energy types associated with an object are changing we say the object is in an **equilibrium state**.

Explain how it would be possible for the glass to be in an equilibrium state (meaning that its thermal energy is not changing) while it is still involved in the two interactions with the hot water and the infrared camera.

Since no changes in thermal energy take place for the glass while it is in its equilibrium state, we can omit that part of the chain S/R energy diagram.

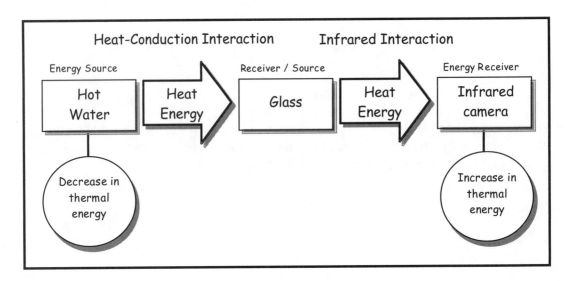

Summarizing Questions

 Discuss these questions with your team and note your ideas.

S1: In what way(s) are the heat-conduction and infrared interactions similar? In what way(s) are they different?

S2: Invent an example of a heat-conduction interaction or an infrared interaction different from the ones discussed in the activity. Draw the S/R energy diagram to describe the interaction.

S3: If two objects are at the same temperature, can heat energy be transferred from one to the other? Why do you think so?

S4: When you go on a picnic a good way to cool down warm sodas is to put them in a cooler full of ice. Write a *scientific explanation* for why a can of soda cools down when in contact with the ice.

Describe the situation using a diagram: (Draw an energy diagram for the interaction responsible for cooling the soda(s).

Write the narrative:

 Participate in a whole-class discussion about these summarizing questions.

Activity 5 Homework—Interactions with the Surroundings
Developing Ideas

Name:_____ Date:_____ Group: _____

Purpose

In Activity 4 you saw that when you rubbed your hands together, the rubbed areas warmed up and increased in thermal energy. In Activity 5 you watched an infrared video of this process and then completed an S/R energy diagram for the infrared (IR) interaction between the warm parts of the hands and the infrared camera. During this interaction, heat energy was transferred from the warm parts of the hands to the camera, but do you think heat energy was only transferred to the camera, or were the warm parts of the hands interacting with other objects as well?

> ## How do warm objects interact with their surroundings and why do they cool down?

What Else Do Warm Objects Interact With?

 As a result of the transfer of heat energy to the infrared camera, what happened to the thermal energy and temperature of the warm parts of the hands?

 Do you think the infrared camera was the only object that the warm parts of the hands were transferring heat energy to? Explain your reasoning.

 What other objects do you think the warm parts of the hand were transferring heat energy to? List as many as you can think of, both touching and not touching.

In answering the previous question you probably named several objects that the warm parts of your hands were interacting with. Some that may have been touching them (such as other, cooler, parts of your hands, or even the air) and maybe some others that were not (such as the table, walls, people etc.). In such a case, rather than identifying all the possible other objects involved, we can group them together as the "surroundings." An energy diagram for all the interactions of a warm part of your hand after being rubbed could then be drawn like this.

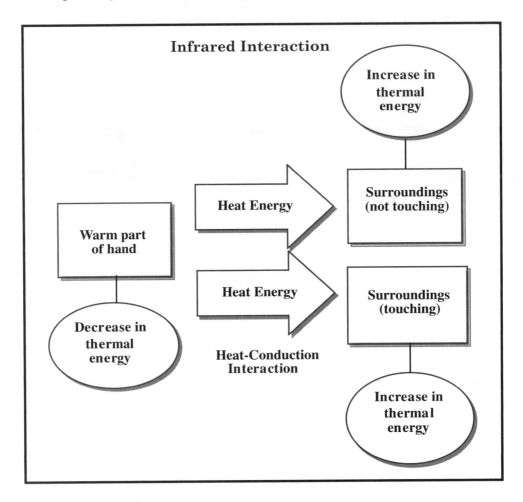

Note that, since the energy source is the same for both interactions, and that both involve the transfer of heat energy to the surroundings, we could also draw the following energy diagram to represent the cooling of the warm part of the hand through its interactions with its surroundings.

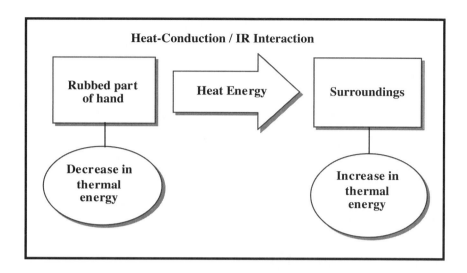

Consequences of Friction

As you discussed at the end of Activity 4, it is almost impossible to eliminate the effects of friction on moving objects here on Earth. In this section, you will consider the consequences of having some amount of friction being present[1].

 As objects move, parts of them will rub on each other, or on the surface they are moving over. Because of the friction-type contact interaction between these rubbing parts, what will happen to the thermal energy of the moving object?

 As a result of this change in thermal energy, will the temperature of a moving object be higher than, the same as, or lower than, its surroundings?

 Because of the difference in temperature (however slight) between a moving object and its surroundings, what two types of interactions (in addition to any contact interactions) will always be involved?

---

[1]Sometimes the effects of friction are so small that we can neglect them, sometimes they are not. This issue will be considered later in this activity.

Because of the difference in temperature (however slight) between a moving object and its surroundings, what type of energy will always be transferred from a moving object to its surroundings?

Friction in Explanations

One of the first decisions that must be made when constructing or evaluating a scientific explanation involving *motion* of an object is whether the effects of any friction-type contact interactions are minor enough to be ignored, or if they play a significant role.

In general, if the explanation concerns an object moving on well lubricated wheels (or across a very smooth surface), with no parts or surfaces rubbing together, and for which other interactions are having a much more significant effect, then friction can usually be ignored. However, if there are surfaces rubbing together, or if there are no other interactions involved, then a friction-type contact interaction is probably itself playing a significant role in what is happening to the object.

For example, consider the situation in which you gave a low-friction cart a quick shove with your hand to start it moving along the track.

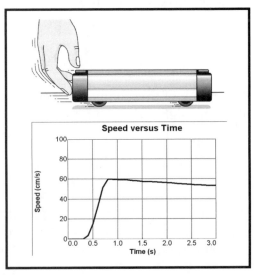

In explaining *"Why does the cart start to move when given a quick shove by the hand?"* the effects of friction on the cart are totally overwhelmed by the effect of the shove, and so can be effectively ignored. However, a friction-type contact interaction would play a significant role in explaining *"Why does the cart slow down gradually after the shove?"* since that is the cause of its decreasing speed.

In any scientific explanation you construct from now on you should consider the issue of friction and, if you consider its effects to be negligible, make sure you make a statement to this effect in your narrative. (If you are considering its effects to be significant you do not need to state this explicitly, as it should be evident in your narrative.)

Summarizing Questions

Be prepared to share your responses to the following questions during the next class period.

S1: Whenever an object starts to move, assuming the effects of friction are **not** negligible, what will happen to its thermal energy? Why does this happen?

S2: At the end of Activity 4 you completed an S/R energy diagram for the interaction in which a cart (with friction pad lowered and rubbing on the track) slowed down gradually as it moved along the track. However, at that point you had not investigated the other interactions that accompany the heating associated with the effects of friction.

Complete this S/R energy diagram so that it describes all the interactions that the cart is involved in as it moves along the track (after the initial push).

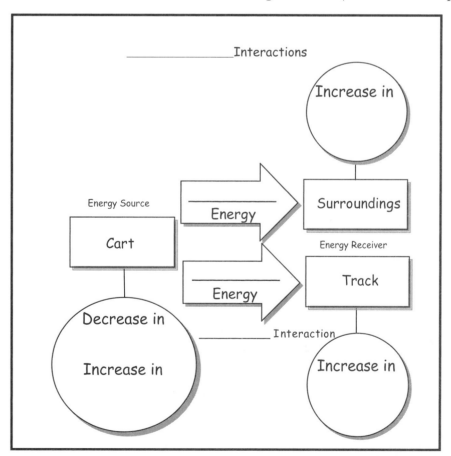

S3: Consider the following situations to be explained. For each one, state whether you would consider the effects of friction to be negligible and briefly justify your choice. (You do not need to construct the explanations themselves!)

Why does the low-friction cart slow down quickly when it runs into the rubber band?

Why does the wood block start to move while it is given a push across the tabletop?

Why does the wood block stop almost immediately after it is given a push across the tabletop?

Why does the hockey puck speed up while the player is hitting it with his stick?

Activity 6–Keeping Track of Energy
Developing Ideas

Purpose

Earlier, in Activity 2, you observed a collision between a launched cart and a target cart. There was a contact interaction between the two carts, which was described with the S/R energy diagram shown here. (Note that the effects of friction are assumed to be negligible during the collision.)

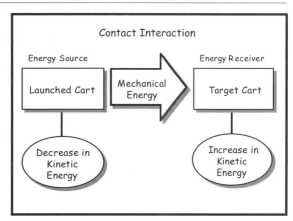

Contact Interaction

Energy Source

Launched Cart

Mechanical Energy

Energy Receiver

Target Cart

Decrease in Kinetic Energy

Increase in Kinetic Energy

This diagram suggests that we can think of the energy transfer between the carts as occurring in two steps, as follows:

> **As the mechanical energy is transferred out from the launched cart it decreases in kinetic energy;**
>
> **then**
>
> **As the mechanical energy is transferred into the target cart it increases in kinetic energy.**

Suppose you were able to measure the amounts of the energy changes and transfers in this contact interaction. How do you think the amount of mechanical energy transferred out of the launched cart would compare with the amount that its kinetic energy decreased over the same period of time? What about the amount of mechanical energy transferred into the cart compared to the increase in its kinetic energy? Would your answer depend on whether the effects of friction are negligible or not?

In this activity we want to determine whether there is any relationship between the energy transfers and changes that occur for objects involved in interactions.

  How are the amounts of energy input, energy output and energy changes for an object related together?

Initial Ideas

In Activity 2 you also gave a cart a push to start it moving along the track. **Assuming the effects of friction are negligible** this situation would be described by the S/R energy diagram on the next page.

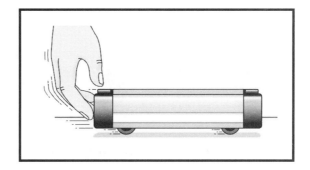

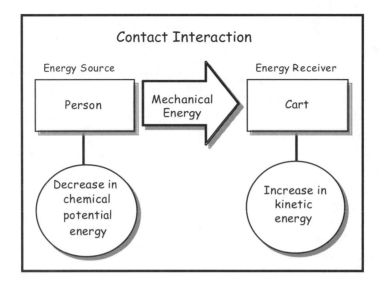

Suppose you were able to measure the amount of mechanical energy transferred from the person to the cart, and also the amount of the increase in the cart's kinetic energy.

 How do you think these two amounts of energy would compare? That is, do you think the amount the cart's kinetic energy increases would be less than, equal to, or greater than, the amount of mechanical energy transferred to the cart from the person? Why do you think so?

 Would your answer to the previous question be different if the effects of friction were **not** negligible? Explain your reasoning.

 Participate in a short class discussion

Input/Output Energy Diagrams

So far in the *PET* course you have used source-receiver (S/R) energy diagrams, like that shown on the previous page. These diagrams are useful when focusing on one particular interaction between specific objects of interest. However, as you have also already seen, such S/R energy diagrams can quickly become very complex when trying to show several different interactions that happen simultaneously. Thus, rather than showing all the interacting objects in an energy diagram, sometimes it is convenient to focus on only one of the interacting objects.

In this case we need show only the interaction types, the energy transferred into the object (called the energy input), the energy transferred out from the object (called the energy output), and the energy changes within the object.

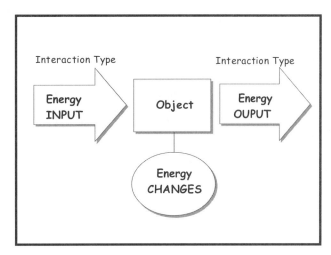

We will call this type of energy diagram an input-output energy diagram, or I/O energy diagram. In the I/O energy diagram we show any energy inputs to, and outputs from, the object of interest, together with the energy changes within that object. **In such an I/O energy diagram we do not include the other energy sources or receivers**.

For example, an I/O energy diagram for the target cart in the collision between two carts would look like this. Note that in this particular case (assuming the effects of friction are negligible) there is no energy output from the target cart. As you will see later on, it is also possible to have situations for which there is no energy input, or no energy changes.

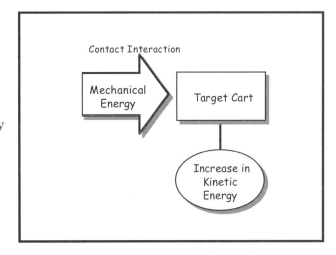

Notice also that we can read this I/O energy diagram from left to right to give us a cause-and-effect storyline for what happens to the cart; mechanical energy is input to the cart and this is the cause of the increase in its kinetic energy (which is the effect).

The previous example seems to suggest that an I/O diagram is identical to a selected part of an S/R diagram. However, in order to show the cause-and-effect storyline, sometimes the I/O diagram may look a little different, as shown by the following example.

During the collision between the two carts, the **effect** on the launched cart was that its kinetic energy decreased. The **cause** of this decrease was the transfer of mechanical energy from the launched cart to the target cart. To show this storyline we would draw the I/O energy diagram for the launched cart during the collision as shown here. Reading from left to right it tells us that the mechanical energy output from the cart is the cause of the decrease in its kinetic energy.

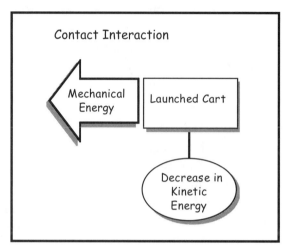

As a final example, in the previous activity you watched an infrared video of hot water being poured into a glass and saw that the glass initially warmed up. In that initial warming situation heat energy was being transferred from the hot water to the glass (via a heat-conduction interaction), meaning there was a heat energy input to the glass. The effect of this heat energy input was that the thermal energy of the glass itself increased. As a result of this increase in thermal energy, the glass became warmer than its surroundings and so heat energy was also being output from the glass to those surroundings (via heat conduction and infrared interactions). The I/O energy diagram describing this situation would look like this:

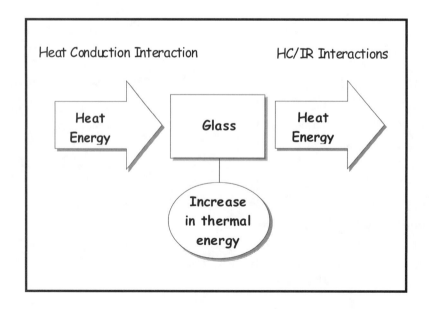

In this activity you will examine several situations where it is convenient to use such an I/O energy diagram to describe how an object interacts with all the other objects around it, and the effect those interactions have on the object itself.

Amounts of Energy

If we are going to find a relationship between amounts of energy, we need to figure out how to measure amounts of energy. We can measure lengths in meters, time in seconds, mass in kilograms, but what units are used to measure energy?

YOU WILL NEED:

- Kilogram mass
- Meter stick (or a 2-meter stick)

STEP 1: Lay the kilogram mass on the floor. Grab it and slowly lift it to a height of 1 meter, trying to maintain a nearly constant speed (except for starting and stopping).

According to scientists, you expended about **10 joules of energy** in lifting the 1-kg mass a vertical distance of 1 meter.

STEP 2: Now imagine lifting the 1-kg mass 2 meters (twice as far).

In that case, you would have expended about 20 joules of energy in lifting the 1-kg mass a vertical distance of 2 meters.

STEP 3: Finally, imagine placing 2 1-kg masses on the floor on top of each other, and then slowly lifting the 2-kg mass 1 meter upward.

In that case, you would have also expended about 20 joules of energy in lifting the 2-kg mass a vertical distance of 1 meter.

Scientists use the **joule** as a common unit of energy. The unit is named after the English scientist James Joule (1818-1889) who performed many experiments involving heat. By carrying out many different types of experiments and inferring mathematical relationships among the variables involved, scientists can calculate the amounts of energy transfers and changes involved in interactions. The simulators you are using in this course were programmed to make the same kinds of calculations. The results of the calculations are represented in energy bar graphs, both numerically and in terms of the relative length of the bars in the graph.

For example, this energy bar graph was taken from the *Interactions and Motion* simulator, and represents the energy inputs, outputs, and changes for a cart when it is pushed along a track with a very small amount of friction present. (In this case the energy values in the graph are shown in units of kilojoules (kJ). A kilojoule is equal to one thousand

Body 1	
ENERGY INPUT	
MECHANICAL	19.81
ENERGY OUTPUT	
HEAT	0.72
ENERGY CHANGES IN SYSTEM	
KINETIC	18.36
THERMAL	0.72

joules.) In other words, over the period the simulator was run the total mechanical energy input to the cart was 19.81 kJ of energy and the total heat energy output from the cart was 0.72 kJ. Over the same time period the kinetic energy of the cart increased by 18.36 kJ, while its thermal energy increased by 0.72 kJ.

> **Important note: The simulator reports energy values to only the second decimal place so values are rounded to the nearest 0.01 (in the appropriate units). Therefore a difference of only 0.01 between two energy measurements should <u>not</u> be considered significant.**

Looking for a Relationship

One way of developing a relationship between the amounts of energy involved in interactions is to examine several examples and look for patterns that connect the amounts of energy inputs, energy outputs, and energy changes. We will start with a simple case and move on to more complex cases. In the end, we want you to come up with a very general mathematical statement (written as an equation) that will work for **all cases**, whether simple or complex.

 EXPLORATION #1: Pushing a cart on a frictionless track

STEP 1: Imagine you were to give a stationary cart a push to make it move it along a track for which effects of friction are negligible. Complete the I/O energy diagram for the period while the cart is being pushed.

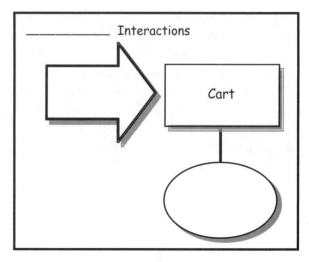

Why is there no energy output from the cart in this case?

 In this case how do you think the amount by which the energy of the cart increases will compare to the amount of energy input to it? Explain your reasoning.

STEP 2: Use the *Interactions and Motion* simulator to check your idea. Open up *Chapter 1 Act. 6 Setup 1* and run the simulation. The cart will be given a short push for two seconds and the simulator will stop automatically after eight seconds. The energy amounts displayed in the energy bar graph represent the total amounts of energy accumulated since the simulator was started.

 Do the types of energy input and energy changes shown in the simulator energy bar graph for the cart match those you represented in your I/O energy diagram? If not, modify your diagram accordingly.

 Does the kinetic energy of the cart change during the push? What about after the push? Why does this make sense?

STEP 3: Now look at the values for the energy input during the push and the amount of the energy change in the cart. Does there seem to be a relationship between them?

 How is the amount of energy input during the push related to the amount of the energy change in the cart during the push? Does this agree with your prediction?

 Express this relationship in the form of a mathematical equation using the variables 'Energy Input' and 'Energy Changes'.

 EXPLORATION #2: Space Heater

STEP 1: Many people use small space heaters to warm up their rooms on cold days and nights. When you plug in your space heater and turn it on, ***electrical energy*** is transferred to it (via an electric circuit interaction). (You will examine interactions involving the transfer of electrical energy in detail in Chapter 5.) Because of this energy transfer, the heater coils warm up. They also emit infrared radiation to the surroundings and warm up the air in contact with the coils. (The warmth you feel from the heater is therefore caused both by the IR radiation and the air that was warmed by being in contact with the coils.)

 Complete the I/O energy diagram describing what happens when the space heater is first turned on.

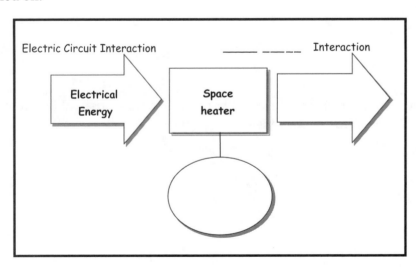

STEP 2: The *EM Devices* simulator has a tool that behaves like a space heater. Open *Chapter 1 Act. 6 Setup 2* and you will see the setup shown here.

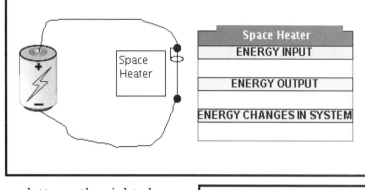

Turn on the simulator. Keep your eye on the energy bar graph and also on the clock above the palette on the right shown here. Run the simulator for about 15 seconds, then turn it off.

 Record the types and amounts of energy input, output, and changes in the table below (in units of kJ).

Space Heater	
ENERGY INPUT	
Type of Energy =	Amount =
ENERGY OUTPUT	
Type of Energy =	Amount =
ENERGY CHANGES IN SYSTEM	
Type of Energy =	Amount =

 Do the various types of energies shown in the simulator energy bar graph for the space heater match those you represented in your I/O energy diagram? If not, modify your diagram accordingly.

STEP 3: In the previous example of the cart being pushed on the frictionless track, the amount of energy change for the cart was **equal to** the amount of energy input. This does not seem to be true for the example of the space heater.

 Why do you think the amount of energy change for the space heater is less than the amount of energy input?

At the end of Example 1 of this activity you wrote down a mathematical equation relating 'Energy Input' and 'Energy Changes' for a system that has an energy output of zero. However, the space heater has non-zero values for all three variables; 'Energy Input', 'Energy Output', and 'Energy Changes.'

Try to write a mathematical equation relating the values for 'Energy Input', 'Energy Output' and 'Energy Changes' for the space heater.

Compare your new equation with that of at least two other groups and try to resolve any differences.

Does this equation also work for the cart being pushed along the frictionless track in Example 1? Explain why or why not.

Let us now consider another example to see whether this relationship works for other systems.

EXPLORATION #3: Heating a gas in a flexible container..

STEP 1: Your instructor will show you a demonstration (or movie) of an experiment in which a bottle of air, with a rubber balloon over the top, is warmed by immersing it in hot water.

Describe what happens when the bottle of air is warmed.

Now think about the **air inside the bottle** as the 'object' in this case.

 When the bottle is immersed in the hot water what type of energy is transferred to the air inside it from the hot water?

 What effect does the energy input you identified in the previous question have on the air? In other words, what type of energy change occurs for the air in the bottle?

Now think about the possible energy outputs from the air in the bottle. First, consider the possibility of an output of heat energy. Usually, when an object warms up, it will output heat energy to its surroundings. However, in this case, the bottle is almost totally immersed in hot water. Under these circumstances the heat energy output from the air in the bottle will be negligible.

 Explain why you think the heat energy output from the air in the bottle will be negligible while it is almost totally immersed in the hot water.

Is there any other type of energy output from the air in the bottle? To answer this question think about what you observed happening when the bottle was immersed in the hot water.

As the air warmed up, did it have an observable effect on any other object? If so, what type of energy was transferred from the air to this object? Explain your thinking.

Complete the I/O energy diagram to show what happens to the air in the bottle when it is immersed in the hot water.

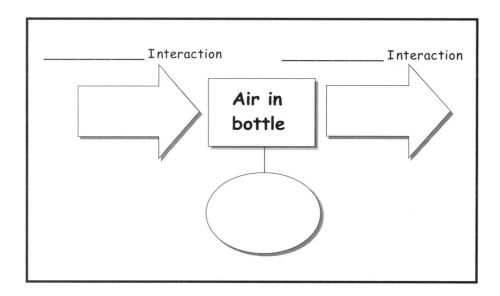

STEP 2: You can use a simulator to check your thinking and examine this situation. When you open *Chapter 1 Act. 6 Setup 3* you will see this setup.

On the left, representing the bottle with air inside, is a container of nitrogen gas. (Air is ~80% nitrogen.) Inside the container is a 'lid' that can move up and down, corresponding to the rubber balloon on the bottle. To the right is an energy bar graph for the gas in the container. There is a heater below the container that will warm it, and hence the gas inside it, when the simulator is run.

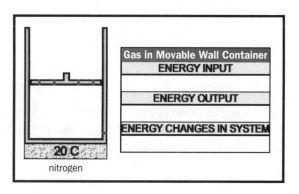

Now turn on the simulator. Watch the energy bar graph and the moveable 'lid' in the container.

Record the types and amounts of energy input, output, and changes in the table below (in units of kJ).

Gas in container	
ENERGY INPUT	
Type of Energy =	Amount =
ENERGY OUTPUT	
Type of Energy =	Amount =
ENERGY CHANGES IN SYSTEM	
Type of Energy =	Amount =

Do the various types of energies shown in the simulator energy bar graph for the gas in the container match those you represented in your I/O energy diagram? If not, modify your diagram accordingly.

STEP 3: At the end of Experiment #2 you developed a mathematical equation relating 'Energy Input', 'Energy Output' and 'Energy Changes' for the space heater. You should now check whether that equation works for the gas in the container.

In the case of the gas in the container, would the mathematical relationship you developed at the end of Experiment #2 accurately connect the amounts of 'Energy Input', 'Energy Output' and 'Energy Changes' in the battery system? Use the values from the simulator to support your answer.

Summarizing Questions

S1: What is the mathematical relationship (equation) that relates the energy input, energy output and energy changes for an object involved in one or more interactions?

S2: Apart from being a mathematical tool, the equation you developed in this activity should tell you something about energy. If a certain amount of energy (say 20 J) is input to an object, what does this equation tell us happens to that energy? Is some of the energy lost, is extra energy gained or does the equation imply something else?

S3: What does this mathematical relationship seem to tell us about energy and whether it can be created or destroyed? Explain how it tells you this.

S4: An electric fan is often used to blow air. When the fan is turned on, the blades start to move and begin to push the air around the room. Think about what energy transfers and changes are involved when this happens and complete the I/O energy diagram below for an electric fan just after it is turned on. (Note that this is a slightly simplified picture of what happens when a fan is turned on. You will examine the fan again in Chapter 5.)

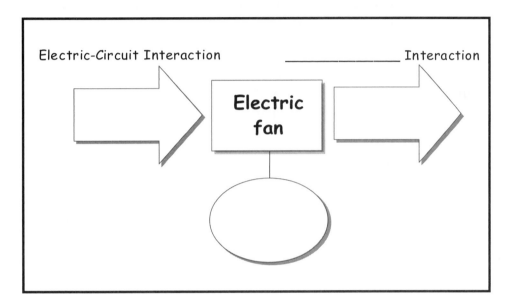

Electric-Circuit Interaction

_____ Interaction

Electric fan

S5: For the fan described in the previous question, fill in the blank spaces in the table below of energy types and determine the numerical value for the energy output (in units of kJ). Below the table, show how you arrived at this value.

Electric Fan	
ENERGY INPUT	
Type of Energy =	Amount = 0.76
ENERGY OUTPUT	
Type of Energy =	Amount =
ENERGY CHANGES IN SYSTEM	
Type of Energy =	Amount = 0.23

 Participate in a whole-class discussion to go over your answers to these questions.

Conservation of Energy

The class should have agreed on a single formulation of the relationship summarized as an equation in S1 and described in words in S2 and S3. This seems to be a very important and significant relationship. It suggests that for any object interacting with its environment, if you take into account all the energy inputs, outputs and changes inside the system, then you can make a claim about how these energies are related to each other.

An equation like this is useful because if you either know, or can measure, the amounts of all but one of these energies, the mathematical relationship can be used to determine the unknown amount.

Scientists have found this relationship to be useful for all the kinds of interactions they have studied. They call it the **Law of the Conservation of Energy.** *Conservation* in this case means that something remains the same as time goes on. If you look at the equation you will notice that it suggests that all the energy input into a system appears either as an energy change in the system or as an energy output from the system. In other words, *energy is not created nor destroyed, it is only changed into another kind of energy.*

Activity 6 Homework—Energy Conservation and Friction
Developing Ideas

Name:_____ Date:_____ Group: _____

Purpose

While developing your ideas about energy conservation in the previous activity, you considered interactions in which there was a single type of energy input and output. In those situations there was only one type of energy change in the object you were considering. However, you also saw earlier that when a friction-type contact interaction is involved, there is more than one type of energy change. There is also more than one type of energy output. Do you think energy is still conserved in such cases?

Is energy still conserved during a friction-type contact interaction?

Initial Ideas

In a Summarizing Question in the Activity 5 Homework, you completed an S/R energy diagram for a friction-cart slowing down as it moved along the track **after** being given an initial push.

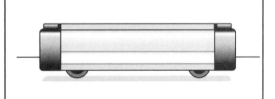

While there was no energy input in this case (because the initial push had ended), there were two energy outputs from the cart, and two types of energy change for the cart itself.

 What two types of energy were output from the cart as it moved along the track? What interactions were responsible for these outputs?

 What two types of energy changed in the cart itself? What effect did each of these energy changes have on the cart?

Which of the interactions the cart was involved in (and associated energy output) was the *cause* of the energy changes in the cart and what was the other energy output? (In other words, without which interaction would none of the energy outputs and changes have happened?)

Draw an I/O energy diagram for the cart as it slowed down while moving along the track (after the initial push). Remember to draw your diagram so that it can be read as a cause-and-effect storyline from left to right.

In this situation, with friction acting to slow the cart down, do you think energy will still be conserved or not? Explain your reasoning.

Collecting and Interpreting Evidence

STEP 1: A group of students in a previous class used the energy bar tool in the *I&M Simulator* to measure the energy changes and outputs for a friction cart as it moved along the track.

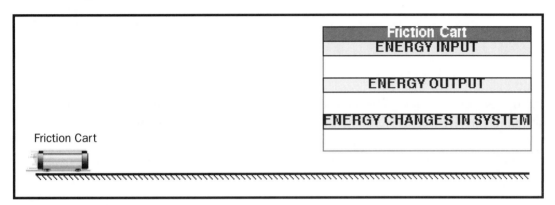

Friction Cart

Their results are shown in the table below, in units of kJ.

Friction Cart	
ENERGY INPUT	
Type of Energy = NONE	Amount = 0.00
ENERGY OUTPUT	
Type of Energy = MECHANICAL	Amount = 0.84
Type of Energy = HEAT	Amount = 0.39
ENERGY CHANGES IN SYSTEM	
Type of Energy = KINETIC	Amount = —4.99
Type of Energy = THERMAL	Amount = 3.76

Do the various types of energies shown in the table for the friction cart match those you represented in your I/O energy diagram? If not, modify your diagram accordingly.

STEP 2: Now consider the following questions about the values recorded by the students in the table.

 In the table, the change in kinetic energy is shown as a negative number, whereas the change in thermal energy is a positive number. What information do you think these signs represent?

 In the case of the friction cart slowing down as it moves along the track, does the mathematical equation you developed in this Activity accurately connect the amounts of energy input, energy output and energy changes in the cart? Use the numerical values from the table to check if that equation still works in this case. Show your work below.

Summarizing Questions

Be prepared to share your responses to the following questions during the next class period.

S1: Is energy conserved during a friction-type contact interaction? What evidence supports your answer?

S2: How is it possible for an object (like the friction cart in this activity) to have no energy input during an interaction yet still have an energy output? Use your ideas about conservation of energy to explain your thinking.

Activity 7–Explaining Phenomena Using Energy Ideas
Applying Ideas

Comparing the Class Consensus and Scientists' Ideas

During the previous activities the class developed ideas about different types of interactions and how to describe them in terms of energy. These ideas should be described in your written responses to the Summarizing Questions at the end of each activity.

Your instructor will give you a copy of the handout *Scientists' Ideas:*

Interactions and Energy. Take a few minutes to review the *Scientists' Ideas* and make sure they correspond to the ideas the class has developed, although perhaps the language may be somewhat different. In the space below each of the *Scientists' Ideas* make a note of any evidence (or examples) you have seen in this chapter that supports each idea.

Scientific Explanations Involving Ideas about Energy

In this chapter you have been developing ideas about how to describe interactions and their effects in terms of energy transfers and energy changes. You have also been practicing writing and evaluating scientific explanations using some of these ideas. However, in the previous activity you developed a very important idea about conservation of energy that seems to apply to all interactions. This idea is very powerful and can be used in the explanation of many phenomena, as you will see and practice in this activity.

Remember, one of the first decisions you must make when constructing or evaluating an explanation involving motion of an object is whether the effects of any friction-type contact interactions are minor enough to be ignored, or if they play a significant role. After you have done so, you should next draw an energy diagram that shows all the interactions, energy transfers, and energy changes relevant to the phenomenon to be explained. The issue of whether to draw an S/R energy

diagram or an I/O energy diagram will depend on the nature of the situation and what is to be explained.

If the question concerns a particular object involved in a *single* specific interaction, then either an S/R diagram or an I/O diagram would be appropriate. However, if the question concerns the behavior of a particular object that is involved in more than one interaction at the same time, then an I/O energy diagram is probably more appropriate. Occasionally, you might be asked to explain the behavior of both objects involved in a particular interaction; in this case an S/R diagram would be better suited.

In either case, whether you draw an S/R or I/O energy diagram, you should try to use ideas about conservation of energy in your written narrative. If you have drawn an S/R diagram you would choose the relevant object (usually *either* the energy source object *or* the energy receiver object) and use energy conservation ideas to explain its behavior. If you have drawn an I/O

energy source object *or* the energy receiver object) and use energy conservation ideas to explain its behavior. If you have drawn an I/O energy diagram, then just apply conservation ideas to the object in the diagram. Also, if you have decided that the effects of friction are negligible, remember to include a statement to that effect somewhere in the narrative, usually at the beginning.

Practice Explanations

The rest of this activity presents you with situations that are to be explained. In the first case we revisit a situation you have already written an explanation for, that of giving a cart a quick shove so that it moves along the track. However, now we can include ideas about friction and energy conservation in the explanation.

 EXPLANATION #1: Why did the low-friction cart start to move when it was given a push by somebody's hand?

The following explanation is intended to be good. Read it carefully and then answer the questions that follow it.

Describe the situation using a diagram:

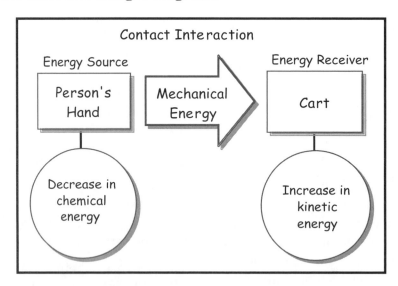

Write the narrative:

> While the hand is pushing the cart, the effects of friction are negligible, which means that the only interaction that really affects the cart during the push is the contact interaction with the hand. During this interaction, mechanical energy is transferred from the hand to the cart. Applying the idea of conservation of energy to the cart, we know that since there is no energy output from it, the energy input must therefore be accounted for by an increase in the cart's kinetic energy. This increase in its kinetic energy means that the stationary cart starts to move.

Why is it reasonable to ignore the effects of friction in this explanation?

 Use a colored pencil (or highlighter) to indicate the part of the narrative in which the idea of energy conservation is used to explain why the cart's kinetic energy increased. How could you make the same argument using the mathematical equation you developed in the previous activity? (Energy Input = Energy Output + Energy Changes.)

 Finally, use a different-colored pencil (or highlighter) to indicate the part of the narrative in which scientific ideas about energy are connected to the actual phenomenon to be explained.

Pay careful attention to the structure of the explanation above and use it as a model to guide you in writing and evaluating other explanations. In the next example, we provide some guiding questions to help you complete an explanation for a common situation encountered in sports.

 EXPLANATION #2: Why does a baseball player slow down as he slides into base?

In a close situation, a baseball player will usually choose to slide into a base rather than just run to it. (This gives him the advantage that he can be safe by just getting his fingers to the base, rather than his whole body. It is also more difficult for a fielder to tag him.)

In this explanation we want you to consider why it is that the player slows down while he is sliding into the base. (Note that this is a question about while he is sliding, not about anything he does before that.) Answering the following questions should help you in constructing an explanation.

 Do you think the effects of friction can be ignored in this situation? Why or why not?

 While he is sliding along the ground what, if anything happens, to the kinetic energy and thermal energy of the player. Why do you think so?

 While he is sliding along the ground, is there an energy input to the player? If so, of what type? Explain your thinking.

 While he is sliding along the ground are there any energy outputs from the player? If so, what type do you think they are and why?

ACTIVITY 7—**Explaining Phenomena Using Energy Ideas**

Describe the situation using a diagram: (Complete the I/O diagram for the player as he slides into base.)

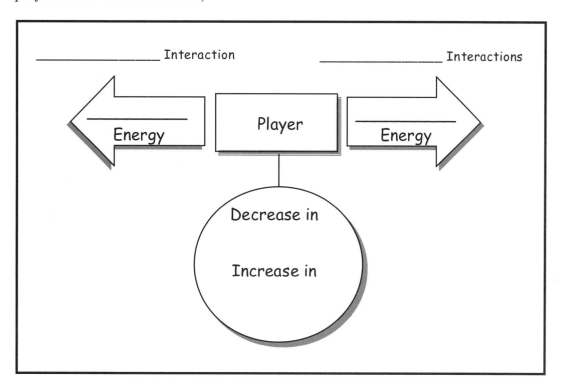

_____ Interaction   _____ Interactions

_____ Energy   Player   _____ Energy

Decrease in

Increase in

Write the narrative: (Fill in the blanks to complete the explanation for why the player slows down.)

As the player slides, he is involved in a(n) _____ interaction

with the ground. During this interaction _____ energy is transferred

from him to the ground and, at the same time, his _____ energy increases.

As a result of this increase in _____ energy, _____ energy is

transferred from him to his surroundings. Since there is no energy _____ to

the player, the _____ means these energy outputs

and increases in _____ energy must be accounted for by a _____ in the

_____ energy of the player. This decrease in his _____

means he _____ as he slides.

In the final section of this activity you will construct your own explanations for two different motions of a popular child's toy.

The Pull-Back Toy Car

YOU WILL NEED:

■ Toy car with rubber-band attachment.

Have you ever played with a toy car that has a 'pull-back' motor? To make the toy work it is placed on a surface and then pulled backwards for a short distance. When released, the toy moves forward on its own without being pushed.

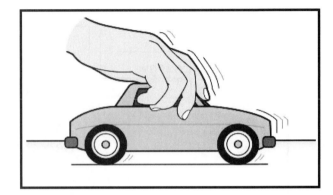

The toy car you have can work as a simple pull-back toy. Test the car and make sure that it works in this way.

 After pulling the car back and releasing it, does it move forward on its own (even if only a short distance)?

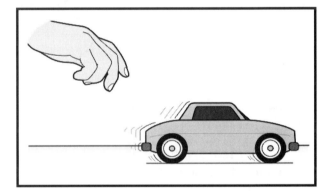

 Now examine the car and describe briefly how you think it works.

In a moment you will consider two aspects of the motion of the toy car: the first while you are pulling it back and making the rubber band (or elastic) stretch, the second just after you let go and the car starts to move. The explanation of these two situations will be much simpler if the effects of friction can be ignored.

 Why would you be justified in neglecting the effects of friction in these two situations?

The Pull-Back Process

As you have probably deduced, as you pull the car back (using your muscles) the car is involved in two contact interactions simultaneously: one with your hand and the other with the rubber band. Answer the following questions about these two interactions.

 Complete the S/R energy diagram below for the contact interaction between the hand and the car while the car is being pulled back.

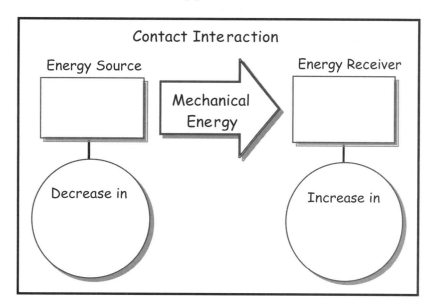

 Now complete the S/R diagram below for the contact interaction between the car and the rubber band that stretches during the pull-back process.

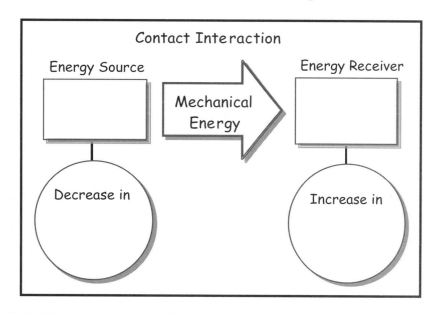

As you know from the evidence you have gathered in this chapter, and as your energy diagrams on the previous page should show, the effect of either of these contact interactions, *acting on their own*, would be to change the speed of the car. (In fact, one interaction would tend to increase its speed, while the other would tend to decrease it.) However, for most of the pull-back process (except at the very start and very end) the toy car was probably moving at a reasonably constant speed.

 Combine the two S/R energy diagram you drew above into a single diagram showing the chain of interactions the car is involved in as it is pulled back at constant speed.

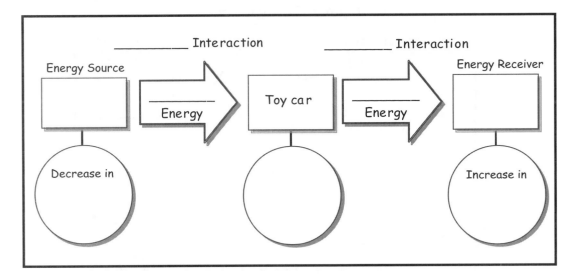

Your task now is to write a scientific explanation, using energy ideas, as to why the speed of the car does not change during the pull-back process represented by this diagram. Guiding questions are provided to help you.

 EXPLANATION #3: Why does the toy car move at a constant speed during the pull-back process?

 While the car is being pulled back, is there an energy input to it? If so, of what type? What about an energy output?

While the car is being pulled back at a constant speed, is its kinetic energy increasing, decreasing, or not changing?

 In order for the kinetic energy of the car to remain the same, would the amount of the energy input have to be less than, the same as, or greater than the amount of the energy output. Use your ideas about conservation of energy to explain your answer.

Describe the situation using a diagram: (Complete the I/O energy diagram for the toy car as it moves back at a **constant speed**.)

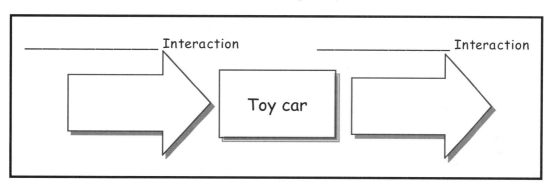

_____ Interaction   _____ Interaction

Toy car

Write the narrative: (Remember to state you are ignoring the effects of friction. Then use the Law of Conservation of energy to explain how the energy input and energy output combine to produce no change in kinetic energy.)

Finally, you should construct your own explanation for why the pull-back toy car starts to move just **after** the hand releases it.

 EXPLANATION #4: Why does the toy car start to move just after it is released?

Describe the situation using a diagram:

Write the narrative:

 Participate in a class discussion to go over the explanations.

Interactions and Forces

Purpose

"There is a contact interaction between the player's foot and the ball. Mechanical energy is transferred from the foot to the ball."

However, scientists often use a different way of describing the **same** interactions, not in terms of energy, but in terms of the pushes and pulls (which they call **forces**) that the objects exert on each other. So, for the example above, we could also say:

"There is a contact interaction between the player's foot and the ball. The foot pushes the ball" **or** *"The foot exerts a force on the ball."*

In Chapter 1 of the course you developed some ideas about how to describe contact interactions between objects in terms of a transfer of mechanical energy between the objects. For example, for a soccer player kicking the ball, previously we might have said:

In this chapter you will be investigating the effects that forces have on the motion of objects. We will start by examining how we can recognize when a force is acting on an object, and when it is not.

When does a force stop pushing an object?

CHAPTER 2

Initial Ideas

Think about a soccer player kicking a stationary ball. As he interacts with it, by kicking it, the ball starts to move. After the kick, the ball rolls across the grass and gradually comes to a halt.

 Sketch a speed-time graph for the motion of the ball. Be sure to include both the motion of the ball while the player's foot is touching it, and its motion after the foot has lost contact with it.

Speed versus Time

Speed

Time

 Using a colored pencil, indicate the period on the graph during which you think the foot was in contact with the ball and briefly explain your reasoning.

 Using a different-colored pencil, indicate the period on the graph during which you think there was a force pushing the ball forward. Again, explain your reasoning.

Why do you think the ball gradually slows down and eventually stops after it has been kicked?

 Now draw two pictures of the ball and use arrows to show what **forces** (if any) you think are acting on the ball at two different times during its motion. Label your arrows to show where the forces come from.

i) During the time foot was in contact with the ball.

ii) After the foot has lost contact and the ball is rolling across the grass.

 Briefly explain the reasoning behind your pictures.

Discuss your ideas with your team and try to agree on what the speed-time graph and 'force' picture(s) should look like. Sketch your team's graph and picture(s) on a large presentation board.

 Participate in a whole-class discussion about these questions. Make a note of any ideas or reasoning that are different from those of your team.

Collecting and Interpreting Evidence

 EXPERIMENT: Is the motion of the cart after it has been pushed the same as during the push?

YOU WILL NEED:

- Low-friction cart
- Track
- Access to a Motion Sensor connected to a computer
- Access to the *I&M Computer Simulator*

STEP 1: Open the Motion Sensor data collection file for this experiment. Place your cart at rest on the track about 20-30 cm in front of the Motion Sensor. Start collecting Motion Sensor data and then have one of your team give the cart a quick push away from the sensor. (Stop the cart when it reaches the other end of the track.)

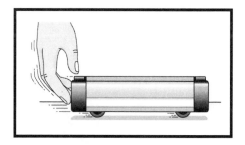

 Sketch the speed-time graph for the motion of the cart.

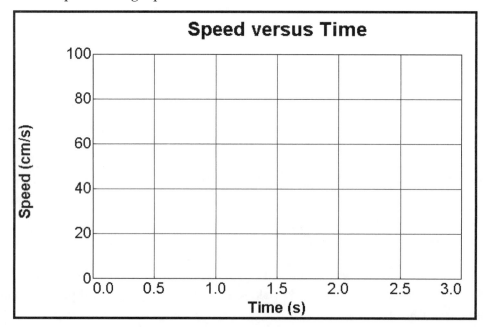

 What happens to the speed of the cart while the hand is actually in contact with it? Does it speed up quickly, slow down quickly, or move at a reasonably constant speed?

After the hand has lost contact with the cart does the behavior of the cart's speed change, or does it continue moving in the same manner as when your hand was in contact with it?

STEP 2: Return the cart to its starting position. Start collecting Motion Sensor data and then have one of your team members give the cart a **gentle** push away from the sensor with their hand. While the cart is moving, and before the data collection stops, give the cart two or three more pushes, in the **same direction** as the first push. (Stop the cart when it reaches the other end of the track.)

 Sketch the speed-time graph for the motion of the cart.

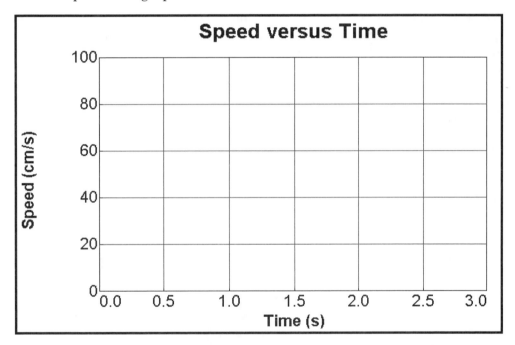

 Each time the hand interacts with the cart, what happens to the cart's speed? Does it speed up quickly, slow down quickly, or move at a reasonably constant speed?

 During the periods when the hand is not interacting with the cart what happens to the cart's speed? (Is it increasing, decreasing, or fairly constant?) Does the cart move in the same manner as when the hand is interacting with it, or is the speed behaving differently?

What evidence would you look for to tell you that a force is acting on the cart? To illustrate your thinking, use a colored pencil to indicate on the two speed-time graphs above the sections of the graph during which you think there is a force pushing the cart. Explain your reasoning below.

STEP 3: Three students are discussing the motion of the cart and the force acting on it. They all agree that while the hand is pushing it there is a force acting on the cart, but have different ideas about what happens during the periods when the hand is not in contact.

The force of the hand is transferred to the cart and is carried with it. That's why the cart keeps moving after the push.

The force of the hand stops when contact is lost, but some other force must take over to keep the cart moving.

After contact is lost there are no longer any forces acting on the cart. That's why it moves differently.

Samantha   **Victor**   **Amara**

 Do you agree with Samantha, Victor, or Amara, or with none of them? Explain your thinking.

Simulator Exploration

On the right is a speed-time graph taken from an *I&M Simulator* setup that models the experiment from STEP 2 where you pushed the cart two or three times.

Indicate the periods on the speed-time graph when you think the cart in the simulator was being pushed. How do you know?

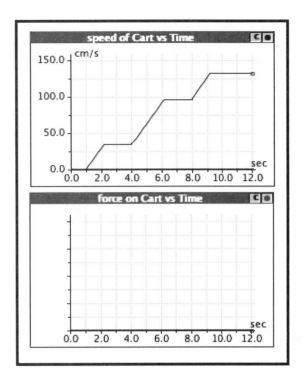

The *I&M Simulator* can also 'measure' the force acting on the cart in the simulator model. On the blank force-time graph above, sketch how you think the force acting on the simulator cart varies (if at all) during the same 12-second time period shown on the speed-time graph. (Note: It is only the shape of the graph that is important for now, so no values for the force are shown.)

Explain the reasoning that led you to draw your force-time graph the way you did.

STEP 4: You can use the *I&M Simulator* to compare your ideas with those scientists' ideas upon which the simulator model is based. Open the simulator setup file for this activity. (See your instruction sheet if you've forgotten how to do this.) The setup shows a cart on a track, together with speed-time and force-time graphs

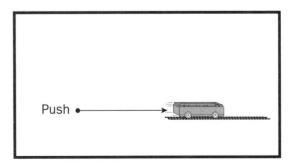

While the simulator is running you can give the cart a 'push' by pressing on the spacebar of your computer keyboard. The push will continue (at a constant strength) as long as you hold the spacebar down. The simulator will stop on its own after 12 seconds.

Run the simulator a few times (remember to click 'rewind' to get back to the start) and check that you understand how the spacebar 'push' works. When you are ready, try to reproduce the speed-time graph from STEP 3.

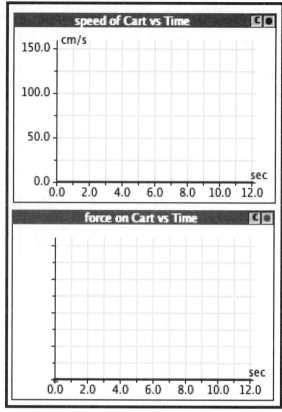

 Sketch the speed-time and force-time graphs from the simulator.

 During the periods when the simulator cart was being pushed was there a force acting on it? What evidence from the simulator graphs supports your idea?

 During the periods in between the pushes, was there a force acting on the simulator cart? Again, what evidence from the graphs supports your idea?

Forces and Force Diagrams

The pushes you used in this activity are examples of forces. Whenever one object is pushing or pulling on another object we say it is exerting a force on the other object. Notice that this means the pushes and pulls you used in Chapter 1 to investigate contact interactions could also be described in terms of forces exerted on the cart by a person, another cart, or a rubber band.

Just as with the energy description of contact interactions you developed in Chapter 1, we can also draw a diagram to help us analyze and explain the force description of the same interactions. In such a force diagram, we identify the object of interest and all the forces (pushes and pulls) being exerted on it by **other** objects at a **particular moment in time**. We represent these forces with 'force arrows' on the diagram, which are labeled to show what they represent. For example, the force of your hand pushing the cart could be represented like this:

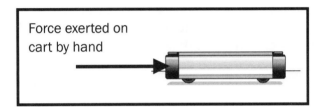

As you might expect, the direction of these force arrows indicates the direction of the forces they represent. In addition, the length of the arrows is drawn to indicate the relative strengths of the forces. So, for example, if you pushed the cart in the other direction, with a stronger push, the force diagram would look like this (note the longer arrow):

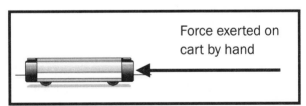

Notice that the force diagram shows only one of the objects involved in the interaction (the cart), and that the other object involved (the hand) is only mentioned in the labeling of the arrow representing the force it is exerting. In this sense these force diagrams are very like the Input/Output (I/O) energy diagrams you drew at the end of Chapter 1.

The strength of a force is measured in units of newtons (N), named in honor of Sir Isaac Newton, a famous English scientist you will learn more about later on. Your instructor will give you a spring-scale that can be used to measure the strength of forces in units of newtons. Pull on the scale to get a feeling for forces of different strengths (in newtons).

CHAPTER 2

Sometimes it may be necessary to add information on the strength of a force to a force diagram. For example, if a hand pulls on a cart with a force of 2 N, that would be represented by the following diagram[1]:

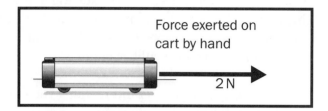

Finally, if the object is moving at the moment in time for which we are drawing the force diagram, then it is important to know in which direction. When this is relevant we can show this by drawing a speed arrow above the object (just like the speed arrow in the *I&M Simulator*). (We use a half-arrow so as not to confuse it with the force-arrows, since it represents the speed of the cart, **not** a force acting on the cart.) The length of the speed arrow represents the relative speed of the object. For example, when you gave the moving cart a push in the same direction as its motion, the force diagram would look like this:

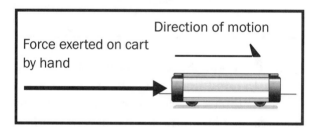

Note that the speed arrow only tells about the speed of the object at the particular moment in time for which the force diagram is being drawn. It does not tell anything about whether the object's speed is in the process of changing, or whether it is remaining constant.

You may have noticed that all the situations discussed above show only one force acting on the cart. It is certainly possible for more than one force to act on an object at the same time, but it is important to understand the effect of a single force before considering situations involving multiple forces. Thus, in the activities that follow, you will study the effect that a single force has on an object. Later in this chapter you will examine situations where more than one force acts on an object at the same time.

---

[1] As you saw in Chapter 1, a push and a pull of the same strength have exactly the same effect on the motion of an object. Thus, we could equally well represent this pull to the right using exactly the same force arrow as we would use for a push to the right. Since the effect is the same, whether we choose to distinguish between pushes and pulls is a matter of choice. In this course, we will always draw force arrows on the side of the object from which the force is applied. Hence, a push will always be represented by a force arrow pointing toward the object, and a pull will always be represented by an arrow pointing away from the object.

Summarizing Questions

 First discuss these questions with your team and note your ideas. Leave space to add any different ideas that may emerge when the whole class discusses their thinking.

S1: While the hand is exerting a force on the cart, what is the motion of the cart like? What evidence from this activity supports your idea?

S2: Do you think the force of the hand was transferred from the hand to the cart during the interaction between them, and then continued to act on it after contact was lost? What evidence supports your idea?

S3: At what moment do you think the force of the hand stopped acting on the cart?

S4: During a contact interaction, what do you think is transferred from the source to the receiver: energy, force, both, or neither? Explain your reasoning.

Comparing Force and Energy Diagrams

In Chapter 1 you explained the behavior of objects during contact interactions in terms of a transfer of mechanical energy from one interacting object to the other. In this chapter you are developing ideas that will help explain the same interactions in terms of the force that one of the interacting objects exerts on the other.

To help you start thinking about how these two ways of describing contact interactions relate to each other, consider the situation of a stationary cart that is given a quick shove with a hand to start it moving. Shown at right is a timeline of I/O energy diagrams showing how the energy transfer to the cart and changes in its kinetic energy are related to the interaction.

 Below the energy diagrams are three pictures of the cart. Use these pictures to draw force diagrams, representing the force (due to the contact interaction between the cart and the hand) acting on the cart at the same three points in time as the energy diagrams. (Be sure to include force and speed arrows as you think appropriate. However, if you think there is no force acting at a particular time, then do not draw a force arrow.)

 Participate in a whole-class discussion to go over your answers to the Summarizing Questions and force diagrams.

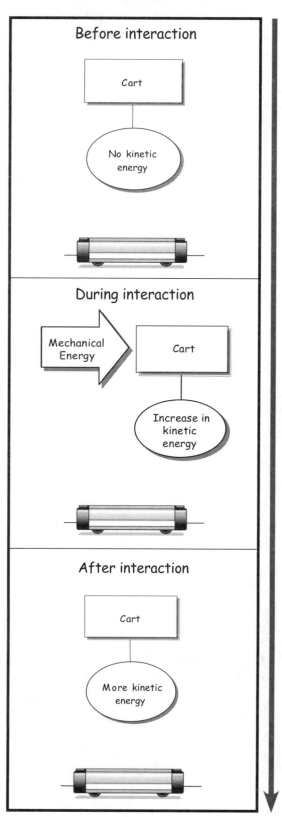

Purpose

In Activity 1 you saw the effect that quick pushes had on the motion of a

cart. This is like the situation in many sports, where the players move the ball (or puck) around using quick pushes of their hands, feet, or a bat/racket of some kind.

But what would the motion of an object be like if it were involved in a contact interaction for a long time, that is, if a constant strength push were applied to it **continuously**? For example, suppose your friend was standing balanced on a skateboard and you pushed, and kept on pushing, with the same strength force, in the same direction. What would his motion be like?

 How does an object move when a single force of constant strength continuously acts on it?

Initial Ideas

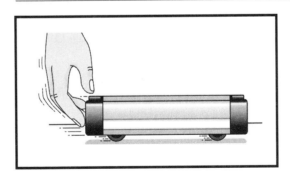

Imagine you had a low-friction cart at rest at one end of the track in front of you. Now, suppose you were to interact with it by pushing the cart continuously from behind with a **constant-strength push.**

 What do you think the motion of the cart would be like under these circumstances?

Sketch a speed-time graph to illustrate your idea.

Speed versus Time

Speed

Time

 Briefly explain your reasoning.

Sketch your team's speed-time graph on a presentation board and participate in a short whole-class discussion about everyone's ideas. Make a note of any ideas, or reasoning, that are different from your own.

Collecting and Interpreting Evidence

 EXPERIMENT: What happens to the cart when it is given a continuous push?

YOU WILL NEED:

- Low-friction cart
- Track
- Fan unit
- Glove (optional)
- Access to a Motion Sensor connected to a computer
- Access to the *I&M Computer Simulator*

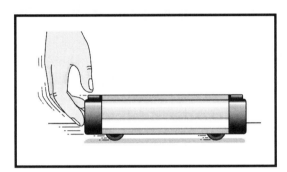 **STEP 1:** Place the cart near one end of the track (or table). Each member of your team should try using **one finger** to push the cart along the track. (Make sure you push the cart from behind and do not grip it with your fingers.) Try to maintain a constant-strength push as the cart moves.

 How does the cart seem to behave as you push it?

 How easy did it seem to maintain a continuous, constant-strength, push? Why do you think this is?

In reality, most people find it very difficult to maintain a continuous push of a constant strength. We will now check to see if there is a better way to arrange for such a force to act on the cart.

STEP 2: Fix the fan unit to the cart and place it, at rest, on the track (or table).

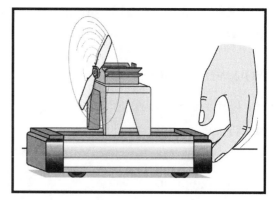

> The team member operating the fan may wish to use a glove for protection if the fan blades are exposed.

Turn the fan unit on and have one of your team place a finger in front of the cart to stop it from moving. This person should concentrate on the push they feel from the cart while the fan is running. At the same time, another team member should listen to the sound the fan unit makes while it is running. Keep the fan running for several seconds and then turn it off.

 How does the push of the cart seem to behave while the fan is running? Does the push seem to stay constant or does it seem to increase or decrease significantly?

 Does the sound that the fan makes change as it is running, or does it sound about the same the whole time?

 Do you think the fan unit exerted a constant-strength force on the cart while it was running? What evidence supports your idea?

CHAPTER 2

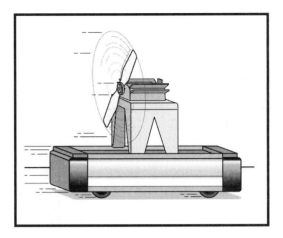

STEP 3: Place the cart (with fan unit attached) on the track. Turn the fan unit on and then release the cart. (Do **not** give it any sort of push or pull with your hand.) One team member should listen carefully to the sound of the fan while the cart is moving.

Carefully stop the cart before it reaches the other end of the track and turn the fan unit off.

 How does the cart seem to move as the fan unit pushes it along the track? Does it seem to move at a reasonably constant speed, or does it seem to speed up as it moves?

 Do you think the fan unit exerted a constant strength force on the cart as it moved along the track? What evidence do you have to support your answer?

STEP 4: Open the Motion Sensor data collection file for this activity. Place the cart about 20-30 cm in front of the Motion Sensor and collect data while the fan unit pushes the cart away from the sensor.

Sketch the speed-time graph for the motion of the cart below.

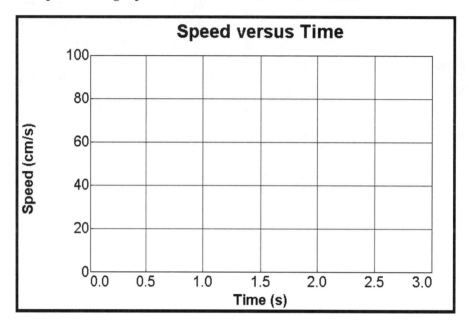

What does the speed-time graph tell you about the speed of the cart while the fan unit was pushing it? Does this confirm your idea from STEP 3?

STEP 5: Suppose you could repeat this experiment using a longer track. Do you think the fan-cart would continue to speed up in this case, or do you think something else would happen?

Suppose you could join three tracks together end-to-end and release the fan cart from one end of this extended track. Do you think the fan-cart would continue to speed up as it moved along all three tracks, or do you think something else would happen? Explain your thinking.

Your instructor will now show you a video of a previous class testing their ideas by running a fan-cart along one, then two, then three tracks.

 What does the video show? Does the speed of the cart keep increasing, even over the length of three tracks?

Simulator Exploration

STEP 6: Again, you can use the *I&M Simulator* to compare your ideas with the simulator model. Open the simulator setup file for this activity. Run the simulator and hold the spacebar down to apply a **continuous constant-strength force** to the cart. (As the fan unit does to the real cart.)

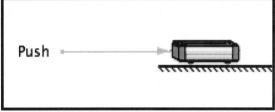

 Sketch the speed-time and force-time graphs from the simulator.

 Based on the evidence you have gathered in this activity, what happens to the speed of an object while a single force is acting on it in the same direction as its motion?

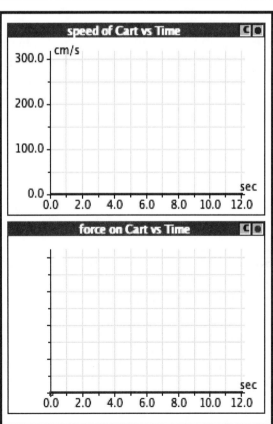

Look back at your initial ideas for the behavior of the speed of the cart at the beginning of this activity. Do the results from these experiments confirm your initial ideas, or not?

Summarizing Questions

First, discuss these questions with your team and note your ideas. Leave space to add any different ideas that may emerge when the whole class discusses their thinking.

S1: If a cart is at rest and a single force acts on it, what happens? If the same force continues to act on the cart what happens to the cart's speed?

S2: In general, during the time a single force with a **constant strength** acts on a moving object, in the **same direction as its motion**, what is the object's motion like? Does it move at a constant speed, does its speed continuously increase, or does the speed only increase at first and then become constant after a short time? What evidence from this activity supports your thinking?

S3: When you were using your finger to try to push the cart with a constant strength force, you probably noticed the cart was 'getting away' from you. (If not, try it again.) Why do you think the cart behaved in this way?

CHAPTER 2

S4: Suppose that, while the cart was being pushed along the track by the fan unit, a wire suddenly broke so that the fan unit stopped pushing on the cart. What do you think would happen to the speed of the cart? Explain your reasoning.

S5: At the beginning of Activity 1 of this chapter you sketched a speed-time graph for a soccer ball that was given a quick kick and then slowed to a stop as it rolled across the grass. Sketch this graph again below, with any changes from the original you wish to make.

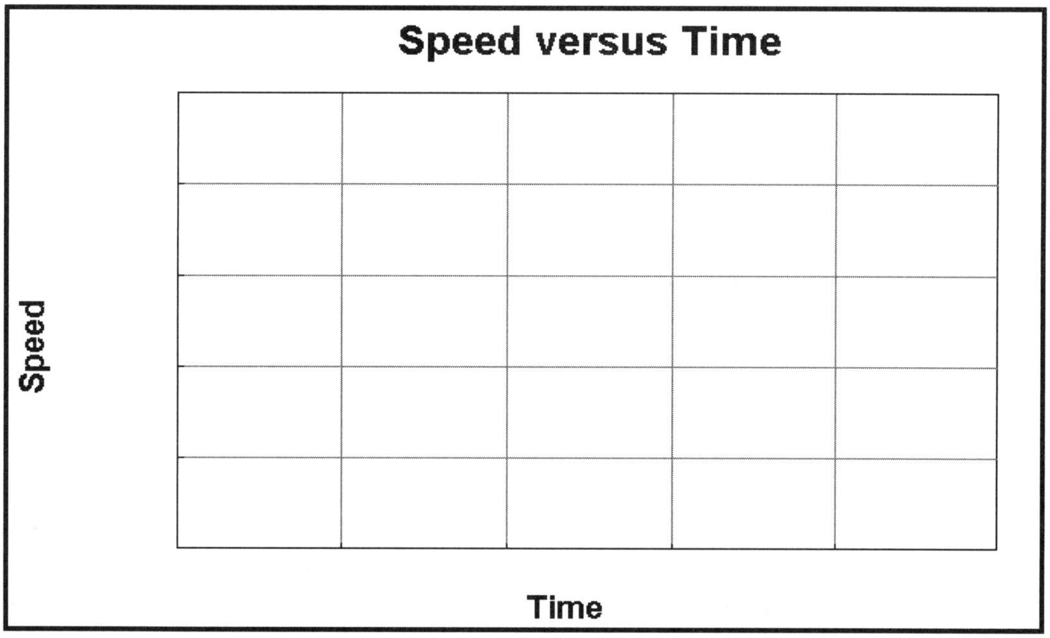

Speed versus Time

Speed

Time

If you made any changes from the graph you drew in Activity 1, briefly describe them, and your reasoning for making them.

S6: On the graph you drew in the previous question, use different colored pencils to indicate:

a) The section (or sections) of the graph during which there was a contact interaction between the foot and the ball

b) The section (or sections) of the graph during which a force acted on the ball in the same direction as its motion

Explain your reasoning for choosing these sections.

Do You Think the Speed Keeps Increasing?

Two students in a previous class were discussing what they thought would happen if they could join many, many tracks together and arrange for a fan unit to push a cart along this extremely long track.

I think that as long as the fan keeps pushing on it, no matter how long the track is, the cart will keep speeding up.

I agree that the cart will speed up for a while, but I just don't believe it could keep speeding up forever. I think that at some point its speed will become constant.

Han

Samantha

 Do you agree with Han, Samantha, or neither of them? Explain your thinking.

Writing Scientific Explanations Using Force Ideas

As previously stated, the contact interactions you are examining in this chapter are the same as those you were introduced to in Chapter 1. However, in Chapter 1 you described these interactions in terms of ideas about energy transfers and changes; in this chapter you are developing ideas about forces and their effects that will allow you to think about these same interactions in a different way.

The process of writing scientific explanations of phenomena using force ideas is very similar to the process you used in Chapter 1 when using energy ideas. However, instead of drawing an energy diagram, you should draw a **force diagram.** (The procedure for drawing and interpreting force diagrams is given in Activity 1 of this chapter.) Also, instead of writing a narrative that describes the behavior of an object in terms of energy transfers and changes, you should do so in terms of the **forces** acting on the object and the effect they have on its motion (if any).

When writing your scientific explanations you should keep in mind the criteria of *accuracy*, *completeness*, *logical reasoning* and *clarity* introduced in Chapter 1. You should also use these criteria to evaluate the explanations written by others. (As a reminder, if all the criteria are met, the explanation should be considered *good*. If one or more of the criteria is not met, then the explanation should be considered *poor* and in need of revision.)

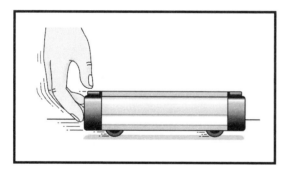

To illustrate the similarities between energy-based and force-based explanations, consider the following two parallel explanations of why a stationary cart begins to move when it is given a quick push by someone's hand.

These explanations do not mention friction since we have not yet considered its effect in developing our ideas about forces. However, since we are dealing with a low-friction cart, it can be assumed that the effects of friction are negligible.

EXPLANATION: Why does a stationary cart begin to move when it is pushed?

Describe the interaction using a diagram:

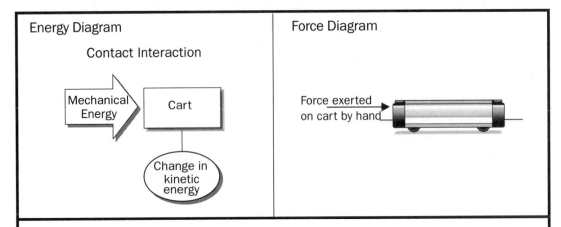

Energy Diagram

Contact Interaction

Mechanical Energy → Cart

Change in kinetic energy

Force Diagram

Force exerted on cart by hand

Write the narrative:

During the contact interaction between the hand and the cart, there is a transfer of mechanical energy to the cart. According to the idea of Conservation of Energy, since there is no energy output, this input of energy must be accounted for completely by an increase in the kinetic energy of the cart. Since the cart is initially at rest, this increase in kinetic energy means that the cart starts moving.

The only force acting on the cart is that exerted by the hand. When a single force acts on an object at rest, the object starts to move in the direction of the force, so the cart starts to move in the direction of the force exerted by the hand.

So one explanation says that the cart starts to move because Conservation of Energy suggests that the mechanical energy input to the cart results in an increase in its kinetic energy, while the other says it moves because the hand exerts a force on it during the interaction between them. Which explanation is better? They are **both** good – they are just two different ways of looking at the **same interaction**, one based on the ideas of energy, the other on the ideas of forces. Further, as you are seeing in this chapter, though these two sets of ideas are different, they are closely related.

The previous explanation was meant to show you how both energy and force ideas can be used to explain the same phenomenon. For the remaining explanations in this chapter you should consider, and use, **only** force ideas.

In this activity you saw that a cart with a fan unit attached started to move when the fan was turned on, and continued to speed up as it moved along the track. You should now use one of the ideas you developed about force and motion in this activity to write a scientific explanation for why this happened.

 EXPLANATION: Why did the cart with a fan-unit attached continue to speed up as it moved along the track?

Describe the situation using a diagram: (Draw a force diagram for the cart while it is moving along the track and being pushed by the fan unit.)

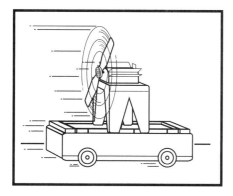

Write the narrative: (Use the idea you developed in this activity about what happens to the speed of a moving object when a continuous force acts on it in the same direction as its motion.)

 Participate in a whole-class discussion about the summarizing questions and scientific explanation.

Name:_____ Date:_____ Group: _____

Purpose

In this homework activity you will practice using your developing ideas about how the motion of an object is related to the force acting on it. Imagine you see your friend **coasting** toward you on his skateboard. (How he started moving is not a concern here.)

■ From the moment you first see him it takes four seconds for him to reach you.

■ As he reaches you, you begin to push him in the same direction as his motion, with a **constant-strength push**. You continue to push in this way for four seconds and then you stop pushing.

■ Your friend continues to move, coasting in the same direction, for another four seconds.

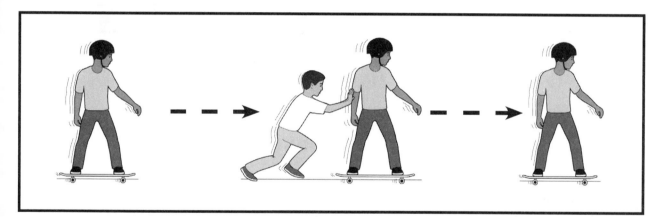

Initial Ideas

 What do you think the motion of your friend would be like (speeding up, slowing down, or constant speed) during each of the four-second periods described above? Would they all be the same or would they be different? Explain your reasoning. (Note: Assume the skateboard is well lubricated, so that the effects of friction can be ignored.)

Sketch what you think the speed-time and force-time graphs for your friend would look like for the whole 12-second period described above.

> **You do not need to worry about particular values for the speed and force. However, you do need to pay attention to the time axis so that any corresponding 'events' in the two graphs line up with each other.**

 Explain why you drew the graphs the way you did.

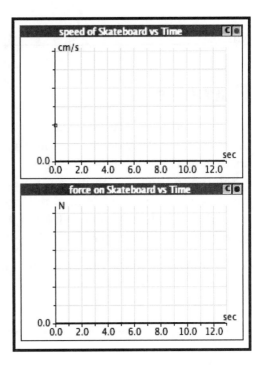

 Using the pictures of the skateboarder below, draw a separate force diagram for each indicated time. (Use your predicted speed-time and force-time graphs above to guide you.) Be sure to include both speed arrows of appropriate lengths **and** any force arrows you think are appropriate.

| 2 seconds | 6 seconds | 10 seconds |

Briefly explain your force diagrams and how the speed arrows and force arrows (if any) you drew on all three diagrams correspond to your predicted speed-time and force-time graphs.

Collecting and Interpreting Evidence

 SIMULATOR EXPLORATION. Now open the *I&M Simulator* setup file for this homework assignment in your web-browser. (See the earlier handout for details on how to do this.) This setup is very similar to those you have already seen in class; you can apply a force to the skateboarder by holding down the spacebar on the keyboard.

 Before running the simulator, describe how you will use the spacebar to reproduce the pattern of forces you drew on your force-time graph.

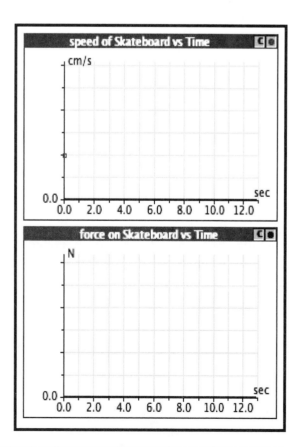

 Now run the simulator and apply the spacebar force as you described above. Sketch the speed-time and force-time graphs produced by the simulator model.

Does the pattern of forces you applied in the simulator model produce a speed-time graph that agrees with your prediction? (Remember, only the shape of the graph is important.)

 If not, return to the simulator and experiment to try and understand why this is. Explain any new ideas you may have.

 Look back at the three force diagrams you drew for the skateboarder before using the simulator. Are the **force arrows** you drew consistent with the simulator model results? If not, describe how you would change the force arrows and why.

 Looking at the same three force diagrams, are the lengths of the **speed arrows** you drew consistent with the speeds shown by the simulator speed-time graph? If not, describe how you would change the speed arrows and why.

Summarizing Questions

Answer these questions as part of the homework assignment. Be prepared to add any different ideas that may emerge during the whole-class discussion.

S1: During which period(s) of time was there a mechanical energy transfer to the skateboarder? (Before he interacted with the person pushing him, during the interaction, after the interaction, more than one, or all of these?) How do you know?

S2: During which period(s) of time was there a force acting on the skateboarder in the same direction as his motion? (Before he interacted with the person pushing him, during the interaction, after the interaction, more than one, or all of these?) How do you know?

S3: Suppose you are watching an ice-hockey game. As the puck is sliding across the ice at a relatively constant speed, it passes close to a player, who hits it (with his stick) in the same direction as it is already moving. After the hit, you notice that the puck is moving much faster than it was before the hit. Use your ideas about forces to write a scientific explanation for why the puck's speed is greater after the hit than it was before.

EXPLANATION: Why was the puck moving faster after being hit?

Describe the situation using a diagram: (Draw a force diagram for the puck during the interaction that made the speed change. Remember to include speed and force arrows as you think appropriate.)

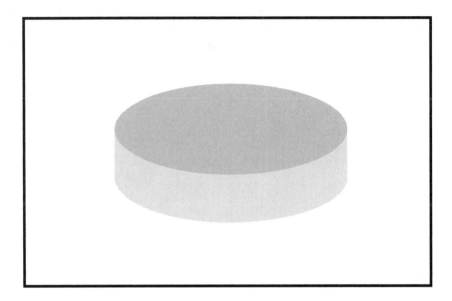

Write the narrative: (Use ideas about forces to connect the increase in speed to the force acting on the puck during the hit.)

Purpose

In the first two activities of this chapter, you saw that when an object is moving, a force applied in the same direction as the motion makes its speed increase. But what if the force is applied in the opposite direction to that which the object is moving?

For example, suppose that while your friend is coasting along on his skateboard, you gave him a quick gentle push in the opposite direction to that in which he was moving. What do you think his motion would be like during your push? What about after your push?

Would something different happen if, instead of a quick push, you kept up a continuous constant push on your friend?

 What effect does a backward push have on the motion of an object?

Initial Ideas

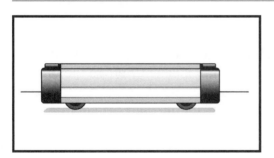

Imagine you started a low-friction cart moving along the track (or table) in front of you and then, while it was still moving, you gave it a very gentle tap with your hand in the **opposite direction** to its motion. After your tap you note that the cart is still moving in its **original direction.**

Sketch a speed-time graph for the motion of the cart. Be sure to include the motion of the cart before you tap it, while you are touching it, and after your hand has lost contact with it.

Speed versus Time

Speed

Time

 Briefly explain the reasoning behind your graph.

 Use the pictures below to draw three force diagrams (including both force and speed arrows where appropriate) for the cart; one for a moment **before** the tap (for which the speed arrow is already included), one **during** the short time that you were tapping it, and a third for a moment just **after** your tap. Remember to label any force arrows you draw.

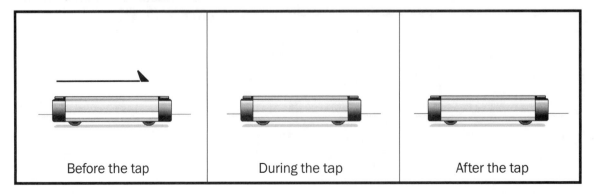

Before the tap   During the tap   After the tap

Briefly explain the reasoning behind your force arrows and speed arrows.

Collecting and Interpreting Evidence

 EXPERIMENT #1: What effect does a short backward push have?

YOU WILL NEED:

- Low-friction cart

- Track

- Access to a Motion Sensor connected to a computer

- Access to the *I&M Computer Simulator*

STEP 1: Place your cart at rest on the track Now one of your team should give it a quick push, just to get it started. As the cart is moving, someone else should give it some **very gentle** taps in the direction opposite to its motion.

STEP 2: Now open the Motion Sensor data collection file for this experiment. Place your cart at rest on the track (or table) about 20-30 cm in front of the Motion Sensor. Start collecting Motion Sensor data and then repeat the procedure from STEP 1.

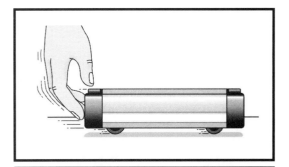

Practice doing this first and make sure that these taps are gentle enough that the cart does not stop moving until after at least three taps.

Sketch the speed-time graph for the motion of the cart.

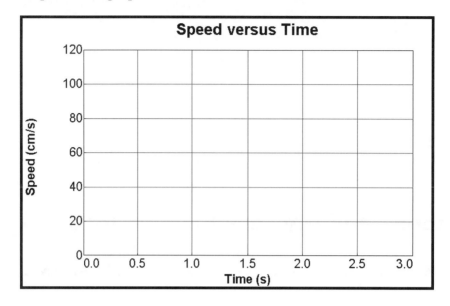

 What was the motion of the cart like during the short periods of time that the hand was interacting with it? Was it speeding up quickly, slowing down quickly, or moving at a reasonably constant speed?

 In between the taps how does the cart appear to move? Does it appear to speed up significantly, slow down significantly, or move at a reasonably constant speed?

Simulator Exploration

STEP 3: You can use the *I&M Simulator* to compare your ideas with the simulator model. Open the simulator setup file for this activity. In this setup the cart is given a quick push to get it going; then you can apply gentle backward taps by holding down the spacebar for a short time.

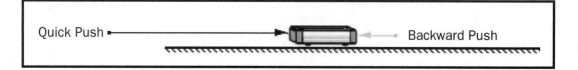

Start the simulator and after about two seconds apply a backward tap by holding down the spacebar for about one second. Apply two or three more similar backward taps before the simulator stops. Sketch the speed-time and force-time graphs for the cart and mark the short periods where a backward tap was applied.

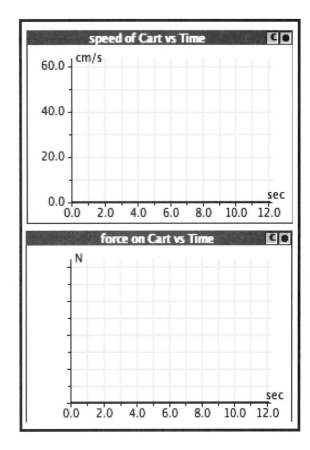

 What do you think the strong force shown at the beginning of the force-time graph represents?

 What happens to the speed of the cart during each backward push?

 In the simulator model does a force act on the cart during these pushes? What evidence supports your idea?

 In between the backward pushes how does the speed of the cart behave?

Does a force act on the cart during these times? How does the force-time graph tell you this?

EXPERIMENT #2: What effect does a continuous backward push have?

YOU WILL NEED:

- Low-friction cart
- Track
- Fan unit
- Glove (optional)
- Access to a Motion Sensor connected to a computer
- Access to the *I&M Computer Simulator*

STEP 1: Now imagine that, after giving the cart a quick push to start it moving, you applied a **continuous**, **constant-strength** push in the opposite direction to its motion (instead of applying gentle backward taps).

What do you think the motion of the cart would be like in this case? Explain your reasoning.

Sketch what you think the speed-time graph would look like in this case.

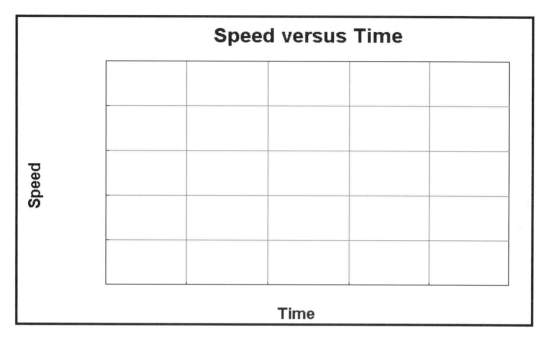

STEP 2: Open the Motion Sensor data collection file for this experiment. Mount the fan unit on the cart. Place the cart at rest on the track about 20-30 cm from the Motion Sensor, so that the fan unit will push **TOWARD** the sensor.

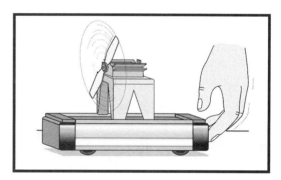

Turn the fan unit on and hold the cart still. Start the data collection and then give the cart a quick push **AWAY FROM** the sensor with your hand. Allow the cart to return to the starting position before stopping it and turning the fan off.

 Describe the motion of the cart.

Sketch the speed-time graph for the motion of the cart.

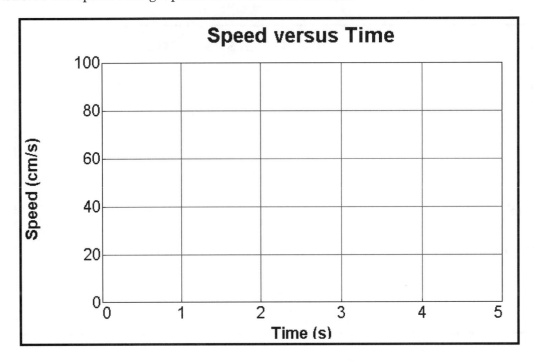

 While the cart is moving **away** from its starting position (**after** the initial push) is it speeding up, slowing down, or moving at a reasonably constant speed? Why do you think this is?

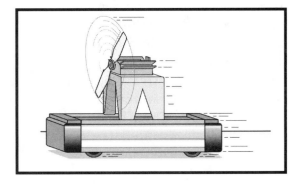

 While the cart is moving back **toward** its starting position, is it speeding up, slowing down, or moving at a reasonably constant speed? Why is the cart moving in this manner now?

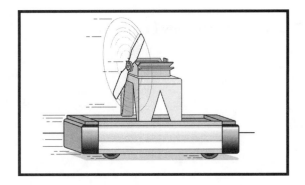

Simulator Exploration

STEP 3: You can again use the *I&M Simulator* to compare your ideas with the simulator model. Use the same setup file as before, but this time use the spacebar to apply a continuous backward push to the cart for the whole period the simulator is running.

 Sketch the speed-time graph for the cart.

 Mark the point on the speed-time graph where the cart changed direction. Explain briefly how you knew where this point was on the graph.

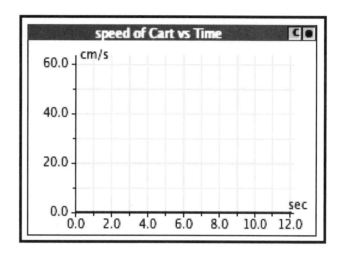

Run the simulator again and pay attention to the directions of both the speed arrow and the force arrow representing the push of the fan unit on the cart.

 When the speed arrow and the force arrow are pointing in the same direction, what is happening to the speed of the cart?

 What about when they are pointing in opposite directions?

Summarizing Questions

S1: If an object is **already moving**, what effect on its speed does a single force applied in the direction **opposite** to its motion have? If such a force continues to act, what else may happen?

S2: Shown below are two force diagrams for a moving cart upon which a force (from a fan unit) is acting. What will the motion of the cart be like in each case? (Speeding up, slowing down, or constant speed.) Explain your reasoning.

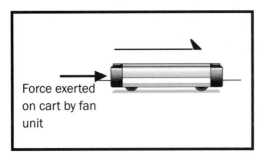

Force exerted on cart by fan unit

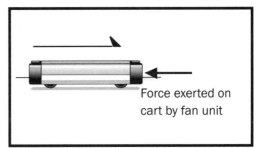

Force exerted on cart by fan unit

S3: In the last three activities you have studied the effect of a single force acting on an object under different circumstances. When an object is moving, what would be evidence that it is currently being acted upon by a single force?

S4: In an experiment you performed in Activity 2 of Chapter 1 you pushed a cart so that it moved along the track. You then gave it a quick tap with your hand to change its direction and send it back toward its starting point.

Using the ideas you developed in this activity, you should now be able to explain this change in direction in terms of the force the hand exerted on the cart and the effect it had on the cart's motion.

Complete the following scientific explanation for why the cart reversed direction when it was hit by the hand.

 EXPLANATION: Why did the cart reverse direction when it was hit by the hand?

Describe the situation using a diagram: (The force diagram currently shows a cart moving to the left. Draw and label the appropriate force arrow for the interaction with the hand that will make the cart reverse direction.)

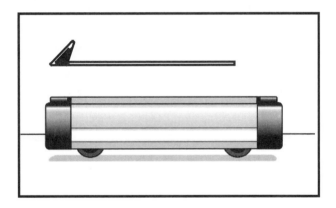

Write the narrative: (Fill in the blanks to complete the explanation.)

After the initial push, the cart was moving along the track at a _____

speed. When it came into contact with the hand, the _____ exerted a

force on the _____ in the _____ direction _____

motion. When a force acts on a moving object in the _____ direction

_____ motion its speed will _____, and if the

force continues the object will eventually _____ and then

_____. The force of the _____ continues to act on

the _____ and so it _____ and then _____.

Connecting Force and Energy Ideas

In the first three activities of this chapter you have developed some ideas about how the motion of an object is affected when a single force is exerted on it. Two students were discussing how these ideas are related to the ideas developed in Chapter 1 about how to change the kinetic energy of an object.

I think energy and force are both the same. During a contact interaction both energy and force are transferred from one object to another. So, after the interaction, one object has more energy and force than it had before, and the other has less energy and force.

I don't think they are the same. I think that the force is only there while the two objects interact with each other and that's when the energy is transferred. When there is no interaction, there is no force, and so no energy transfer.

Dave

Luisa

 Do you agree with Dave, Luisa, or neither of them? Explain your thinking.

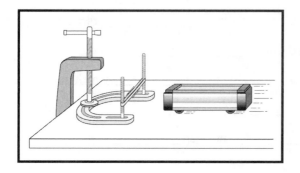

In Activity 3 of Chapter 1 you pushed a cart so that it rebounded from a rubber band. In that activity you described this rebound in terms of two separate contact interactions; one in which the cart was an energy source and the other in which it was an energy receiver.

To further explore the connection between force and energy ideas, let us think about this situation using both sets of ideas. Consider four separate moments in time:

A. A moment sometime after the cart was given its initial push, but **before** it hit the rubber band.

B. A moment **during** the short period when the cart was slowing down as the rubber band was being stretched.

C. A moment **during** the short period while the rubber band was pushing the cart away again.

D. A moment **after** the cart has rebounded from the rubber band and is moving back toward its starting point.

In the left column of the table below are several statements about interactions, energy, and forces that could apply to the cart rebounding from the rubber band.

 If you think a statement is true for one of the four moments listed above, place a check mark in the appropriate box in the table. If you think it is false for that moment, leave the box blank.

> **You can assume the effects of friction are negligible.**

Statement	A	B	C	D
There is a contact interaction between the cart and the rubber band.				
Mechanical energy is being transferred from the cart to the rubber band.				
Mechanical energy is being transferred from the rubber band to the cart.				
The kinetic energy of the cart is decreasing.				
The kinetic energy of the cart is increasing.				
A force in the direction opposite to its motion is being exerted on the cart by the rubber band.				
A force in the same direction as its motion is being exerted on the cart by the rubber band.				

Shown below are both I/O energy diagrams and force diagrams that give the complete 'storyline' for the cart reversing direction. Look at the diagrams and pay careful attention to when the kinetic energy of the cart changes, when mechanical energy transfers occur, and when a force acts on the cart.

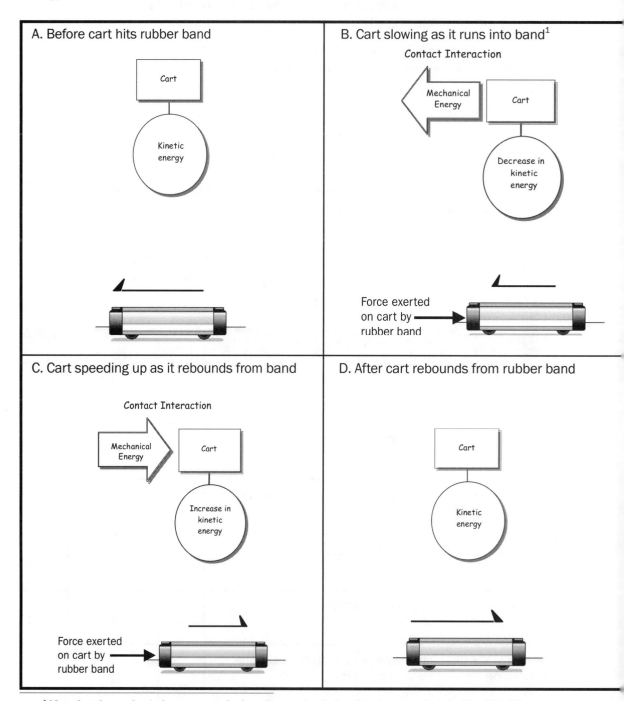

---

[1] Note that the mechanical energy transfer from the cart (to the hand) is shown on the left side of this I/O energy diagram, because this transfer can be regarded as the cause of the decrease in kinetic energy and so can be thought of as happening first. This left-to-right cause-and-effect interpretation of I/O energy diagrams was discussed in Chapter 1.

Now answer these questions about the relationship between the direction in which a single force acts on an object and the transfer of mechanical energy in the corresponding contact interaction.

 When a single force acts on an object in the **same** direction as its motion, is mechanical energy transferred into or out of the object? How do you know?

 When a single force acts on an object in the direction **opposite** to its motion, is mechanical energy transferred into or out of the object? Again, how do you know?

 Participate in a whole-class discussion to go over your answers to the Summarizing Questions and to discuss your thinking about how force and energy ideas are connected.

Activity 3 Homework 1—Combinations of Forces
Developing Ideas

Name:_____ Date:_____ Group:_____

Purpose

Up to now you have considered situations where only a single force has acted on an object. But what if there is more than one force? For example, suppose two hockey players try to hit the puck at the same time? How should we treat the forces acting on the puck to understand its motion? In this homework you will use the *I&M Simulator* to investigate scientists' ideas about how forces combine to affect the motion of objects.

> **How do objects behave when more than one force acts on them?**

Initial Ideas

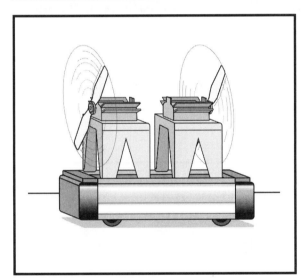

Imagine you had a cart with two fan units mounted on it, so that they push on the cart in opposite directions and with **different strengths**.

Now suppose you turned both the fan units on and gave the cart a quick shove along the track in the same direction that the **stronger fan** is pushing.

 What do you think the motion of the cart would be like just **after** your push? Would it speed up, slow down, or move at a reasonably constant speed? Explain your reasoning.

Suppose that you repeated the experiment, but this time gave a quick shove in the same direction that the **weaker fan** is pushing. How do you think the speed of the cart would behave now, just **after** your push? Again, explain your reasoning.

Collecting and Interpreting Evidence

 SIMULATOR EXPLORATION #1: What effect do combinations of forces have on an object at rest?

In these steps you will use the simulator model to examine scientists' ideas about the effect that a combination of two forces has on an object that is **initially at rest**. You will also consider what strength a single force, acting on an otherwise identical cart, should have to produce the same effect.

STEP 1: Open the first simulator setup for this activity. The upper cart in the setup (Cart 1) has two fan units pushing on it in the **same** direction, with individual force strengths of 30 N and 20 N. A speed-time graph for this cart is shown on the lower left.

 The cart is initially at rest. How does Cart 1 move when you run the simulator? (Speed up, slow down, or constant speed.)

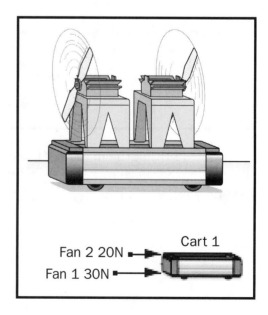

STEP 2: The lower cart in the setup (Cart 2) represents an identical cart (with the same total mass) but with only one fan unit, pushing with a force strength of 30 N. Its speed-time graph is shown at the lower right. This cart is also initially at rest, but as the simulator was running you probably noticed that Cart 2 did not speed up as quickly, and so lagged behind Cart 1.

Suppose you wanted Cart 2 to move in exactly the same manner as Cart 1. (That is, you want them to remain side-by-side as they move along.)

If you could vary the strength of the force with which the fan unit on Cart 2 pushes, what value do you think it should have to make Cart 2 speed up in exactly the same manner as Cart 1, so that they stay side-by-side as they move? Briefly explain your reasoning.

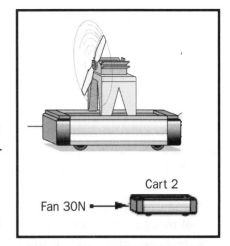

Throughout this activity you should only think about adjusting the strength and/or direction of the single force on Cart 2, NOT adding any other forces.

Rewind the simulator and adjust the strength of the single force acting on Cart 2 to the value you predicted above.

To change the strength of a force, first rewind the simulator. Then double-click on the head of the black force arrow itself to bring up the 'properties box' of the force. (If the 'Properties of Background' box appears, close it and try again.)

You can now change the strength of the force using the control at the top right. You can either adjust the value using the slider control, or type in a new value.

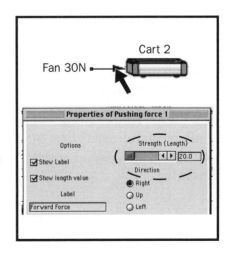

After adjusting the strength of the force on Cart 2, run the simulator again.

Do the carts speed up in the same manner now? (If so, they will stay side-by-side as they move.) Why do you think this is? (If they don't move together, return to the simulator and adjust the strength of the fan on Cart 2 until they do. Then comment briefly on your findings here.)

STEP 3: Now, rewind the simulator, and remove the 20 N force (Fan 2) from Cart 1. Then add a new 20 N force pushing to the **left**.

To remove a force, first use the selection tool to select the force arrow. Once the force is selected, just hit the Delete or Backspace key on your keyboard.

To add a force to the cart, first click on the Pushing force tool in the tool bar.

Next, click on the object, and holding the mouse button down, drag out a force arrow to the right of the cart. The value of its strength will increase as you drag.

If you do not get the right value for the strength, you can change its value in the way outlined in STEP 2 on the previous page.

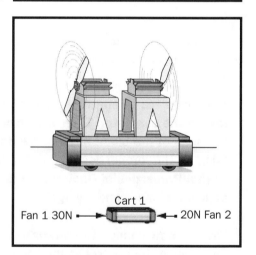

This new setup for Cart 1 represents an arrangement with two fan units, pushing in opposite directions. The fan unit pushing to the right is stronger than that pushing to the left.

Before running the simulator consider the following questions:

How do you think Cart 1 will move now, if at all, when released? (Not move, speed up, slow down, or constant speed.) Explain your reasoning.

Do you think the weaker 20 N force will have **any** effect on the motion of the cart, or will it behave in exactly the same manner as if **only** the 30 N force were acting on it? Explain your thinking.

 What value do you think the strength of the single force on Cart 2 should have now, so that its motion will match that of Cart 1 with the two opposing forces? Again, explain your reasoning.

Adjust the strength of the single force on Cart 2 to the value you suggested above and then run the simulation.

 Does the speed of Cart 1 behave in the way you predicted?

 Does the motion of Cart 2 match that of Cart 1? (If not, return to the simulator and adjust the strength of the fan on Cart 2 until it does. Then comment on your findings here.)

Unbalanced Combinations of Forces

When more than one force acts on an object, the effect they cause is due to the combination of all the forces together. When the total strength of all the forces acting in one direction is bigger than the total strength in the opposite direction (as shown below) we say that the forces are **unbalanced**.

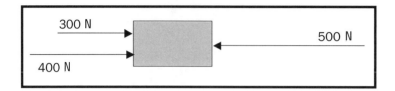

(When the total strength of all the forces pushing one way is exactly the same as the total strength pushing in the opposite direction, we say that the forces on the object are **balanced**. You will examine the effect of a balanced combination of forces on an object in a later activity.)

In the first part of this activity you examined the effect that an unbalanced combination of forces has on an object that is initially at rest.

 When **unbalanced** forces act on an object that is initially **at rest**, what effect does the simulator model suggest they have on it? After it has started moving, does its speed increase, decrease, or remain constant?

 Does the simulator model suggest that a single force can have the same effect on a stationary object as an unbalanced combination of forces? If so, describe how you would calculate the strength of that single force.

SIMULATOR EXPLORATION #2: What effect does an unbalanced combination of forces have on an object that is already moving?

In this second set of steps you will use the simulator model to examine scientists' ideas about the effect that an unbalanced combination of two forces has on an object that is **already moving**. (How the object started moving is not important here, just that it is already moving.)

STEP 1: Open the second simulator setup for this activity. It is very similar to the first setup except that the forces on Cart 1 are already arranged to oppose each other, and at the moment the simulator starts, both carts are **already moving to the right at the same speed,** as shown by the equal-length speed arrows.

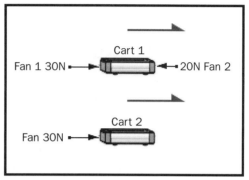

When the simulator is run, what effect do you think this **unbalanced** combination of forces will have on the motion of Cart 1? Will it slow down speed up, or continue moving at a constant speed? Explain why you think so.

Now run the simulator. What is the motion of Cart 1 like? (Speed up, slow down, or constant speed.) Is this what you predicted above?

What value do you think the force strength of the single fan unit on Cart 2 should have to make the two carts move side-by-side? Explain your reasoning.

Check your idea using the simulator and record the result below.

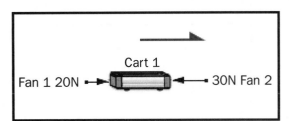

Fan 1 20N → Cart 1 ← 30N Fan 2

STEP 2: Now suppose you changed the force strength of the two fan units on Cart 1, so that the force acting opposite to the direction of motion was stronger than the force in the same direction as the motion, as shown at left.

 What effect do you think this **unbalanced** combination of forces will have on the motion of Cart 1? Do you think it will speed up, slow down, move at a constant speed, or would something else happen? Explain your thinking.

 What do you think you would have to do to the direction and strength of the single force acting on Cart 2 to make the two carts continue to move side-by-side? Explain your reasoning.

 Again, check your ideas using the simulator and record the results below.

 Suppose the simulator were to run for several seconds longer. What do you think would happen to the carts? Explain your thinking.

Rewind the simulator, then set it to run for 20 seconds instead of 10 seconds.

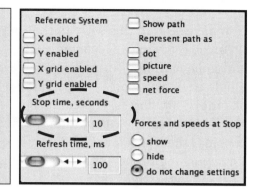

To extend the running time of the simulator, double-click on the white background of the simulator window to bring up the Properties of Background box.

You can now change the length of time the simulator runs using the control on the middle left.

 Now run the simulator again. Do the carts behave as you predicted?

STEP 3: Use your results from this simulator exploration to answer the following questions:

 If an object is already moving, what effect (if any) does the simulator model suggest an **unbalanced** combination of forces has on its speed? Does the speed change, or does it remain constant?

 What happens to the speed of a moving object if the force acting in the same direction as its motion is stronger than the force acting in the direction opposite its motion?

 What if the stronger force acts in the direction opposite to the motion?

Net Force

You have seen in this activity that when an unbalanced combination of forces acts on an object, you can also find a single force that would make the object move in the same manner. Further, you have seen that the strength and direction of this single equivalent force can be found by adding and/or subtracting the strengths of the individual forces, depending on the direction in which they act. Scientists call the result of such a calculation the **net force** acting on the object. For example, consider the box below. The total force pushing to the right is 700 N, while the force pushing to the left is 500 N. Thus, the net force on the box would be 200 N pushing to the right.

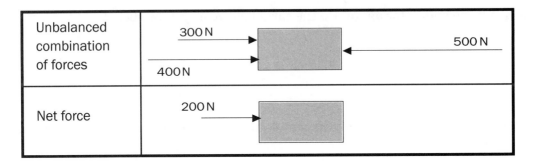

Summarizing Questions

S1: When an **unbalanced** combination of forces acts on an object (either at rest or in motion), does the speed of the object change, or does it remain constant? Is this the same as, or different from, the effect of a single force? Why does this make sense?

S2: In a previous class a student made the following statement:

"When more than one force acts on an object only the strongest force matters. It's as if the weaker forces were not there and the object moves in the same way as if only the strongest force were acting on it."

Do you agree or disagree with this student? What evidence from this activity supports your thinking?

S3: Four people push on a large box with the forces shown in the diagram below.

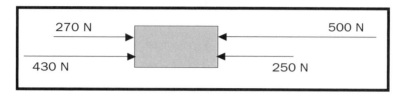

What is the net force (strength and direction) acting on the box? Explain how you determined your answer.

S4: In the Initial Ideas section of this homework activity you were asked about the motion of a cart with two fan units of **unequal strength** attached. Students in a previous class performed this experiment and noticed that, **after** their initial push, the cart slowed down gradually.

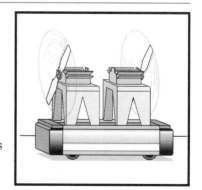

The students were not sure which of the two fans was the strongest, but one of them wrote the following explanation for why the cart slowed down.

CHAPTER 2

EXPLANATION: Why did the cart with two opposing fans on it slow down after being given an initial push?

Describe the situation using a diagram:

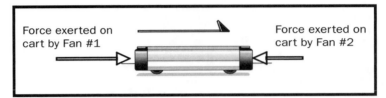

Write the narrative:

The initial push gets the cart started moving to the right, but after the hand loses contact the only forces acting on the cart are from the two fan units. When a weaker force opposes a stronger force, an object will move in the direction of the stronger force, but will slow down as it does so. Because Fan #1 is the stronger force, and is pushing in the same direction as the motion, the cart keeps moving to the right. However, Fan #2 exerts a weaker force in the direction opposite the motion, so the cart slows down.

Evaluate this explanation: Decide whether this explanation (including both the force diagram and narrative) is *good* or *poor* by reviewing each of the following criteria:

Present	Criterion
Yes/No	Completeness: All ideas needed are included.
Yes/No	Accuracy: All ideas included correspond to established ideas.
Yes/No	Logical reasoning and clarity: Narrative connects ideas to the phenomenon, and is well written.

If you find this explanation to be good, give your reasons below. If you find it to be poor, give your reasons and correct the explanation.

Name:_____ Date:_____ Group: _____

In this article we provide a broad outline of educational research on student ideas about forces and motion. The last 20 years of research on children's ideas has revealed that there are some common ideas that students use to explain their experiences with moving objects. In the educational research literature, student ideas have been referred to as misconceptions, pre-conceptions, intuitive knowledge and/or naïve theories of motion. These ideas are often consistent, reliable, and reasonable to students even though they are not necessarily consistent with scientists' ideas.

Educational researchers Gunstone and Watts (1985) classified the findings of the research on students' ideas about force and motion into general categories. Physics education researcher Michael McCloskey (1983) also studied the types of ideas students have acquired about motion through experience with moving objects. He found that a large majority of college students interviewed consistently explained motion using what McCloskey calls the "impetus theory." This naïve theory of motion leads to common student ideas that are not consistent with scientists' ideas.

Common ideas from the work of Gunstone and Watts (1985) and McCloskey (1983) are described below.

Common Idea 1: Impetus Theory–Internal Force.

According to this idea, the act of setting an object in motion imparts to the object an internal force or "impetus" that serves to maintain motion. In the physics class this is often stated in terms of "force being transferred" from one object to another during an interaction.

Common Idea 2: Impetus Theory–Force Runs Out.

According to this idea the moving object's impetus gradually dissipates and as a result the object gradually slows down and comes to a stop. In the physics classroom this often appears in statements such as "the force runs out."

Common Idea 3: Forces have to do with living things.

This idea was investigated by Jean Piaget in the 1920s. By interviewing children while they worked on force problems, he found that children tend to think of force as something having to do with living things. Children often use animistic terms to describe how inanimate objects can exert a force. For example, children often refuse to believe that a spring exerts a force on a car because the spring is not alive.

Common Idea 4: Constant motion requires constant force.

Children of all ages (including many undergraduate physics students) often develop a general rule that an object moving at a constant speed must be experiencing a constant force. This idea is expressed in statements such as, "If it is moving, there must be some kind of push on it," or "if it is moving, it has to have some kind of force *in* it." The former illustrates the notion that objects cannot "do something" without a reason, in this case a force. The latter is an example of the notion that during a mechanical interaction such as a push, force is transferred from the hand to the object. This force is now "in" the object and when it runs out, the object slows down and eventually stops moving. This idea is very common in elementary school, middle school, high school, and college. It is possible that part of the reason that these types of ideas develop is that people never actually experience a world with no friction. As a result, there is always an invisible force acting against the motion of objects, whether it is friction or air resistance. In most people's experience, some kind of push is indeed often needed to keep objects like blocks and couches moving at a constant speed.

Common Idea 5: The amount of motion is proportional to the amount of force.

The idea that constant motion requires constant force (common idea 4) often implies that no force means no motion. This is further generalized by many students to mean that the quantity of force is proportional to the quantity of movement. So, for example, a child might say that an object slowed down because a small amount of force was applied. The child might go on to explain that this means that a small

amount of force will give rise to a "slow" speed but a large amount of force will give rise to a "fast" speed. This is very different from the scientists' idea that any unbalanced force in the direction of motion will cause an object to speed up and any unbalanced force opposite the direction of motion will cause an object to slow down.

Common Idea 6: If a body is not moving there is no force acting on it.

There is a subtle difference between this idea and the idea that no-force-means-no-motion, discussed in the previous section. In this case, the learner believes that a stationary object has no forces acting on it at all. This does not account for an apple hanging on a tree or a person standing on the ground. This idea is not consistent with the scientists' idea that an object with balanced forces acting on it might not be moving at all.

Common Idea 7: If a body is moving there is a force acting on it in the direction of motion.

Children typically associate the direction of motion with the direction of the force acting on the object. A classic example of this can be found when students study circular motion. When students are asked to hit a moving ball with a club so that it goes in a circle on the floor, they often try to hit the ball around a circular path. After trying this several times, they ultimately discover that the ball must be hit towards the center of the circle.

Summary

Common Ideas 3 through 7 initially reported by Gunstone and Watts (1985) fall under the broader heading: *Motion Implies Force.* The Common Ideas 1 and 2 were originally reported by McClosky and fall under the broader heading of impetus, or something imparted to and contained within an object. Researchers and practitioners have found that these ideas are common at all grade levels up to and including college. These ideas are often found to be consistent with students' everyday experiences, largely because we live in a world full of friction. For this reason, the idea that *motion implies force* and the idea that *impetus is imparted to an object* is very resistant to change, even in the face of evidence. Gunstone and Watts (1985) quote physics education researcher John Clement:

"In conclusion, the data support the hypothesis that for the majority of these students, the 'motion implies a force' preconception was highly resistant to change. This conclusion applies to the extent that students could not solve basic problems of this kind where the direction of motion does not coincide with the direction of force." (p. 97)

As learners, it is important to keep in mind that we come into the classroom with our own ideas about how the world works. Some of these ideas work very well in the conditions under which we live. In science, however, we are often asked to imagine a broader range of possible conditions and to extend our explanations to account for them. As learners, we must become aware of our own ideas and the ideas of others. We must also become aware that our own misconceptions, pre-conceptions, naïve theories or ideas are seeds from which more powerful ideas can grow. We should always be mindful of the fact that we are not blank slates; we have ideas—good ideas. Our initial ideas may not always be consistent with the ideas of scientists. Awareness of these ideas has allowed teachers and curriculum developers to design lessons and curricula that can help students build on their own ideas. Our ideas, and our childrens' ideas, should be respected and valued. Through carefully crafted classroom experiences, childrens' ideas can be modified and developed by the children themselves into ideas that have a broader range of application.

References

Gunstone, R. & Watts, M. (1985). Force and Motion. In *Children's Ideas in Science,* R. Driver, E. Guesne, and A. Tiberghien, Eds. Taylor and Francis Inc. Chapter 5, p. 85-104.

McCloskey, M. (1983). Naive Theories of Motion, in Genter and Stevens Eds., *Mental Models,* Lawrence Erlbaum associates, New Jersey.

Activity 4–Children's Ideas about Force, Motion and Energy
Learning about Learning

Purpose

In Chapter 2 you are developing ideas about how the forces acting on an object affect its motion. The purpose of this activity is to help you apply your current ideas about forces and motion to understand the ideas of elementary students.

Before starting this activity, read the supporting article titled *Children's Ideas about Force and Motion*. The article should help you begin to recognize physics ideas of elementary students and some of your own prior ideas about force and motion.

What types of ideas do elementary students have about force and motion?

Initial Ideas

Imagine that 5th grade students were asked the following question: *"What forces are involved in the motion of a soccer ball before and after it is kicked?"* What ideas about force and motion do you think students would use when answering this question? Draw on your own experience as well as on the information contained in the article, *Children's Ideas about Force and Motion*

Collecting and Interpreting Evidence

Your instructor will show you a DVD. After watching the DVD, review the transcript.

Read through the transcript and note places where students are expressing their ideas. What ideas about force and motion did the children in the DVD express? Cite evidence from the DVD transcript to support your claim(s). (You can cite the time codes from the transcript in the following table.)

Nikhel and Alana (00:08:05 to 00:09:14)

Claim (What idea did you infer from the transcript or DVD?)	Evidence (What specific comments led you to make the inference in the preceding column?)

Ian and Aaron (00:09:19 to 00:10:46)

Claim (What idea did you infer from the transcript or DVD?)	Evidence (What specific comments led you to make the inference in the preceding column?)

Discuss any **similarities** you found between your inferences about the children's ideas and common ideas described in the article *Children's Ideas about Force and Motion*.

Inference about Children's Ideas (from tables above)	What Common Ideas are Similar? (please write out the name of the idea as well as the number)

Summarizing Questions

S1. At about DVD time 00:09:00 a student states that the ball "still had some more force to move it a little bit" after the kick, and that this force came from the foot. Another idea that was expressed by the students is that the ball stopped moving "because the force ran out."

Why do you think these ideas **make sense** to the students? You might consider what they actually mean by the term "force."

S2. In what ways were the ideas expressed by your *PET* classmates (see Chapter 2 Activity 1 Initial Ideas) **similar** to the ideas expressed by the children in the movie? In what ways were they **different**?

S3. You are much older than the children in the DVD and have had many more life experiences. Why do you think your ideas would be so similar in some cases?

 Participate in a class discussion to share your answers to these questions and challenge or support the answers of others.

What forces act on the ball? Why does it slow down?

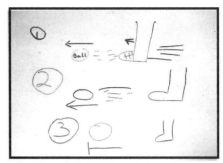

Figure 1. Ian and Nikhel, Alana, and Stacey's diagram referred to from 08:20 to 09:22

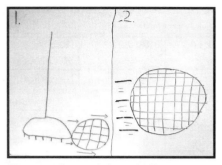

Figure 2. Ian and Aaron's diagram referred to from 09:24 to 10:47

\multicolumn{3}{c}{**What forces act on the ball? Why does it slow down?**}		
00:08:05	Interviewer	... and watch how it moves. It doesn't have to go very far, but I want you to think about how it moves when you're kicking it and how it moves after you kick it. OK? So go ahead and kick the ball.
00:08:19	Interviewer	So tell me about your first picture, that's while your foot is kicking the ball?
00:08:23	Nikhel	Yes
00:08:24	Interviewer	OK, so what forces do you think there are then?
00:08:27	Nikhel	Your foot and the ball...(see Figure 1)
00:08:29	Interviewer	...and the ball? So the ball is a force too?
00:08:33	Alana	No
00:08:33	Nikhel	No, wait a minute... your foot, yeah.
00:08:36	Interviewer	Your foot is the force?
00:08:37	Stacey	Yes.
00:08:38	Interviewer	OK, so I need a force to make it move?
00:08:40	Alana	Uh-huh.
00:08:41	Interviewer	OK, I see.
00:08:42	Nikhel	... and energy will make it move.
00:08:43	Interviewer	... and energy to make it move? Alright. Um... so, after you kicked it, it was still moving, right?
00:08:50	Nikhel	Yes
00:08:50	Alana	Uh-huh
00:08:51	Interviewer	Er... so, was there a force then?
00:08:56	Nikhel	It probably still had some more force to move it a little bit, but then it probably ...
00:09:05	Interviewer	So where do you think that force came from?
00:09:07	Nikhel	The foot (points to foot on picture)
00:09:09	Interviewer	The foot? So, so there was still some force from the foot... making it move?
00:09:13	Nikhel	Uh-huh
00:09:13	Alana	Uh-huh (nods agreement)

		What forces act on the ball? Why does it slow down?
00:09:13	Nikhel	Uh-huh
00:09:13	Alana	Uh-huh (nods agreement)
00:09:14	Interviewer	(to Stacey) Is that what you think too? OK. And then it stopped, why?
00:09:19	Nikhel	Because there was no more force to push it.
00:09:22	Interviewer	There was no more force to push it.
00:09:24	Interviewer	So...what were you saying then, Ian, about the forces?
00:09:28	Ian	Er... I can't explain the forces in a picture. (see Figure 2)
00:09:30	Interviewer	OK. Well... Aaron, why don't you tell me about the first picture, what's this?
00:09:36	Aaron	This is the foot kicking the ball, and the force behind it which is making it move.
00:09:40	Interviewer	So what, what makes the force?
00:09:43	Aaron	The foot, ... your foot.
00:09:43	Interviewer	Your foot makes the force? Alright, and Ian, you tell me about the second picture.
00:09:45	Interviewer	Go ahead... tell me about the second picture.
00:09:48	Ian	OK... that's for wind... that's for moving (indicates lines behind ball on picture) Um... it still has the force of the foot behind it, but the foot isn't pushing the ball, but it still has the force that the foot put on it.
00:10:02	Interviewer	What makes you think that?
00:10:03	Ian	Because it keeps... the foot pushes the ball... and, when the foot isn't touching it, that ... means...
00:10:15	Interviewer	Go on, go ahead.
00:10:16	Ian	...that is... it keeps moving because it still has the force of the foot on the ball.
00:10:21	Interviewer	So, what would happen if it didn't have the force of the foot on there?
00:10:24	Ian	It would just stop.
00:10:26	Interviewer	So why do you think the ball does stop eventually?
00:10:29	Aaron	Because the foot isn't pushing it any more.
00:10:32	Interviewer	OK.......................What were you gonna say?
00:10:32	Aaron	......The force runs out....................The force runs out.
00:10:34	Interviewer	The force of the foot runs out?
00:10:35	Aaron	Yes
00:10:36	Interviewer	OK...Alright...um...So if...suppose that force of the foot didn't run out, what would happen?
00:10:43	Ian	It would keep moving and moving forever.
00:10:46	Interviewer	It would keep moving and moving along forever....

Purpose

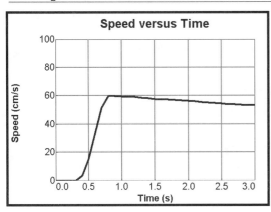

Speed versus Time

In a previous activity you saw that when a force is exerted on a moving object, in a direction opposite to that of its motion, the object slows down. Is such a force always responsible

when things slow and stop, or would a moving object eventually slow and stop on its own?

In previous activities you have probably noticed (from your Motion Sensor speed-time graphs) that the cart you were using in your experiments was slowing down slightly even when there was not a hand or a fan unit pushing it 'backwards.' Why do you think this was?

Was some other force responsible for this slowing, or is it just something that happens to all moving objects around us, anyway?

 Is friction a force and how does it work to slow moving objects?

Initial Ideas

Three students in a *PET* class discuss the very first experiment in Activity 1 of this chapter, where someone gave a cart a quick push and then let it move along the track on its own (before someone else stopped it). They notice

that their speed-time graph (shown above) indicates that the cart was slowing down very gradually after the initial push, and discuss why they think this was happening.

I think a friction-type contact interaction is slowing the cart down, but since I can't see anything pushing on the cart I don't think a force is involved.

I agree that friction is slowing the cart down, but I do think friction is a force. I just don't know how it works

I know we learned in Chapter 1 that friction slows things down, but I'm not sure in this case. Even without friction, I think it would slow down anyway, because the force of the initial push gradually runs out.

Daryl   **Kristen**   **Samantha**

 Do you agree with Daryl, Kristen, Samantha or with none of them? Explain your thinking.

 Use the pictures below to draw force diagrams for the cart in the experiment described above; the first while it is speeding up during the initial push, the second after the push, while the cart is gradually slowing down. Explain briefly why you drew your diagrams as you did.

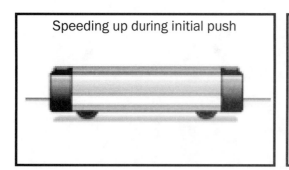

Speeding up during initial push

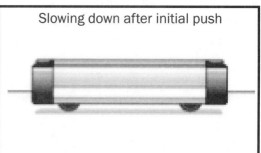

Slowing down after initial push

When you examined friction-type contact interactions in Chapter 1, you gave a wooden block a push across the table and saw it slow and stop. We said this was due to 'friction' but how do you think friction actually works?

 Whether you think friction is a force or not, explain what you think was actually happening to slow the block down.

 Participate in a whole-class discussion about these ideas. Make a note of any ideas or reasoning that are different from those of your team.

Collecting and Interpreting Evidence

 EXPERIMENT #1: Is friction a force?

YOU WILL NEED:

- Low-friction cart with friction attachment
- Track
- Fan unit
- Glove (optional)
- Colored pencils
- Access to a computer and Motion Sensor

STEP 1: Examine the cart and note the friction attachment that, when lowered, allows a felt pad to touch whatever surface the cart is placed on. For now, make sure the pad is raised so that it will not rub. Mount the fan unit on the cart.

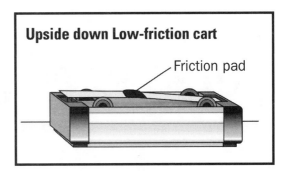

Upside down Low-friction cart

Friction pad

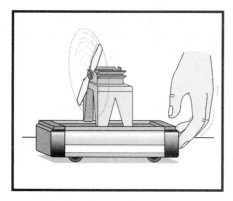

Place the cart at rest about 20-30 cm in front of the Motion Sensor. Make sure that, when the cart is given a quick push away from the sensor, the fan unit will push on the cart in the opposite direction to its motion.

Open the Motion Sensor data collection file for this activity. Hold the cart steady and turn the fan unit on.

After starting to collect data, give the cart a quick push away from the sensor. Hold the cart with your hand at the moment it comes to a stop, **before it starts to move back toward the sensor.**

 Describe the motion of the cart from the moment just **after** you gave it the quick push, to the moment you stopped it.

 Sketch the speed-time graph for the motion of the cart and label it FAN.

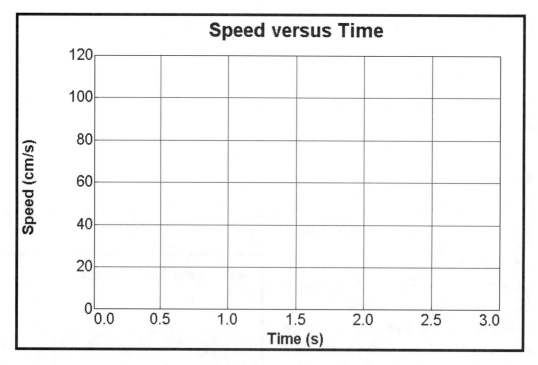

STEP 2: Now remove the fan unit from the cart and, using the adjustment screw, lower the friction pad so that it rubs **lightly** on the surface when the cart moves.

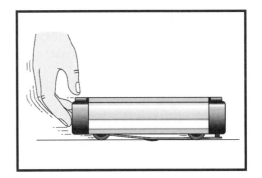

Adjust the level of the friction pad so that, after being given a **similar** quick push, the cart comes to a stop in about the same place as the fan-cart did in STEP 1.

> When recording Motion Sensor data try to make the start and stop times on the graph close to the same as the graph you drew in STEP 1, and also try to match the initial pushes by having the graph rise to about the same maximum value as it did in STEP 1.

 When you are satisfied with the adjustment of the pad, use a different color pencil to sketch the speed-time graph on the same set of axes you used in STEP 1. Label the graph FRICTION.

 How does the motion of the cart with the friction pad lowered compare with the motion when the fan unit was pushing backward on it? (Are the motions reasonably similar, or are they very different?)

 Look at the graph you labeled FAN on the previous page. What evidence does this graph provide that, after the initial push, a force was acting on the cart in a direction opposite its motion? What force was this?

 Now, look at the graph you labeled FRICTION above. Does this graph provide evidence that a force was acting on the cart (after the initial push)? If not, why not? If so, in what direction did the force act?

If your Motion Sensor graphs were not labeled, would it be possible for someone who did not see the experiments to tell which one was produced using the fan unit to slow the cart, and which was produced using the friction pad?

 What do your answers to the previous questions imply about whether friction is, or is not, a force that acts on moving objects in a direction opposite their motion?

 EXPERIMENT #2: What causes friction?

YOU WILL NEED:

- Sticky notes
- Wooden block
- Launcher and clamp
- Meter stick
- 2 sheets of sandpaper
- Tape
- Magnifying lens

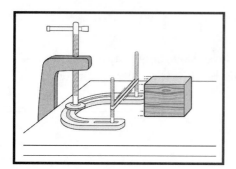

STEP 1: Mount the launcher on the end of the table (do **not** use a track for this experiment). Push the wooden block against the rubber band, so it is stretched back about 1 cm, and hold the block still by pushing down on top of it. Release the block, so that it slides across the table and stops. Measure how far it travels. Do **not** enter this value in the table!

Repeat the process from STEP 1, stretching the band back a little further each time, until you reach a point where the block travels a distance of at least 50 cm before stopping. Use a sticky note to mark how far back the rubber band must be stretched to achieve this 50 cm travel distance.

> **This is how far back you will stretch the band in EVERY step from now on. Do not remove this marker until you have completed the whole activity.**

STEP 2: Each member of your team should now take a turn launching the block (stretching the rubber band back to the **same** marked point each time) and measure how far the block travels.

Enter these measured values on the top row of the table below, and calculate the average distance traveled by the block across the table.

Surface	Distance traveled (cm)			
	Trial 1	Trial 2	Trial 3	Average
Tabletop				
Sandpaper				
Stickies				

STEP 3: Now slide a sheet of sandpaper under the launcher, so that the **back edge** of the sheet lines up with your launching mark.

Place a second sheet of sandpaper in front of the first and slide its edge about 2 mm **under** the first sheet. Tape the corners of the sheets of sandpaper to the table.

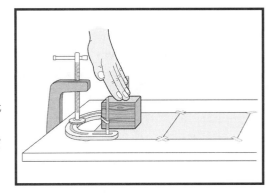

CHAPTER 2

Repeat the experiment from STEP 2, each time stretching the rubber band back to the same previously marked point. (You do not need to determine a new launching point.)

 Complete the second line of the table.

 How does the average distance the block travels on the sandpaper compare with the distance it travels on the bare tabletop? Why do you think this is?

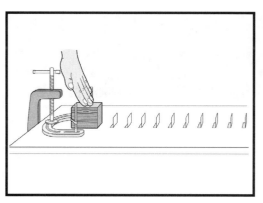

STEP 4: Remove the sandpaper and place 15 sticky notes, about 4 cm apart, in front of the launcher, so that they will be in the path of the block, when it is launched, as shown below.

Now launch the block in the same way as you did before and measure how far the block travels. (Make sure to 'reset' the sticky notes before each trial.)

 Complete the last row of the table.

 How does the average distance the block travels over the sticky notes compare with the distance it travels on the bare tabletop?

 Why do you think that the block does not travel as far before stopping when the sticky notes are in the way? (Hint: During their interaction, does a sticky note exert a force on the moving block? If so, in what direction?)

The sticky notes can serve as an analogy to help you think about what might be happening when the block slides across a surface. (An analogy in science is when two situations or processes have certain characteristics in common. Observing, or thinking about, how one process operates can help you visualize how the other also operates.)

STEP 5: Examine the surface of the sandpaper with the magnifying lens and your fingers.

 Describe what you see and feel.

 The sticky notes slow the block down because each one exerts a weak force on the block in a direction opposite to its motion. How do you think the sandpaper slows the block down?

Examine the surface of the table and the wooden block with the magnifying lens and with your fingers.

 Do the table and the block both look and feel perfectly smooth, or can you see some imperfections? How would these affect the motion of the block as it slides across the tabletop?

Students were comparing their ideas about how friction works with the first experiment in Activity 3, in which you applied several very gentle 'backward' taps to a moving cart, thereby slowing it down in several 'steps'. One student made the following statement:

"When we slowed the cart down in Activity 3 we were applying several weak 'backward' forces to it. Each one of these forces made the cart slow down a little, until eventually it stopped. But friction is different, there are no backward forces acting on the block, it's just the rubbing on the surface that makes it slow down. "

 Do you agree or disagree with this student? Explain why.

Summarizing Questions

 First discuss these questions with your team and note your ideas. Leave space to add any different ideas that may emerge when the whole class discusses their thinking.

S1: When you see a moving object slow and stop, what do you think is causing this to happen (if anything)?

S2: What evidence from this activity suggests that friction is a force that opposes motion?[1]

---

[1] As discussed in Chapter 1, under certain circumstances the effects of friction can be taken to be negligible. In terms of forces, you should make this decision based on whether or not there are much stronger forces acting on an object, such that the friction force itself will have only a negligible effect.

S3: How does the row of sticky notes serve as an analogy to help understand how friction works in slowing down a moving object? That is, how does thinking about why the sticky notes slow the block down help you think about why the block slows down when sliding across the sandpaper or the table?

S4: Why do you think the block slows down more rapidly on the sandpaper than on the bare tabletop? Why does it slow down at all on the apparently smooth tabletop?

S5: Why do you think the cart slows down very gradually, even when no friction pad is used, but slows quickly when the pad is rubbing on the track? Use the pictures below to draw force diagrams to illustrate the difference between the two situations. Explain your reasoning below the diagrams.

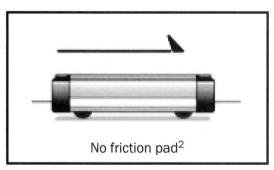

No friction pad[2]

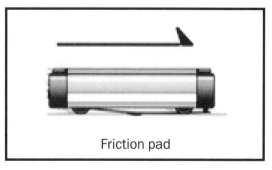

Friction pad

___

[2] In this case the most important source of friction is the interaction between the wheel bearings and the axles on the cart itself, not between the wheels and the track. However, this is still a 'backwards' force acting on the cart.

S6: Suppose you could start an object moving and then arrange for absolutely <u>**no**</u> <u>**forces**</u> to act on it. How would it move from then on? To help you think about this question consider the following:

Suppose a spacecraft is at rest in deep space, far from any stars or planets, so that no form of friction or gravity is acting on it. The main engine, at the rear of the spacecraft, is fired for a period of 2 seconds (to start the spacecraft moving) and is then shut off.

What do you think the motion of the spacecraft would be like after the engine is shut off? Explain your reasoning.

Name:_____ Date:_____ Group: _____

Purpose

The purpose of this activity is to help you understand that although ideas expressed by students may not sound like scientists' ideas, they usually represent a partial (or full) understanding. In this activity you will make inferences about students' knowledge at different points throughout a lesson on friction.

 What types of ideas do second and third grade students have about why moving objects eventually slow down and stop?

Children's Ideas

Before a teacher began an activity on friction, she had the following target ideas in mind for her second and third grade students:

1. Toy cars slow down and stop at different distances on different surfaces.

2. Toy cars slow down because the surface exerts a push against the car in the direction opposite to the motion of the toy car.

Initial Ideas

 Imagine that second and third grade students were asked to explain why they think a car slows down and stops when it is given an initial push on the sidewalk. What types of answers do you think they would give, and what reasoning do you think they would use to justify their answers? Draw on the article *Children's Ideas about Force and Motion* (from Chapter 2 Activity 3 Homework 2) and your own personal experiences.

CHAPTER 2

Collecting and Interpreting Evidence

The movies and associated transcripts can be found on the *PET* DVD in your Student Resources folder for Chapter 2.

Note: Use headphones when viewing videos and make certain that the volume on your computer is at its maximum setting.

Video Clip 1

What ideas do second and third grade students express when asked "Why does the object slow down?"

Two weeks before the discussion that takes place in the movie *Friction_Initial*, students were given about 10 minutes to play with sandpaper, toy cars, and ramps. In the movie, the teacher asked students why they think a car slows down when it is given an initial push on the sidewalk.

 Open the movie *Friction_Initial* and watch the movie.

 1. Do any of these students seem to be thinking about friction as a push (force) against the car in the opposite direction of motion? Which students seem to be thinking about friction as a force and which students seem to be thinking something else about why objects slow down? Use comments from the video (and cut and paste statements from the electronic transcript at the end of this activity) to support your interpretation of students' thinking.

2. Do you think any of these students are thinking about force in one or more of the ways outlined in the article, *Children's Ideas about Force and Motion?* Provide evidence from the movie and the transcript.

Video Clip 2

Experiments with Sandpaper and Sticky Notes

In the movie *Friction_experiment*, two second grade students are performing an experiment with sandpaper, a car, a ramp, and a board with sticky notes lined up (rather like a *PET* experiment). The sticky notes had little hands drawn on each one to suggest the idea of "pushing."

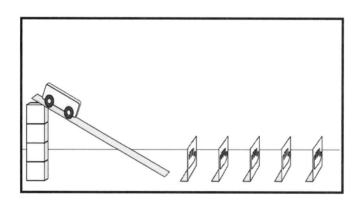

Students were given coarse, medium, and fine sandpaper to help them develop the idea that even as the surface gets smoother, there is still some type of push slowing the car down.

Open the movie *Friction_experiment* and watch it.

3. At video time 00:48:23 Adriana articulates an idea about some differences between the motion of the car on the ramp surface and its motion on the sandpaper surface. Elizabeth then expresses her idea. What ideas do Adriana and Elizabeth use to explain why the car slows down on the sandpaper? Use examples from the entire video and transcript to support your interpretation of the children's ideas.

Video Clip 3

Students' Final Ideas about Friction

In the movie *Friction_final*, students presented their final ideas following the sandpaper/sticky note experiment.

Open the movie *Friction_final* and watch it. Then review the movie *Friction_initial*.

Summarizing Questions

S1: Compare the types of comments students made about why cars slow down in *Friction_initial* to the types of comments students made in *Friction_final*. Were there any general differences in their explanations for why a car slows down? Use examples from the movie and transcript as well as the content on the students' **dry-erase boards** (in *Friction_final* from 00:03:40 to 00:04:40) to show differences in the ways students talked about slowing down before and after the experiment.

S2: Do you have any evidence to support the claim that the students learned something? Make some claims about what students learned and support your claims with evidence. You may wish to focus on one or two students.

S3: In *Friction_final*, Charlie and Harley presented their final explanation for why cars slow down and stop. What was their explanation for why cars slow down, and what do you think they understand about friction at the end of the activity? Do you think their explanation is a good explanation? Why or why not? Use evidence to support your claims.

S4: Based on the discussion in *Friction_experiment,* do you think Adriana and Elizabeth seemed to learn anything? That is, did their ideas change in any ways throughout the experiment? Do you think these students established a full understanding of friction as a surface push against the car? Use evidence from the movie to support your claims.

 Participate in a whole-class discussion to share your answers to these questions and challenge or support the answers of others.

Name:_____ Date:_____ Group: _____

Friction_Initial.mov

00:05:09	Teacher	Ok, we want you to imagine if you had a little car and there was no ramp, it was just on something flat like the sidewalk and you gave it a push, just imagine what would happen to that car. If you think it might start slowing down after a while, why do you think it would slow down?
00:27:18	Jacqueline	Maybe if you push it not that very hard it will go slow because of the-maybe the sidewalk has bumps like the rough um, the rough um sandpaper that we had and it didn't went that fast so if you push it like kind of, like kind of fast like that, it might go really fast but it might stop really quick.
00:53:03	Harley	Um, may-, um I agree to what Jacqueline said, if it's bumpy but um maybe it's 'cause it's not like have batteries 'cause if it has batteries the tires move by themselves so you don't have to give them a push you just have to turn it on but if you give it a push and it doesn't have batteries so it won't keep on going.
01:15:23	Felix	I think that if the, like the sidewalk has little rocks to it um that the car won't go that fast.
01:26:12	Katie	I think if you gave it a hard push it would go over a- two or one crack but then stop because those cracks might make it stop when the tire goes on them.
01:42:06	Teacher	Do you have any idea how those cracks might make it stop?
01:45:26	Katie	Because they're a little deep for those little cars.
01:51:02	Harley	I think um, when you push the car why it slows down and stops is be-not it's kind of has to do with gravity a little bit cause the gravity helps um it cause um maybe it needs a little bit more power, instead of just pushing it needs like electricity and pushing.
02:16:08	Teacher	To keep going?
02:17:19	Harley	(nods)

Friction_Experiment.mov

00:04:26	Elizabeth	'kay.
00:10:18	Researcher	Do you guys know what we're doing?
00:12:12	Elizabeth	Um, we're gonna test these three, these three um, these three sands with the car and we need to test how, how much inches, ah we need to put how much inches did it go.
00:36:22	Researcher	Right. Okay there's your, here's your ramp, here's your blocks so we're gonna have it two blocks high.
00:42:14	Elizabeth	Thank you.
00:43:16	Researcher	Like that, and then the car–.
00:48:23	Adriana	I think it goes fast here but when it gets to here it gets slower.
00:53:21	Elizabeth	Yeah, because there's bumpy things.
00:56:14	Adriana	And it's like stickers something.
00:59:07	Elizabeth	No, they're bumpy things.
01:02:01	Elizabeth	Seven inches.
01:04:22	Adriana	Yeah? You sure?
01:06:18	Elizabeth	Yeah! Seven inches.
01:09:01	Adriana	Seven inches.
01:13:17	Elizabeth	Okay, now so for the smoothest it went.
01:18:25	Adriana	Seven inches.
01:20:28	Elizabeth	Seven inches.
01:25:01	Elizabeth	Okay now the other one.

Friction_Experiment.mov

01:43:16	Adriana	Oh, I think it's gonna
01:54:29	Elizabeth	Six inches.
02:10:19	Teacher	Everybody should be on their whiteboard now, or almost done with their experiment explaining why the cars are slowing down.
02:23:03	Elizabeth	Okay.
02:32:20	Adriana	Four Inches.
02:34:10	Elizabeth	Four inches.
02:39:03	Elizabeth	Yeah, you write them okay.
02:41:27	Adriana	All of them okay.
02:42:28	Elizabeth	Yeah, and I'll measure.
02:52:17	Teacher	Now what do you think, look at this special board that Valerie made, it might help you explain what's going on with the sandpaper (shows a board with small sticky notes). These are little hands on the board (hands are drawn on the sticky notes).
03:05:26	Teacher	Will you set your ramp up again and let's try using this board and see if it can help us explain what's going on. Will you set your ramp up again. It might not help you but it might help you explain.
03:15:24	Elizabeth	Okay.
03:28:13	Teacher	So if you have, oops let's move this...these are little hands, what do you think they're doing. What are they doing?
03:39:09	Elizabeth	(rolls the car into the row of sticky notes. The car is stopped quickly)
03:44:21	Adriana	Maybe trying to stop the car?
03:46:15	Teacher	What are they doing?
03:48:12	Elizabeth	Maybe they're hands and they're signs of, of it to stop?
03:55:24	Adriana	Yeah, maybe the car (inaudible) stopping?
03:59:10	Teacher	When it hits one of those does something get in its way?
04:02:18	Adriana	Yeah, and it gets slower?

Friction_Experiment.mov

04:04:03	Elizabeth	Oh, yeah.
04:05:00	Teacher	So what are those hands doing?
04:06:24	Elizabeth	They're trying to, um, stop the car?
04:10:11	Adriana	Yeah, they're trying to stop the car.
04:11:20	Teacher	Would that help you explain what the sandpaper might be doing?
04:18:06	Elizabeth	Yeah, when we put it, um the little roughness-
04:23:22	Teacher	Is this the most rough?
04:25:09	Elizabeth	Yeah.
04:25:23	Adriana	Yeah.
04:26:11	Elizabeth	It, it, it will stop.
04:30:02	Teacher	What's going on then?
04:31:19	Elizabeth	Um, the rough- it needs something um to go fast and this is not smooth it's rough.
04:40:22	Teacher	And so what is the rough doing? What is it doing?
04:43:11	Elizabeth	Stopping, stopping the car.
04:45:15	Teacher	What's a word you could call that?
04:46:28	Elizabeth	um...
04:54:02	Teacher	Stopping works. Is there another word you can think of though? (gives Elizabeth a little push). What's that?
04:59:08	Elizabeth	Pushing!
05:00:09	Teacher	Is that what maybe they're doing? Maybe? Those hands might be-(rolls the car into the sticky notes).
05:08:22	Adriana	Pushing this way (moves her hand in the direction of the motion of the car).
05:10:16	Teacher	Which way is the car going?
05:12:05	Adriana	That way (moves her hand in the direction of the motion of the car).
05:12:16	Elizabeth	That way (moves her hand in the direction of the motion of the car).

Friction_Experiment.mov

05:12:16	Elizabeth	That way (moves her hand in the direction of the motion of the car).
05:13:11	Teacher	...If it's pushing, what way is it pushing?
05:15:07	Elizabeth	Oh, it's pushing this way (both move their hand in the direction opposite the motion of the car).
05:16:22	Teacher	Maybe that's why it's slowing down and stopping.
05:20:08	Elizabeth	Um, yeah.
05:21:10	Teacher	What do you think?
05:21:28	Elizabeth	Yeah.
05:23:29	Teacher	Maybe. You guys put what you think, though.
05:27:28	Elizabeth	Okay.
05:28:22	Teacher	Does this help?
05:29:20	Elizabeth/ Adriana	Yeah.
05:31:11	Teacher	You guys can keep it there if you want.
05:44:13	Researcher	So the bumpiest one went the least?
05:47:08	Jacqueline	Yeah.
05:48:03	Researcher	How come?
05:48:20	Jacqueline	I think because from the bumps and this one look- where's that card? Look- and when we tried this (rolls the car into the sticky notes) wait-when we tried that it went right here and it grabbed like that and it doesn't pull it really hard but I think because since they have right here they're tapted, I think because they don't let them go see?
06:19:23	Researcher	Oh.
06:20:24	Jacqueline	So this one went really slow then the bumpy one. Wait, let me put the ruler right here.

Friction_Final.mov

06:22	Felix	This reminds me, to get to my parking lot there's a bump that slows my mom's car down. That's all.
00:18:04	Teacher	Interesting. Okay Kevin you go.
00:20:24	Felix	I didn't even pick! Kevin go.
00:27:09	Kevin	I think the um, I think, I think it stops because, because the bumps push it back.
00:39:10	Teacher	Can you show?
00:40:13	Kevin	I don't have my picture.
00:42:08	Teacher	You just wrote words? Okay. Ah, Lupe you guys go.
00:46:27	Sylvester	Um, I'm not done.
00:48:30	Teacher	Okay, Lupe go.
00:51:11	Sylvester	Just read that for me.
00:53:30	Lupe	Okay. Um, Sylvester wrote he said, "I think the bumps make them stop." And he drew some pictures of the sandpaper and the car running. And I drew a little picture of mine and up here it says "caution bump." And I think why it stops is because um when it goes on the bumps there's too much bumps and when it keeps on going on the bumps it doesn't get used; it just like gets tired and it stops because there's too much bumps.
01:28:22	Teacher	Too many bumps?
01:30:21	Lupe	And you need to give it another um push to make it go again.
01:35:07	Teacher	What are the bumps doing to the car?
01:37:04	Lupe	Stopping it because the wheels are just really thick. They're like just little round circles and the bumps are big, big um things like rocks.
01:49:02	Teacher	'kay, we're trying to answer why are these cars doing what they're doing on the sandpaper.
01:57:04	Harley	Um me and Charlie think that um the cars are stopping because the bumps stop the cars and it kind of blocks the cars, it blocks the cars from going really really um fast-and then it loses its speed and then um and then the bumps are kind of like other cars that it crashes into but um when it crashes into um the bump, it can like go over it a little to go to the other side then it will stop. So the bumps are kind of like just blocking it a little bit.
02:57:03	Charlie	And I drew a picture over here about a car um crashing into a bump and then it's losing its speed and, and it's kind of like crashing into it and then starting all over but with less speed. And right there I drew a closeup where it shows the car crashing into the car and then it went um it kind of starts over but with less speed. And here I drew a key that's the car, those lines are the things that show it crashed and the green thing is the floor and the little red things are other bumps.
03:39:22	Teacher	Thank you.

Purpose

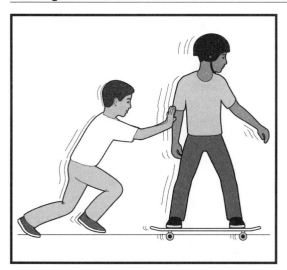

In the previous activities of this chapter you have seen that during a contact interaction, when a single force acts on an object, its speed either increases or decreases, depending on whether the force acts in the same direction as the motion, or opposite to it. Do you think a force of **any** strength will produce the same effect on any object, or will the motion of the object depend on its mass and the strength of the force?

If you were to continuously push your friend on his well-oiled skateboard, would his motion depend on how hard you pushed? If so, how? Would his motion depend on the value of his mass? How do you think these two factors would affect his motion if you were to push against him as he moves?

 When a force acts on an object, how is the object's motion affected by the strength of the force and the object's mass?

Initial Ideas

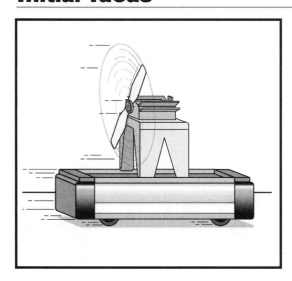

In Activity 2 of this chapter you investigated the motion of a cart while it is being pushed along the track by a fan unit and saw that its speed continuously increases. Suppose you were to repeat the experiment with two otherwise identical carts, one of which has a fan-unit that pushes with a stronger force than the other.

Assuming the effects of friction are negligible, would the motion of the two carts be exactly the same, or different in some way?

Sketch (and label) two lines on the blank speed-time graph below for the two otherwise identical carts being pushed by a 'weaker' and a 'stronger' force.

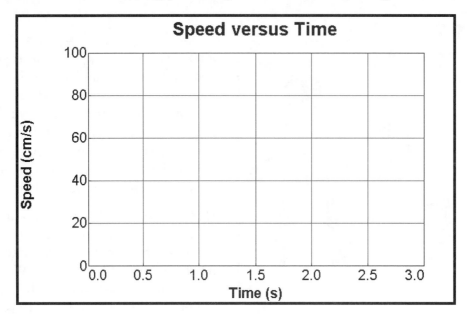

 Briefly explain the reasoning that led you to draw the graphs the way you did.

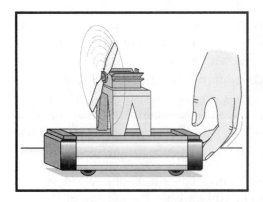

In Activity 3 you also used a fan-cart, but this time gave it a quick push to get it started and then used the fan unit to exert a continuous force in the direction **opposite** to the motion. This caused the cart to slow down, stop momentarily, and then move back toward its starting position, speeding up as it did so.

Imagine you have two such carts, with fan-units of **equal strength**. You then add some extra mass to one of the carts, start both fans, and then give both carts a push away from you so that they start moving side-by-side at the same speed (with the fan units pushing **opposite** the direction of motion).

Which cart do you think would be the first to stop and start moving back toward you – the one with **less mass**, the one with **more mass**, or would they act the same? Explain your reasoning.

 Participate in a whole-class discussion about these questions and make a note of any ideas or reasoning different from those of your team.

Collecting and Interpreting Evidence

 EXPERIMENT #1: How does force strength affect speeding up and slowing down?

YOU WILL NEED:

- Low-friction cart
- Track
- Fan units
- Access to a Motion Sensor connected to a computer
- Color pencils
- Spare batteries and dummies

STEP 1: In Activity 2 you established that the fan-unit provides a constant strength push on the cart. For this experiment you will need to have a way of changing the strength of the fan unit's push on the cart. One suggestion was that changing the number of batteries powering the fan unit might be a way to do this.

To check this idea, first mount the fan unit on the cart. Next, turn the fan unit on and have one of your team place a finger in front of the cart to stop it from moving. This person should concentrate on the push they feel from the cart while the fan is running. At the same time another team member should listen to the sound the fan makes while it is running. Keep the fan running for several seconds and then turn it off.

Repeat this procedure with different numbers of real batteries mounted in the fan unit (and the rest of the spaces taken up with dummies).

 Does the push of the cart seem to change, or stay the same depending on how many batteries are used? What about the sound the fan makes?

 Do you think the strength of the force exerted by the fan unit on the cart depends on the number of batteries used? What evidence supports your idea?

> **Note: This experiment calls for starting with two batteries and adding two more, one by one. Depending on your particular circumstances you may have to start with only one battery, and add two more.**

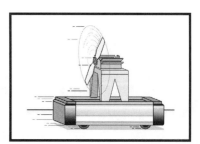 **STEP 2:** Open the Motion Sensor data collection file for this experiment. Insert two real batteries in the fan unit and place the cart about 20-30 cm from the Motion Sensor so that the fan will push it **away** from the sensor. Turn the fan unit on and hold the cart steady. Start the data collection and then release the cart.

 What is the motion of the cart like after you release it? Why does it move in this manner?

STEP 3: So that it is available for comparison you should now store the current Motion Sensor data on the computer. (See the *How to Use the Motion Sensor* Appendix for instructions on how to do this, or ask your instructor).

Now put a third real battery in the fan unit (replacing one of the 'dummies') and repeat the experiment. Store this data also, then add a fourth battery and perform the experiment again.

 Using different color pencils, sketch the three speed-time graphs below. Label each one according to how many batteries were used.

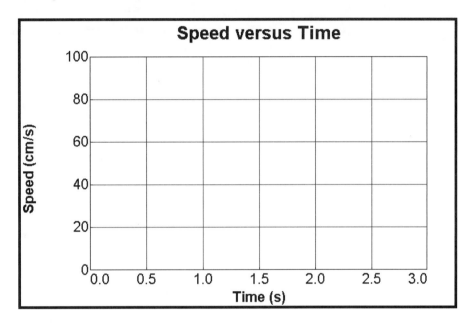

 What is similar about how the speed of the cart behaves, even when different strength forces are acting on it?

 What is different about how the speed of the cart behaves when different strength forces are acting on it?

STEP 4: First, clear all the Motion Sensor data on the computer. (See *How to Use the Motion Sensor* for instructions on how to do this, or ask your instructor.) Also, remove the two extra batteries from the fan unit and replace them with dummies.

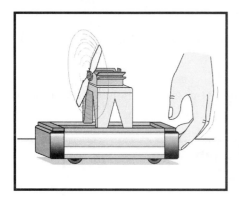

Now, place the cart about 20-30 cm from the Motion Sensor, this time so that the fan unit will push it **toward** the sensor. Turn the fan on and hold the cart steady. Start the data collection and then give the cart a quick push away from the sensor.

> **Stop the cart just as it starts to move back toward the sensor.**

 How does the speed of the cart behave **after** your quick push? Why does it move in this way?

STEP 5: Store the Motion Sensor data and then repeat this procedure using three, then four, batteries in the fan unit. In each case try to make sure the cart is moving at about the same speed, just after the push. *(To check this, make sure each graph rises to about the same maximum value at about the same time.)*

 Using different color pencils, sketch the three speed-time graphs below. Label each one according to how many batteries were used.

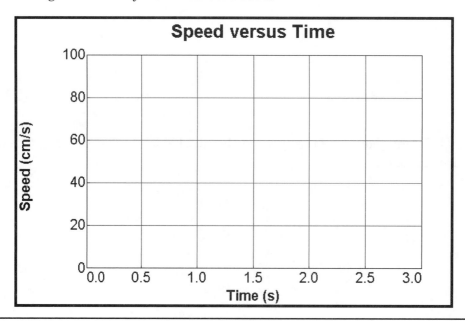

What is similar about how the speed of the cart behaves after the initial push, even when different strength forces are acting on it?

 What is different about how the speed of the cart behaves after the initial push, when different strength forces are acting on it?

Rate of Change of Speed

In the previous experiment you investigated how the manner in which an object's speed changes depends on the strength of the force applied to it. When comparing the motion of the cart with different force strengths acting on it, you or your group members may have used phrases like 'it gets quicker more slowly', or 'it gets slower more quickly.' In cases like this, using the same terminology to describe both the process of changing speed (gets quicker or slower), and how quickly it happens (quickly or slowly), can easily lead to confusion and misunderstanding, so here we introduce some different terminology that you may find useful.

When scientists talk about how quickly something changes, they call it the **rate** at which it changes. For example, when the price of goods we buy increases, we talk about the rate of inflation. If the prices change quickly (say by an average of 10% over the course of a year) economists say there is a high rate of inflation. However, when prices increase more slowly (perhaps by 2% over one year) it is said that the rate of inflation is low

CHAPTER 2

We can also use this 'rate of change' terminology to compare how the speed of an object changes[1] under different conditions. Consider the following questions about the experiment you have just completed.

In the first part of the experiment you examined the motion of a cart while a single force was pushing it along the track, making it speed up.

 How does the rate at which the speed of the cart increases depend on the strength of the force acting on it in the same direction as its motion? Does the speed increase at a higher, or lower, rate when a stronger force is applied? How can you tell this from the speed-time graphs?

Now consider the second part of the experiment, in which you examined the motion of a cart while a single force was acting on it, making it slow down (after an initial push to get it started).

 How does the rate at which the speed of the cart decreases depend on the strength of the force acting on it in the direction opposite to its motion? Does the speed decrease at a higher, or lower, rate when a stronger force is applied? Again, how can you tell this from the speed-time graphs?

 Check your answers to these questions with at least two other groups and try to resolve any differences.

---

[1] Scientists use the term 'acceleration' to refer to a change in speed (increase **or** decrease) and define an object's acceleration to be the rate at which its speed changes. However, in everyday use the word 'acceleration' is usually understood to mean only an increase in speed. Therefore, to avoid confusion we will not use the term acceleration in the *PET* activities.

EXPERIMENT #2: How does mass affect speeding up and slowing down?

YOU WILL NEED (SHARE WITH ANOTHER TEAM, IF NECESSARY):

- 2 Low-friction carts
- 2 Tracks
- 2 Fan units
- Extra masses (metal bars)
- Ruler
- Access to the *I&M Computer Simulator*

STEP 1: Place the two tracks side-by-side. Mount a fan unit on each of the carts and place one on each track. Make sure you have two fan units that provide about the same strength of push. To do this, turn on the fan units, line up the carts side-by-side (on separate tracks), and let them go at the same time.

Assuming the two carts are identical, what should happen if the fan units are about the same strength?

If the two fan units do not appear to have close to the same strength, try changing the number of batteries, or try different fan units.

STEP 2: Now, put two of the metal bars on one of the carts. (Make sure they will not interfere with the fan blade.) Again, hold the carts side-by-side, turn on the fan units, and release both carts at the same time.

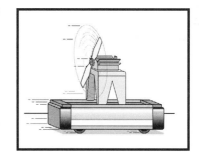

Describe the motion of the two carts. If they were in a race, which one would win? (After the experiment, leave the tracks and carts where they are as you will need them again in STEP 3.)

When the same strength force acted to speed up the two carts, which cart gained speed at a faster rate, the one with less mass, or the one with more mass? How do you know?

STEP 3: Return the carts (one should still have its added mass) to the starting point and turn them around so that the fan units will push them in the opposite direction. Turn the fans on, and give both the carts a quick push, against the fans, to start them moving at the **same speed**.

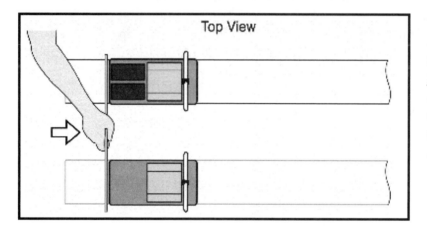

To have both carts moving at about the same speed, one person can push both of them, using a ruler, as shown in the top view here.

Repeat the experiment three times, using a different person to push for each trial.

 Which cart slows to a stop first, the one with less mass, or the one with more mass? Does your observation agree with your prediction in the Initial Ideas section?

 When the same strength force acted to slow down the two carts, which cart slowed down at a faster rate, the one with less mass, or the one with more mass? How do you know?

In the cases you have seen in this experiment (both speeding up and slowing down) which cart's speed changed at a higher rate when the same strength force acted on it, the one with less mass, or the one with more mass?

STEP 4: In STEP 2 you held a race between two carts that had different masses but the same strength force pushing on them. Now, suppose you wanted to make a race between the two carts end as a tie.

 To make the race a tie, what would you have to do to the strength of the fan unit pushing on the more massive cart? Explain your reasoning.

 SIMULATOR EXPLORATION: You can compare your ideas with those of scientists by using the *I&M Simulator*. In the setup file for this activity you will see two carts. One of these carts has no added mass and the other has two metal bars added, making its total mass three times greater than the other. (Each metal block has a mass equal to that of a single cart.) Each cart has a fan with a force-strength of 20N acting on it. Run the simulator and watch the motion of the carts.

 Which simulator cart has the added mass? How do you know?

 To make both carts speed up at the same rate, and hence make the race a tie, what strength should the fan acting on the more massive cart push with? (Remember, its mass is three times greater than the lighter cart.) Explain your reasoning.

Use the *I&M Simulator* to check your idea. Change the strength of the 20 N force on the more massive cart to your predicted value and run the simulator.

To change the strength of a force, first rewind the simulator. Then double-click on the head of the black force arrow to bring up the Properties box of the force.

You can now change the strength of the force using the control at the top right. You can either adjust the value using the slider control, or type in the new value

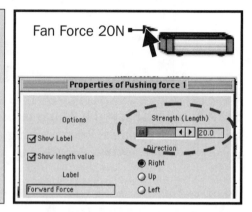

 Does the race between the two carts now end in a tie? Why do you think this is? (If the race is not a tie, first return to the simulator, adjust the force strength until it does, record it here and then answer the question.)

Summarizing Questions

 First, discuss these questions with your team and note your ideas. Leave space to add any different ideas that may emerge when the whole class discusses their thinking.

S1: When a single force acts on an object, how does the rate at which its speed changes depend on the strength of that force? Is this true for both speeding up and slowing down? What evidence supports your answer?

S2: To the right is a speed-time graph for a cart that was given a quick push along the track and then gradually slowed down. Which force do you think was stronger, the initial push, or the one that slowed it down? How do you know?

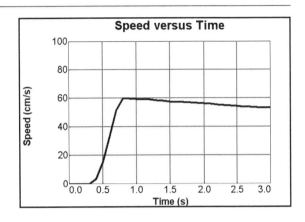

S3: How does the mass of an object affect the rate at which its speed changes, while a force acts on it? What evidence supports your answer?

S4: Which would be easier to start moving, a soccer ball or a bowling ball? Which would be easier to stop if they were moving at the same speed? Why do you think this is?

CHAPTER 2

S5: At a practice session a soccer goalie is practicing rolling a soccer ball along the ground. The coach measures the speed of the soccer ball and sees that, when the goalie pushes as hard as he can, the ball has a speed of 15 m/s just after it leaves the goalie's hands. A teammate plays a joke on the goalie and substitutes a bowling ball (appropriately painted) for the soccer ball. When the goalie pushes as hard as he can on the bowling ball the coach measures the ball's speed to be only 2 m/s just after it leaves the goalie's hands.

Assuming the goalie pushed with the same strength force, for the same amount of time, on both balls, write a scientific explanation for why the bowling ball's speed is much less than the soccer ball's speed, just after they left the goalie's hands.

 EXPLANATION: Why was the bowling ball's speed much less than the soccer ball's speed just after the goalie had pushed them both with the same strength force, for the same amount of time?

Describe the situation using a diagram: (Draw two separate force diagrams, one for each ball.)

Write the narrative: (Use the idea you developed in this activity about how the effect of a force on an object depends on the object's mass.)

Putting It All Together

You have seen in this activity that when a force pushes or pulls on an object, the effect that it has (the rate at which the object's speed changes) depends on **both** the strength of the force **and** the mass of the object. But what if you had two objects that had **different masses**, acted on by forces of **different strengths**? How could you predict which object's speed would change at a faster rate?

Two students were discussing their ideas about a relationship that they could use to help them decide:

We saw that the greater the force strength, the faster the speed changes. I also think that the more mass an object has, the faster it slows down, so increases in the force strength and mass both produce a faster change in speed. That makes me think the rate at which the speed of an object changes depends on the force strength multiplied by the mass.

I agree with what you say about the force strength, but the speed of the cart with more mass increased at a slower rate, not a faster one. I think you have to divide the force strength by the mass to find out about the rate at which the speed will change.

Amara

Han

In terms of a mathematical relationship, Amara thinks:

Rate of change in speed ⌣ Strength of force × Mass of object,

(where the '⌣' sign means 'is related to' or 'depends on') while Han thinks:

$$\textbf{Rate of change in speed} \smallsmile \frac{\textbf{Strength of force}}{\textbf{Mass of object}}$$

 Do you agree with Amara, Han, or neither of them? What evidence from this activity supports your thinking?

In Summarizing Question S5 on a previous page, you thought about the motion of a soccer ball and bowling ball when the same strength force acted on them for the same period of time. What if the coach now rolled the balls toward the goalie at a speed of 15 m/s, so that he could practice stopping them? In this case, the goalie will have to reduce the speed of both balls from 15 m/s to zero over the same time period.

 How would the force strength the goalie has to apply to the soccer ball to do this compare with the force strength he has to apply to the bowling ball? Explain how your answer fits with the mathematical relationship you chose above.

 Participate in a whole-class discussion to go over the summarizing questions and your ideas about the mathematical relationship.

Name:_____ Date:_____ Group: _____

Purpose

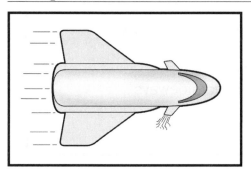

You have seen that when an object is already moving, a force acting on it in the same direction as its motion will make it speed up, while a force in the opposite direction to the motion will make it slow down. But what if the force is applied in a direction that is from the side with respect to the motion? What effect will such a force have?

For instance, what would happen to the motion of a spacecraft if it fired a small engine on its side while it was moving forward?

What effect does a sideways force have on an object that is already moving?

Collecting and Interpreting Evidence

EXPERIMENT #1: What happens if a moving object is tapped on the side?

YOU WILL NEED:

- Soccer ball (or similar)
- Stick (or some other object than can be used to tap the ball firmly)

STEP 1: Start the ball rolling across the floor by giving it a sharp tap with the stick. While it is moving, give it a second sharp tap, but this time at right angles to its direction of motion. (See picture on next page.) **Pay careful attention to both the speed and direction of the ball after this second tap.**

> It is very important to make sure that the strength of the sideways tap you apply to the ball is of about the same strength as the tap you used to start the ball moving in the first place.

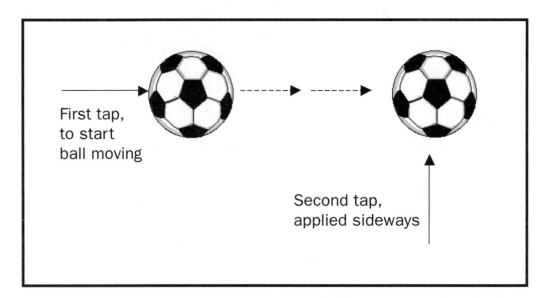

First tap,
to start
ball moving

Second tap,
applied sideways

 On the diagram above, sketch the path of the ball, after the sideways tap.

 After the sideways tap, is the ball's motion in the same direction as before the tap, in the direction of the sideways tap itself, or somewhere in between the two? (If you are not sure, you may wish to repeat the experiment, making sure the strength of both the initial and sideways taps is close to the same.)

 Why do you think the direction of the ball's motion, after the sideways tap, is different from its original direction?

 Why do you think the direction of the ball's motion, after the sideways tap, is different from the direction of the sideways tap itself?

In this experiment the direction of the ball's motion changed as a result of the force exerted on the ball by the stick during the interaction between them.

Do you think a force is always needed to change the direction of motion of a moving object, or can the direction change on its own? Why, or why not? Give two other examples to illustrate your thinking.

 SIMULATOR EXPLORATION #2: What happens if a continuous sideways force acts on a moving object?

YOU WILL NEED:

■ Access to the *I&M Computer Simulator*

STEP 1: As before, imagine that there is a soccer ball (or a ball of similar size and mass) rolling across the floor in front of you. At some point you give it a quick sideways tap that changes its direction, as shown below. A short time later you give it another sideways tap (relative to its new direction of motion).

Suppose you were to keep giving such sideways taps (always relative to the direction of motion at that time) at regular intervals, and always from the same side of the ball. What would the path of the ball look like in this case?

 Sketch your idea on the picture to the right, showing the path of the ball and its position when the taps are applied.

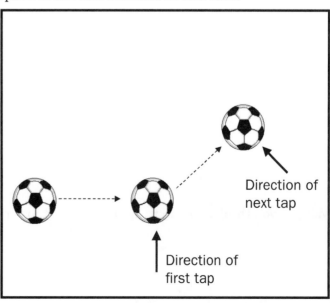

Explain your reasoning.

STEP 2: You can compare your ideas with those of scientists by using the *I&M Simulator*. Open the first setup file for this homework assignment. You will see an object that is already moving toward the top of the screen (or will be when you run the simulation).

*Note: as before, the red half-arrow is a **speed-arrow** for the ball, representing the speed and direction of its motion. Any forces acting on the object will be represented by black arrows, as in the other simulators.*

Run the simulation and, while the object is moving, apply some sideways taps at **regular intervals** (using the spacebar on the keyboard) to try and make the object follow the octagonal path shown on the setup.

 Sketch the path, and indicate the points at which you had to give the object a tap to get it to follow that path.

 Why do you think you had to apply a tap at those particular points?

In between each pair of sideways taps, what is the path of the object like? Why do you think this is?

STEP 3: In the simulator, the taps are represented with black force arrows. Run the simulator again, and watch carefully the direction in which each tap is aimed.

 Is each individual tap aimed in the object's direction of motion before the tap, its new direction after the tap, or in a direction between the two?

 Are all the taps aimed in the same direction, or is there some other simple way to describe how they are directed? (For example, is there some common point they are all aimed toward?)

Now, suppose that, instead of quick taps, you were able to apply a continuous sideways force to the object as it moves.

 What shape do you think its path would be then? Explain your reasoning.

STEP 4: To check your idea, open the second simulator setup file for this homework assignment. This setup shows an object that is initially moving diagonally up and to the right. (Note the direction of the speed arrow.) However, when the simulation is run, a **continuous force** will be applied that is always directed sideways with respect to the direction of motion.

 Run the simulation, and sketch the path of the object below. Choose four points on the path and draw the object at those points, together with its **speed arrow** and an arrow representing the **force** acting on it at that point.

 (Alternatively, if you are completing this homework assignment electronically, you can use the 'snapshot' tool in the simulator and then paste the pictures into this document.)

 At any particular moment in time how would you describe the direction of motion of the object? Is it headed outward (away from the center of the circle), inward (toward the center of the circle), or at a tangent to the circle?

 What is the relationship between the direction of motion of the object and the direction of the force acting on it? Do they always point in the same direction, opposite directions, or are they related in some other way? Please describe.

Is there a common point toward which the force always points? If so, what is it?

 What do you think would happen if, while the object was moving in its circular path, the sideways force were to disappear? How do you think the motion of the object would change? Explain your reasoning.

You can remove the continuous sideways force by tapping on the spacebar in this setup. Start the simulation running again, let it run for a few seconds, and then remove the force.

 Sketch the path of the object, both before and after you remove the sideways force. Again, choose some points on the path (both before and after you removed the force) and draw the object at those points, including its speed arrow and force arrow (if relevant).

CHAPTER 2

Did the behavior of the object when the force was removed agree with your prediction? If not, try to explain it.

Two students in a previous class were discussing what happens to an object moving in a circle, when the force making it do so is removed.

I think that, since there is no longer a force to make it change direction, the object will move in a straight line, in the direction it was headed at the moment the force was removed.

I'm not so sure. I do think it will move in a straight line, but the direction will be the same as the direction of the last force that acted on it.

Samantha

Kristen

 Who do you agree with? Samantha, or Kristen, or neither, and why?

Summarizing Questions

 Write your own answers to these questions. Leave space to add any different ideas that may emerge when the whole class discusses their thinking.

S1: What effect does a sideways force have on the motion of an object? Does it seem to change the speed, as forward and backward forces do, or does it change some other aspect of the motion (or both)?

S2: If a continuous sideways force acts on an object while it is moving, and always points toward one place, what will the object's path be like?

S3: If no sideways forces act on a moving object, what will its path be like? Explain your reasoning.

S4: Imagine tying a stuffed toy to a string and swinging it around in a horizontal circle above your head at a **constant speed**. (A top view is shown here. The curved arrow simply indicates the direction of rotation.) Does a sideways force act on the toy? How do you know?

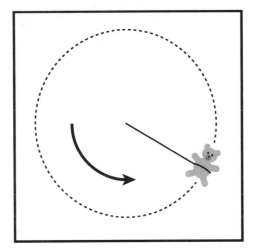

What other object do you think is exerting this force on the toy?

On the picture above, draw a speed arrow and an arrow representing the force acting on the toy.

S5: Now, suppose that after the toy has moved a bit further round the circle, the string were to break when the toy was in the position shown in this diagram. Draw a line on the diagram to show what the path of the toy would be after that happened. Explain your reasoning below.

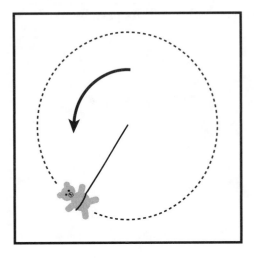

The Nature of Sideways Forces

It is important to realize that the forces that cause objects to change direction (moving in a circular path is just a continuous change in direction) are the same as the forces that cause objects to speed up or slow down. For example, if your second tap in Experiment #1 had been in the same direction as the motion of the ball, then the ball would have sped up, rather than changed direction. If the tap had been in the opposite direction to the motion, it would have slowed down. The difference in effect was due to the **direction** in which the force was applied, relative to the motion, rather than anything different about the force itself.

This is true of all forces. For example, a hit from a hockey stick could be used to make a puck speed up, slow down and stop, or change direction, depending on how it is applied. Another example would be the force of gravity (which you will study in the next chapter), which makes objects fall to the ground, but is also responsible for keeping the Moon in its (nearly) circular orbit around the Earth.

 In the Summarizing Questions you considered a force exerted by a string (which scientists call a 'tension' force) that made a stuffed toy continuously change direction, and so move in a circular path. Describe and sketch two other situations, one in which the tension force in a string is being used to make an object speed up, the other in which the same force is being used to slow an object down.

Activity 7–Motion with Balanced Forces
Developing Ideas

Purpose

In a previous homework activity you saw that when an **unbalanced** combination of forces acts on an object, the speed of the object changes in the same way as when a single force acts on it.

But what if the combined strength of the forces pushing (or pulling) in one direction is exactly equal to the combined strength of the forces pushing (or pulling) in the opposite direction? In this case we say the forces are **balanced**. If such a balanced combination of forces acted on an object at rest, would it start to move? If it were already moving, what would its motion be like?

For example, suppose the two men above push the box with a force of 200 N each, while a frictional force of 400 N opposes them. What would the

motion of the box be like in this case? Would your answer depend on whether it started at rest, or was already moving?

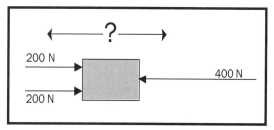

 How does an object behave when the forces acting on it are balanced?

Initial Ideas

Imagine having one of the low-friction carts with two fan units mounted on it. Further, when operating, these fan units push on the cart in **opposite** directions with exactly the **same** strength.

Suppose you held this cart stationary on a level surface, turned both fans on, and then let go.

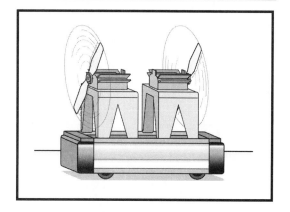

How do you think the cart would move (if at all)? Briefly explain your reasoning.

Now, suppose you were to give the cart a quick push with your hand (in one direction or the other) to start it moving.

 How do you think the cart would move **after** your push? (Speed up, slow down, or maintain a reasonably constant speed?) Why do you think it would move in this way?

 Participate in a whole-class discussion about these ideas. Make a note of any ideas or reasoning that are different from those of your team.

Collecting and Interpreting Evidence

 EXPERIMENT #1: How do balanced forces affect motion?

STEP 1: Your instructor will show you a cart with two fan units mounted on it. These fan units have been adjusted so that, when turned on, they push in opposite directions with the same strength force. Your instructor will hold the cart at rest, turn on both fans, and then release the cart.

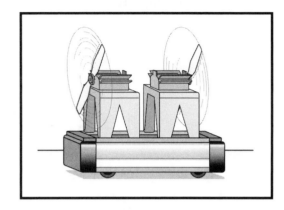

 Describe the behavior of the cart.

 Why do you think the cart behaves in this way?

 In general, if balanced forces act on an object that is at rest, what do you think happens to it?

CHAPTER 2

STEP 2: With the fans still running, your instructor will give the cart a quick push in one direction.

 Describe the motion of the cart **after** the quick push. Does it speed up or slow down quickly, or does its speed seem to stay about the same?

STEP 3: Now your instructor will turn the fans off and repeat STEP 2.

 Describe the motion of the cart **after** the quick push.

 Compare the motion of the cart with the fans running to its motion with them turned off. Does there seem to be any significant difference? Why do you think this is?

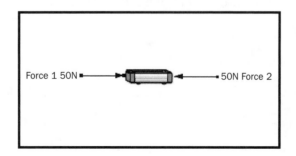

STEP 4:
Simulator Exploration

You can compare your ideas with those of scientists by using the *I&M Simulator*. When you open the simulator setup for this experiment you will see a cart **at rest** with two 50 N forces acting on it, in opposite directions.

When you run the simulator, what is the speed of the cart while the balanced forces act on it? Does the speed change or does it remain constant?

Rewind the simulation and run it again. This time, give the cart an initial push (using the spacebar) for about one second.

 Sketch the speed-time graph for the cart below on the blank graph titled 'Balanced Forces.' (You will use the other blank graph later.)

Balanced Forces   **No Forces**

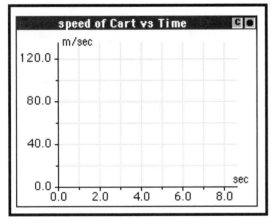   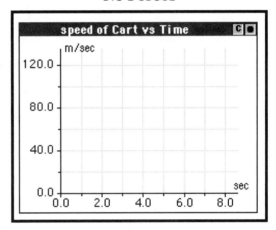

 After the initial push, when **only** the balanced forces act on the cart, does the speed of the cart change or does it remain constant?

 Do you think the motion of the cart **after** the initial push would depend on the strengths of the two balanced forces? (For example, would the motion be different if they both had a strength of 100 N, rather than 50 N?) Explain your reasoning.

STEP 5: To check your idea, rewind the simulator and change the values for the strengths of the two opposing forces, remembering to keep the values **the same** so that the forces are still balanced. Run the simulator again and give the cart the same initial push as before. Do this several times, each time using a different value for the strength of the two opposing forces, always remembering to keep them **balanced**.

 Describe the results of your investigation with the simulator. Does the motion of the cart **after** the initial push depend on the strength of the balanced forces? Why do you think this is?

STEP 6: Finally, rewind the simulator and delete the two opposing forces. (To do this, click on each force arrow and then hit the Delete key on the keyboard.) Run the simulation, and again give the cart an initial push for about one second.

 Sketch the speed-time graph for the cart above on the blank graph laleled 'No Forces.'

 After the initial push, when **no forces** act on the cart, does the speed of the cart change or does it remain constant?

 Is the motion of an object with balanced forces acting on it similar to, or different from, an object with no forces acting on it? Why do you think this is?

EXPERIMENT #2: Are the forces balanced or unbalanced?

YOU WILL NEED:

- Low-friction cart with friction pad
- Track
- Fan unit
- Access to a Motion Sensor connected to a computer

STEP 1: Make sure the friction pad on the cart is raised up so that it will **not** rub on the surface when the cart moves. Mount the fan unit on the cart and place it on the track (or table) about 20 cm from the Motion Sensor, so that the fan unit will push the cart away from the sensor.

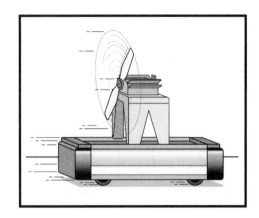

Open the Motion Sensor data collection file for this activity. Turn the fan on, start the data collection, and then release the cart.

 Look at the speed-time graph on the computer. Do you think the forces acting on the cart after you released it were **balanced** or **unbalanced**? How can you tell?

STEP 2: Now, lower the friction pad very slightly, so that it **rubs lightly** on the surface, and repeat the experiment. (If the cart does not move after you lower the pad and turn the fan on, you have lowered it too much!)

 Do you think the forces acting on the cart now are **balanced**, or **unbalanced**? How can you tell from the speed-time graph?

What forces do you think were acting on the cart while it was moving along the track? Which force do you think was strongest? Explain your reasoning.

STEP 3: Keep lowering the pad in very small steps, until you get to a point where the cart will not move when you turn the fan on and release it.

 Do you think the forces acting on the cart now are **balanced**, or **unbalanced**? How can you tell?

 Again, what forces do you think were acting on the cart? Which force do you think was strongest? Explain your reasoning.

STEP 4: Finally, very carefully adjust the friction pad until you get to a point where, **after being given a quick push to get it started**, the cart moves at a fairly constant speed. (You can use the Motion Sensor to collect data to check whether the speed is constant.)

 Assuming the cart did move at a constant speed **after the push**, do you think the forces acting on the cart (after the push has ended) are **balanced**, or **unbalanced**? How can you tell?

 What forces do you think were acting on the cart while it was moving along the track? Which force do you think was strongest? Explain your reasoning.

Summarizing Questions

First, discuss these questions with your team and note your ideas. Leave space to add any different ideas that may emerge when the whole class discusses their thinking.

S1: When the forces acting on an object are balanced, what happens to its speed? Does its speed change or does it remain constant? What evidence supports your idea?

S2: How does your answer to the previous question apply to an object at rest, with balanced forces acting on it?

S3: Use the pictures below to draw three force diagrams for the cart with balanced fan units acting on it; one **before** the initial push, one **during** the initial push, and one **after** the push. Explain your diagrams below the pictures.

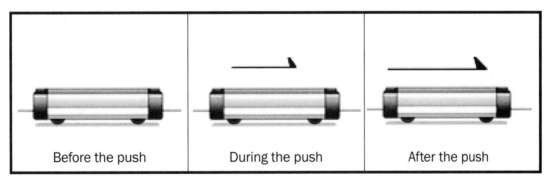

| Before the push | During the push | After the push |

S4: Two students were discussing their ideas about balanced forces:

I just can't see how an object with balanced forces acting on it can be moving at a constant speed. Surely, if it's moving in any way, the force in the direction of motion must be stronger than the opposing force.

What I can't understand is how an object with balanced forces can be moving at all. After all, didn't we learn that an object at rest, with balanced forces acting on it, will stay at rest?

Dave

Luisa

How would you respond to Dave's and Luisa's concerns?

S5: Give two examples of everyday objects on which a **balanced** combination of forces acts. (One of your examples should be an object that is in motion.) Draw a force diagram for each of the objects and make sure you identify the forces acting on it. Below each diagram explain how you know the combination of acting forces is balanced.

S6: Imagine you want to push a heavy sofa across a carpeted floor on which a friction force opposes any movement, or attempt at movement. Answer the following questions about this situation:

If the sofa were at rest, what would you have to do to start it moving? Push with a force strength less than, equal to, or greater than the friction force resisting the movement of the sofa? Please explain the reasoning behind your answer.

S7: After you start the sofa moving, what would you have to do to make it move across the floor at a **constant speed**? Push with a force strength less than, equal to, or greater than the friction force resisting the movement of the sofa? This time, write a scientific explanation to show your thinking.

CHAPTER 2

EXPLANATION: Why does the sofa move across the floor at a constant speed?

Describe the situation using a diagram: (Draw a force diagram for the sofa while it is moving across the floor at a constant speed.)

Write the narrative: (Use the idea you developed in this activity about motion at a constant speed to explain why you think the strength of your push should be equal to, or greater than the friction force.)

S8: You have seen in this chapter of activities that once an object is moving, if **no forces** act on it, it will continue to move at a constant speed. However, based on their real-world experiences, many people hold the idea that a continuous constant force **is** needed in order to maintain a constant speed. Why do you think this is such a common idea? (Hint: Think about what you have learned in this activity about motion at a constant speed, together with the forces that act on an object in the real world.)

Activity 8–Explaining Phenomena Using Force Ideas
Applying Ideas

Comparing the Class Consensus Ideas and Scientists' Ideas

During this chapter you have developed ideas about how the forces acting on an object affect its motion.

 Your instructor will give you a copy of the handout: *Scientists' Ideas: Newton's Laws*. With your team, review the similarities and differences between the class ideas and the *Scientists' Ideas*. In the space below each of the scientists' ideas, make a note of any evidence (or examples) you have seen in this chapter that supports the idea.

Scientific Explanations Involving Forces

In this chapter of activities, you have been developing ideas about how to describe contact interactions and their effects in terms of the forces that the objects involved exert on each other. You have also been practicing writing and evaluating scientific explanations using these ideas. In this activity, you will apply your ideas about forces to explain some more everyday phenomena.

Remember, to construct a scientific explanation using ideas about forces, you should first draw a force diagram that shows all the relevant forces acting on the object of interest. You should also draw a speed arrow, if relevant. When writing your narrative, you should keep in mind the criteria of *accuracy*, *completeness*, *logical reasoning* and *clarity* first introduced in Chapter 1.

As was also stated in Chapter 1, it is very important to state explicitly in your narrative if you are taking the effects of friction to be negligible. This can be the case if you are dealing with situations that involve a vehicle with well-lubricated wheels or an object sliding across a very smooth surface (such as ice), especially if other forces acting on the object are much stronger than any friction forces. If you decide the effects of friction are not negligible, then the force of friction should play a part in the explanation.

Your first task is to evaluate some explanations written by previous students.

Explaining the Motion of an Ice Hockey Puck

After a hockey player gives a puck a quick hit with his stick, the puck slides across the ice at a speed that is essentially constant. (Note: this could also apply to a well-lubricated cart that is given a quick shove along the track!) Three students in a previous class offered the following force diagrams and explanations in terms of the forces acting on the puck.

 EXPLANATION #1: Why does the puck move at a constant speed after it is given an initial hit by a player?

Describe the situation using a diagram:

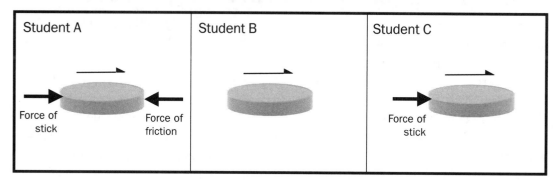

| Student A | Student B | Student C |

Write the narrative:

Student A	Student B	Student C
The force of the stick was transferred to the puck and exactly balances the force of friction opposing the puck's motion. When balanced forces act on an object, its speed will remain constant.	After the stick has lost contact with the puck, no forces act on it and so there is nothing to change its speed.	The initial hit is what starts the puck moving. After the hit has stopped, it moves at a constant speed.

Evaluate these Explanations

Decide whether each explanation is **good** or **poor** by reviewing each of the following criteria.

Student A	Student B	Student C	Criterion
YES/NO	YES/NO	YES/NO	Complete: All ideas needed are included.
YES/NO	YES/NO	YES/NO	Accurate: All included ideas correspond to established ideas.
YES/NO	YES/NO	YES/NO	Logical reasoning and clarity: Narrative connects ideas to the phenomenon, and is well written.

 Participate in a whole-class discussion about these explanations and make any notes you think necessary.

Taxiing a Plane

When taxiing a plane around an airport (before take-off or after landing) the pilots use the engines to push the plane along the ground. (The engines work in the same way that the fan units push on the carts you have used.) When the aircraft is standing still, with the engines running slowly, the pilot increases the power of the engines to start the plane moving, but when the plane reaches the desired taxiing speed, he reduces the engine power again. Why is this? (If you have never noticed this, next time you are on a plane listen to the engine noise while it is taxiing.)

Your task is to explain why the pilot reduces the engine power once the plane has reached the desired taxiing speed. Answering the following questions should help you think about why this is.

 Do you think a frictional force plays a significant role in this situation or not? Briefly explain your reasoning.

 To start the plane moving and make it speed up, do the forces acting on it need to be balanced or unbalanced?

 Once the plane has sped up to the desired taxiing speed, to maintain that speed do the forces acting on it need to be balanced or unbalanced?

 What do your previous answers imply about the strength of the pushing force needed to start the plane moving and speed it up, versus the force strength needed to maintain a constant speed?

Now write your own explanation to answer the question.

EXPLANATION #2: Why does the pilot reduce the engine power when the plane has reached the desired taxiing speed?

Describe the situation using a diagram: (Draw two separate force diagrams, one while the plane is speeding up, the other while it is taxiing at a constant speed.)

Write the narrative: (Remember to connect the ideas about forces you use to the actual question being asked.)

CHAPTER 2

EXPERIMENT #1: Investigating the motion of objects inside a vehicle that suddenly stops.

You have probably noticed that when a vehicle stops suddenly, objects inside it get thrown about. In this part of the activity you will investigate this motion and then use your ideas to judge the validity of a claim made by a bus passenger.

YOU WILL NEED

- Low-friction cart
- Track
- Small block (to represent a case)

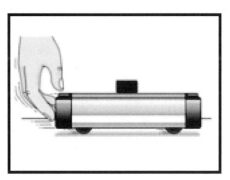

Place the block in the middle of the cart and start the cart moving by giving it a push with your hand. (While you are pushing, hold the block in place in the middle of the cart.)

After your push, let the cart move a short distance on its own, then stop it very **suddenly**, again using your hand. Watch the behavior of the block as you stop the cart.

 Describe what happens to the block during the sudden stop.

Why do you think the block behaves in this way? To help you answer this question, **first** think about the following ideas:

 If an object is already moving, what is needed to make it slow and stop?

If you had two objects moving together, what would happen if a strong force opposing the motion acted on one of them, but no such force (or a very much weaker force) acted on the other?

 Does a strong force act on the cart to slow and stop it quickly? If so, what object exerts that force on the cart?

 During the very short period of time while the cart is stopping, does a strong force also act on the block to slow and stop it? If so, what object exerts that force on the block? If not, what will happen to the speed of the block?

Two students were discussing why the block appears to slide forwards on the cart when the cart is stopped suddenly.

A 'backward' force acts on the cart so it stops moving. When it does so a forward force acts on the block so it is pushed to the front of the cart.

I agree that a force acts on the cart, but no force acts on the block so it just keeps moving forward, while the cart stops.

Han   **Samantha**

 Do you agree with Han, Samantha, or neither of them? Explain your reasoning.

 When the block reaches the front lip of the stopped cart, the block itself then also stops. Why do you think this is?

Using the ideas you thought about above, write an explanation for why the block slides to the front of the cart when the cart is stopped suddenly.

> **First think about the cart and the block separately, drawing separate force diagrams for each. Then combine your ideas in the written narrative to answer the question.**

 EXPLANATION #3: Why does the block slide to the front of the cart when the cart is stopped suddenly?

Describe the situation using a diagram: (Draw separate force diagrams for the cart and block, for the same moment in time while the cart is in the process of stopping.)

Cart: Block:

Write the narrative:

You are the Expert Witness

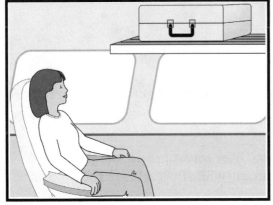

A passenger is suing a bus company for injuries she claims were sustained when the bus had to brake sharply to avoid hitting an obstruction in the road.

The passenger, who was seated in the row of seats behind the luggage rack, claims that the bus braked sharply, causing a case to fly backwards off a luggage rack in front of her and hit her head.

 As an expert in Newton's Laws you have been called to testify as to whether this story is credible or not. How would you respond?

 Explain your reasoning.

 Participate in a whole-class discussion about these ideas.

Interactions
and Systems

Purpose

In the first two chapters of the *PET* course you studied two different ways of talking about the contact interactions that occur when two touching objects interact by pushing and/or pulling on each other. However, there are many other types of interactions in the world. You should recall that the evidence for a contact interaction was a change in the motion of at least one of the objects involved. However, are contact interactions the only ones in which motion changes, or can other interactions result in a change in motion also? If so, what characteristics make these interactions different from contact interactions?

Magnetic effects are used in many different ways in the world around us– from holding notes on your refrigerator, to recording information on computer disks or credit cards.

Think about when you have played with magnets before. Have you noticed if there are any differences between the way magnets interact with each other and the way objects interact with each other during contact interactions?

In this activity you will examine some magnetic interactions to see how they are different from the contact interactions you studied previously, and you will draw some force diagrams to describe the interactions. You will also investigate what kinds of materials are affected by magnets. In addition, you will continue to think about how the idea of a 'system' can be useful in the description of the interaction between objects in terms of energy.

What are some characteristics of magnetic interactions?

Collecting and Interpreting Evidence

 EXPERIMENT #1: Do magnets have to touch each other to interact?

You will need:

■ 2 small magnets

STEP 1: Take the two small magnets in your hands and bring their faces together slowly, but try not to let them touch each other.

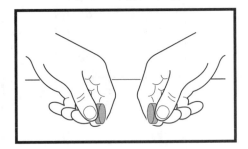

 Describe what you feel as they approach each other.

 Do the magnets exert a force on each other, even though they are not touching? How can you tell?

 Does there seem to be a relationship between the strength of the magnetic force on each magnet and how far apart the two magnets are? How do you know?

 Since you are holding the magnets in place, the forces acting on each magnet must be balanced. At right, draw a force diagram showing the forces acting on magnet A. Label the force arrows.

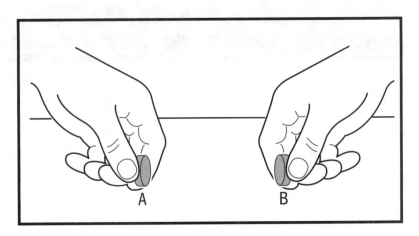

Now turn **one** of the magnets over and bring them together again.

 Do they behave in the same way as before, or does something different happen? If so, what?

 Do the magnets still exert a force on each other when they are not touching? If so, is there anything different about the forces now?

 In this arrangement, does the strength of the magnetic force between the two magnets depend on how far apart they are? If so, in what way?

When two magnets either attract or repel each other in the way you have seen above, we call this a **magnetic interaction**. The magnetic interaction is an example of what scientists call an **'action-at-a-distance'** interaction, that is an interaction in which objects can exert forces on each other without touching. You will see examples of other action-at-a-distance interactions in the following activities.

 How is it possible for two magnets to exert forces on each other without touching? Discuss with your group and try to think of possible ideas to account for how this action-at-a-distance occurs. Make a note of any ideas you find useful.

CHAPTER 3

EXPERIMENT #2: What kinds of materials interact with a magnet?

In this experiment you will be testing various materials to determine if they interact with a magnet in any way.

YOU WILL NEED:

■ Magnet

■ Set of different materials

STEP 1: Before testing any materials, you should record your initial ideas.

 What kinds of materials do you think would be attracted to a magnet? Be as specific as you can.

 Assuming these materials are not themselves magnets, do you think they can also be repelled from a magnet?

STEP 2: Take one item from the set of materials, and record its name in the Table. Determine whether the material is attracted to the magnet.

 Record your result in the Table.

Table: Observations with Magnet and Materials

Material	Attracted to Magnet?

STEP 3: Repeat step 2 for all the available materials. You may also check other materials you are curious about.

 Record your additional observations in the Table.

STEP 4: Choose an object made of a material that is attracted to the magnet. Turn the magnet around, so its opposite pole faces the object.

 Is the object still attracted to the magnet?

 How is the interaction between a magnet and this object different from the interaction between two magnets?

STEP 5: Look over the data in your Table.

 Are all metals attracted to a magnet?

What materials do seem to be attracted to a magnet?

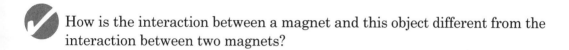

Scientists call materials that are attracted to a magnet 'ferromagnetic materials.' Magnets are also made of ferromagnetic materials. Iron is the most common ferromagnetic material, and objects or materials that include iron in them (like steel) are also ferromagnetic. (Nickel and cobalt are also examples of ferromagnetic materials.)

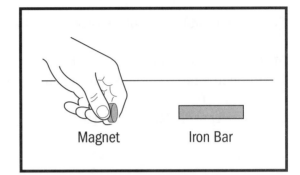

Magnet   Iron Bar

 Draw a force diagram showing the force acting on the iron bar due to the magnet. Label the force arrow.

 EXPERIMENT #3: How can you describe magnetic interactions in terms of energy?

As you have seen in the first two chapters of this course, interactions can be described either in terms of forces or in terms of energy. In the two previous experiments, you drew force diagrams to describe the magnetic interaction in terms of forces. In this experiment you will gather evidence that will enable you to think about how to describe magnetic interactions in terms of energy.

YOU WILL NEED:

■ 2 small disk magnets

■ 2 low-friction carts and track

■ Several heavy metal bars to place on a cart

■ Tape

■ Ruler

STEP 1: Place the two carts on the track. Bring them close to each other and make sure there is not already a magnetic interaction between the two facing ends. (If such an interaction exists, try turning both of the carts around.)

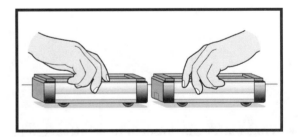

Now, use the tape to attach a small magnet to the center of each of the facing ends (one on each cart). Make sure that these magnets are arranged so that they will **repel** each other when the carts are brought close together.

> **Attaching the magnets to the low-friction carts will allow you to more easily observe the effects of the interaction between the two magnets, but you should remember that all the effects you see are due entirely to the magnetic interaction between the two magnets.**

Hold the two magnet-carts so that the magnets are very close together, but not quite touching. Now release both magnet-carts at the **same time**.

 Describe what happens to the two magnet-carts immediately after you release them.

 What can you say about the effect this magnetic interaction had on the motion of both magnet-carts? Did it have about the same effect on both or did one magnet-cart move very differently than the other? Why do you think this is?

STEP 2: Repeat the experiment from STEP 1 but this time add several of the heavy metal blocks to **one** of the magnet-carts. Watch the motion of the two magnet-carts carefully as you perform the experiment.

 Was anything different about the way the motion of two magnet-carts was affected by the magnetic interaction this time? Why do you think this was?

Suppose you were able to repeat the last experiment but arrange for the mass of one magnet-cart to be **many, many, many times greater** than the other.

 How do you think the motion of each of the two magnet-carts would be affected by the magnetic interaction then? Explain your reasoning.

STEP 3: Remove the metal blocks from the cart. Then remove the magnet from one of the carts, turn it over and fix it back to the cart. (The two facing magnets should now **attract** each other.) Hold the two magnet-carts on the track, about 3 cm apart, release them simultaneously, and watch carefully what happens.

 Describe what happens to the magnet-carts. Does only one of them move, or do they both move? Why do you think this is?

Again, add several of the heavy metal blocks to **one** of the magnet-carts and repeat the experiment. Watch the motion of the two magnet-carts carefully as you release them.

 Was anything different about the way the motion of the two magnet-carts was affected by the magnetic interaction this time? Why do you think this was?

STEP 4: Now use the ideas you developed about energy in Chapter 1 to answer the following questions about the magnetic interactions between the two magnet carts.

 After you released the magnet-carts what effect did the magnetic interaction between them have on the kinetic energy of **both** of them? (Did the kinetic energy of both increase, decrease, or stay the same, or did something else happen?) How do you know?

 Based on the evidence of the change in both their kinetic energies, was there an energy input to both magnet-carts, an energy output from *both* magnet-carts, or did something else happen? How does the evidence support your answer?

 In Chapter 1 the type of energy transferred during contact interactions was defined to be *mechanical energy*. Does the evidence suggest that mechanical energy is also transferred during *magnetic interactions*, or is some other type of energy transfer involved? (In considering this question, you may want to refer back to Chapter 1 Activity 2 to remind yourself of the evidence for a transfer of mechanical energy.)

As you probably deduced, during the magnetic interaction between the two magnet-carts, mechanical energy was transferred to both of them and hence the kinetic energy of both of them increased.

 Assuming the effects of friction are negligible, do you think there was a change in any other type of energy (possibly as yet unnamed) while the kinetic energy of both magnet-carts was increasing during the magnetic interaction between them? Explain how your answer is consistent with the ideas about conservation of energy you developed in Chapter 1.

 What do you think was the energy source for the magnetic interaction between the two magnet-carts?

Summarizing Questions

In this activity you have investigated only some aspects of **Magnetic Interactions**. In another chapter of the *PET* course you will investigate such magnetic interactions further.

 Discuss these questions with your team and note your ideas. Leave space to add any different ideas that may emerge when the whole class discusses their thinking.

S1: An elementary school student asks you for advice about a project she is doing on recycling. She suggests that a large magnet could be used to separate metals from non-metals in the trash passing through a recycling station. What do you think of this idea?

S2: A person holds two small magnets steady so that they are repelling each other. Below, draw a force diagram describing the forces acting on magnet B. Make sure you label the force arrows, and pay attention to their relative lengths.

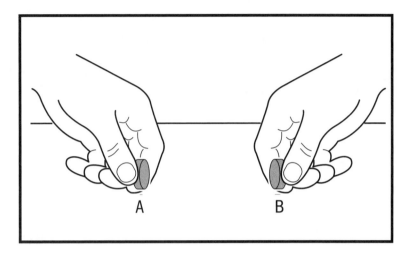

Suppose you held the two magnets in the picture much closer to each other. How would your force diagram change, if at all?

S3: You have observed that one magnet can interact with another magnet even though they do not touch each other. What ideas does your group have that account for this? (How does one magnet 'know' the other one is there, if they are not touching?) Illustrate your group's thinking below.

S4: Use your current ideas about energy in magnetic interactions to complete the S/R energy diagram below for the magnetic interaction between the two equal-mass magnet-carts that pushed them apart (after you released them).

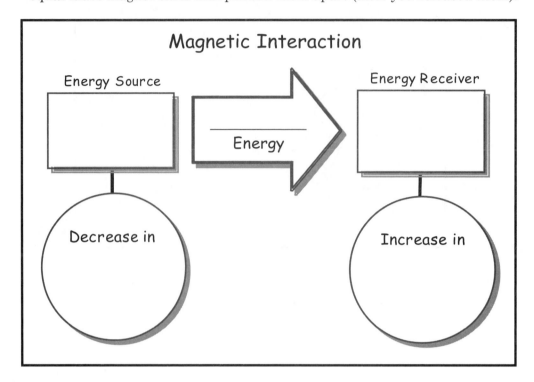

Magnetic Interaction

Energy Source

Energy Receiver

Energy

Decrease in

Increase in

 Participate in a whole-class discussion about these ideas and make a note of any new ideas that seem useful.

The Magnetic Field

A magnetic field can be thought of as an invisible 'field of influence' around a magnet, an idea that scientists find useful to account for the observation that magnetic interactions can occur without physical contact. Your instructor will now give you a bar magnet and a compass which you can use to investigate the *"field of influence"* around the bar magnet, and answer the following questions. (Do not touch the compass to the magnet.)

 Does the strength of the influence on the compass depend on how far it is from the bar magnet? How do you know?

Does the influence on the compass change, depending on which end of the bar magnet it is closest to? Explain how you know.

The idea of a magnetic field is also useful when thinking about magnetic interactions in terms of energy. As you probably deduced, since there was an increase in the kinetic energy of both magnet-carts in the interactions you examined, by the Law of Conservation of Energy there must have been a decrease in some other form of energy associated with the magnets. We will call this **magnetic potential energy**. Further, scientists find it useful to think of the magnetic field as being the energy source during such interactions, with the magnetic potential energy being associated with the magnetic field itself[1].

Systems and Energy Changes

In the above analysis the magnet-carts and their magnetic fields were treated separately in the S/R energy diagram, with an explicit transfer of energy between them. However, it is often convenient to consider interacting objects together as a single 'system' and to draw an Input/Output (I/O) energy diagram to describe the behavior of the whole system together in terms of energy.

Consider the two attracting magnet-carts (including their magnetic fields) that you used in the previous experiment as a **single system**. Then, assuming the effects of friction were negligible, after you released the magnet-carts and they were moving together, the only interaction occurring was between objects *within* this system (the magnetic interaction between the two magnet-carts). During this time, there were no interactions between the magnet-carts and any other objects *outside* the system, meaning that there was *no energy input* to the system and *no energy output* from the system. Thus, the only energy transfer that took place was within the system, from the magnetic field to the magnet-carts. Also, the only energy changes that happened as a result of this transfer were for the components of the system itself.

---

[1]In Chapter 1 you were introduced to *chemical potential energy* and *elastic potential energy* as forms of energy that are 'stored' in different ways and have the potential to produce changes in other types of energy, such as kinetic energy. In the same way, you can think of *magnetic potential energy* as energy stored in the magnetic fields around magnets that has the potential to produce changes in the kinetic energy of the magnets themselves.

CHAPTER 3

Complete this I/O energy diagram for the system of the two attracting magnet-carts[2], for the short time period while the magnet-carts were moving together and speeding up as they did (assume the effects of friction are negligible).

 How do you think the amount by which one type of energy decreased in this system compares to the amount by which the other type of energy increased? Explain your reasoning.

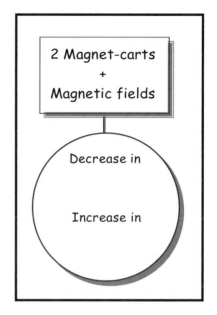

 Compare your response and I/O energy diagram with another group. Try to resolve any differences.

In Chapter 1 you learned about the Law of Conservation of Energy, which can be stated in its general form as follows:

$$\textbf{Energy Input } = \textbf{ Energy Output } + \textbf{ Energy Changes}$$

For the **special case** where you choose a system of interacting objects so that there is no energy input and no energy output, the Law of Conservation of Energy takes on a particularly simple form:

$$\textbf{Energy Changes } = \textbf{ 0}$$

This does not mean that there are no energy changes within the system, but it does mean that any energy changes that do occur must exactly cancel each other out so that the total amount of energy in the system remains constant.

In the example above with the magnet-carts, the Law of Conservation of Energy suggests that the *decrease* in magnetic potential energy must be exactly balanced by the *increase* in kinetic energy, so that the total energy changes would equal zero. (It is important to remember that this particularly simple form of energy conservation only applies to systems for which there are no energy inputs and no energy outputs. If there are energy inputs to, or outputs from, the system then a more general form of the Law applies.)

---

[2]The magnetic fields are shown explicitly in this diagram but it is not necessary to include them since it can be assumed the fields are always there when magnets are part of a system.

Name:_____ Date:_____ Group: _____

Purpose

In Activity 1 of Chapter 3, you saw that the idea of a magnetic field of influence is useful in accounting for magnetic interactions, in terms of both force and energy ideas. Also, from the observation that the kinetic energy in a system of two magnets increases as a result of a magnetic interaction between them, you inferred that there must be a decrease in some other form of energy, called magnetic potential energy. In this homework assignment you will investigate how the magnetic potential energy in a system of magnets depends on how far apart they are.

> **How does the magnetic potential energy in a system of magnets depend on the distance between them?**

Initial Ideas

In the previous activity you saw that the closer together two magnets are, the stronger the magnetic force they exert on each other. Do you think there is a similar relationship between distance and magnetic potential energy?

Do you think the magnetic potential energy in a system of two attracting magnets depends on the distance between them? Why or why not? Do you think the system has more magnetic potential energy when the magnets are close together, far apart, or is the amount of magnetic potential energy the same no matter how far apart the magnets are? Explain your thinking.

Would your answer be the same for a system of two *repelling* magnets? Again, explain your thinking.

Collecting and Interpreting Evidence

 EXPERIMENT #1: Potential energy for attracting magnets

YOU WILL NEED:

- *PET Student Resource DVD*
- Computer to play DVD movie for this assignment

STEP 1: Locate the file *C3A1HW_movie1.mpg* on your *PET Student Resources DVD*. This movie shows two *attracting* magnet-carts (with very strong magnets) interacting. One of the carts is fixed in place while the second cart is free to move, and is released at varying distances from the first. Speed-time graphs for the free magnet-cart are also shown, so you can determine the maximum speed the magnet-cart gains just before colliding with the fixed magnet-cart.

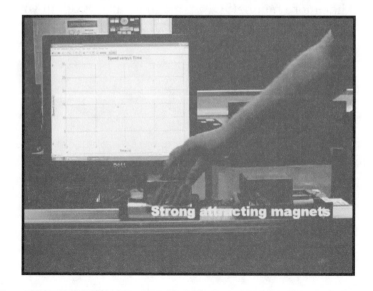

Using data from the movie, complete the table below.

Final speed of free magnet-cart after being released from different distances

Release distance (cm)	Final speed (cm/s)
2 cm	
5 cm	
10 cm	
20 cm	
30 cm	

STEP 2: Now answer the following questions about energy changes in the system of two magnet-carts you saw in the movie[1]. You can assume the effects of friction were negligible for this system. (When thinking about some of these questions you may wish to replay the movie and consult the data in the table above.)

 In each 'run', at what two moments was the *kinetic energy* in the system at its minimum and maximum values? (Just as the magnet-cart was released, just before the collision, or sometime in between?) How do you know?

---

[1] We assume the magnetic fields of the magnets are implicitly included in this system also.

In each run, at what two moments was the *magnetic potential energy* in the system at its minimum and maximum values? (Just as the magnet-cart was released, just before the collision, or sometime in between?) Use conservation of energy ideas to explain your answer.

 Complete the I/O energy diagram for this system as the free magnet-cart moved toward the fixed magnet-cart after being released.

 Explain briefly how the energy changes you indicated in this energy diagram are consistent with your responses to the two previous questions.

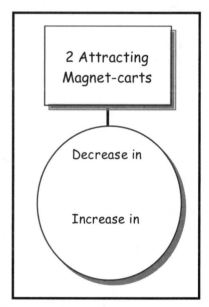

 Does the kinetic energy in the system increase by a greater amount when the magnet-carts start close together or farther apart? Explain how you know.

 Does the magnetic potential energy in the system decrease by a greater amount when the magnet-carts start close together or farther apart? Use your response to the previous question, and the Law of Conservation of Energy to justify your answer.

In all the runs shown in the movie, the system always ends up in the same situation, with the magnet-carts as close together as they can get. Therefore, if the amount of magnetic potential energy in the system does depend on how far apart the magnets are, then in all the runs the system would have ended up with the same amount of magnetic potential energy.

 Do you think that the starting amount of magnetic potential energy in the system was the same for all the runs, or was it different? Explain how you know.

 As two *attracting* magnets get farther apart, does the amount of magnetic potential energy in the system increase, decrease, or stay the same? Briefly explain your answer.

Potential Energy for Repelling Magnets

You have seen that if two *attracting* magnet-carts are held a short distance apart and released, then the magnet-carts move closer together and the kinetic energy in the system increases as they do so. From the observation that the system gains more kinetic energy the farther apart the magnets start, you inferred that the amount of magnetic potential energy in such a system increases as the distance between the magnets increases.

However, when two *repelling* magnet-carts are held a short distance apart and released, we know the system still gains kinetic energy (because the magnet-carts start to move), but this time the magnet-carts move farther apart.

If the kinetic energy in a system of two repelling carts increases as the magnet-carts get farther apart, what must be happening to the magnetic potential energy in this system at the same time? Explain how you know.

 As two *repelling* magnets get farther apart, does the amount of magnetic potential energy in the system increase, decrease, or stay the same? Briefly explain your answer.

Imagine you were to arrange for the two magnet-carts in the video to repel each other, then place the free magnet-cart about 20 cm from the fixed magnet-cart, and give it a gentle shove *toward* the fixed magnet-cart.

 After your shove, do you think the free magnet-cart would speed up, slow down, or move at a constant speed?

 Explain your reasoning in terms of your ideas about forces.

Explain your reasoning in terms of your ideas about energy.[2]

 Complete the I/O energy diagram for this system as the free magnet-cart moved toward the fixed magnet-cart after being given a quick shove.

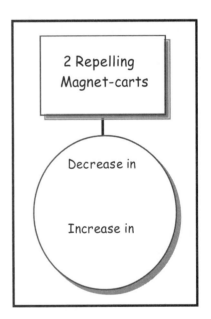

2 Repelling Magnet-carts

Decrease in

Increase in

---

2 You may be wondering how it is possible that for both attracting and repelling magnets as they get farther apart the magnetic force gets weaker in both cases, but yet the magnetic potential energy in the system increases if they are attracting, but decreases if they repelling. This is related to the difference in the direction of the magnetic force in the two cases, and how the magnetic force strength changes as the magnets move under the influence of that force.

When two attracting magnets are released a certain distance apart, the magnetic force acting on them gets stronger and stronger as they move closer together, and so the kinetic energy in the system increases at a faster and faster rate. The farther apart the two magnets start, the more chance there is to increase the kinetic energy. However, if two repelling magnets are released the same distance apart, then as they move even farther apart the magnetic force acting on them gets weaker and weaker, and so the kinetic energy in the system increases at a slower and slower rate. The farther apart they start the less chance there is to increase the kinetic energy. (In the real world friction will eventually become stronger than the weakening magnetic force and they would actually slow down!)

Potential Energy in Systems

In a system of two magnets, we now know that the amount of magnetic potential energy depends on how far apart the two magnets are, or more generally how the components of the system are arranged, or configured, with respect to each other. When scientists are dealing with systems that have two or more interacting components they usually think about potential energy in the following way:

> Potential energy is energy that a system has due to how its individual components are configured, and it changes when the individual components in the system are rearranged.

In the activities that follow, you will think about different types of potential energy that scientists associate with different types of interactions between components within a system.

Summarizing Question

S1: Open the file *C3A1HW_ movie2.mpg* on your *PET Student Resources DVD*. This movie shows a slightly different arrangement of *attracting* magnet-carts, in that although neither magnet-cart is fixed in place, a large amount of extra mass has been added to one of the carts.

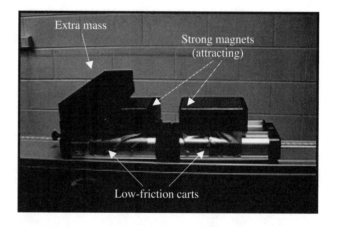

Watch the movie, which shows that after being given an initial push along the track, the lighter magnet-cart gradually slows down, stops momentarily, and then comes back, speeding up as it does so.

Now write a scientific explanation, using your ideas about energy in this system of *attracting* magnet-carts, to explain why the moving magnet-cart slows down as it gets farther away from the stationary magnet-cart. (You should assume the effects of friction are negligible.)

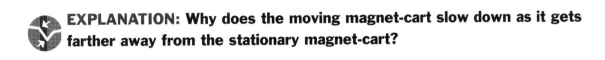 **EXPLANATION: Why does the moving magnet-cart slow down as it gets farther away from the stationary magnet-cart?**

Describe the situation using a diagram: (Draw an I/O energy diagram for the system of the two magnet-carts as the moving cart is slowing down.)

Write the narrative: (Use your ideas about energy changes in a system of interacting magnets to explain how getting farther apart affects the magnetic potential energy in this system and what effect this has on the kinetic energy. Remember to connect your ideas to the phenomenon to be explained).

CHAPTER 3

Purpose

In the previous activity you studied some magnetic interactions and found that a magnet can attract or repel another magnet without touching it. This behavior probably came as no

surprise to you. You may also have heard about electric charges, and that they can interact with each other as well.

You have also undoubtedly felt the effects of these electric charges: getting a shock when walking across a carpet and touching a door knob; or finding that clothes sometimes stick together when you take them out of the dryer. We will call the interaction between such charges the **electric-charge interaction**.

The purpose of this activity is to investigate some properties of this interaction and to see how they can be explained in terms of a simple model of charges in materials.

What are some properties of electric-charge interactions? What simple model can account for these properties?

Collecting and Interpreting Evidence

EXPERIMENT #1: How does one charged object affect another charged object?

YOU WILL NEED:

■ Five 4-inch lengths of sticky tape

■ Pen, or other permanent marker

■ Support stand from which to hang tape. (This could be a meter stick projecting beyond the edge of a table.)

■ Balloon (rubber)

STEP 1: Press one of the 4-inch lengths of tape on the table in front of you.

STEP 2. Fold over about $\frac{1}{2}$ inch of both ends of the four remaining pieces of sticky tape. These ends will serve as 'handles.' **When working with the tapes, only hold them by these handles; try not to touch any of the sticky surfaces.**

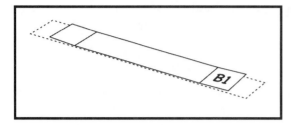

Place one of the pieces of tape, sticky side down, on top of the tape already stuck to the table. Using a pen, or other permanent marker, label one of the handles on this piece B1. (B stands for bottom.)

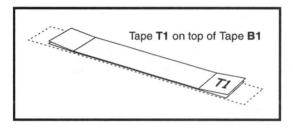

Tape **T1** on top of Tape **B1**

Now place a second piece of tape directly on top of the first, again sticky side down. Label this piece T1. (T stands for top.)

Rub your finger over the three pieces to make sure they are firmly stuck together. (The original piece without the handles will also be stuck to the table, but that is not important.)

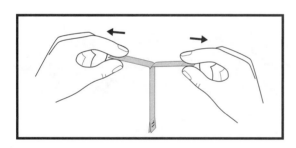

Now **slowly** and carefully peel both pieces of tape, with the handles still stuck together, from the other piece of tape without the handles. (If the two pieces of tape become separated, press them firmly together again.) Holding a handle on each piece of tape in each hand, **quickly** rip them apart. Keep them far from each other so they don't touch.

Finally, stick the two pieces of tape to the support stand so that they hang down vertically below it.

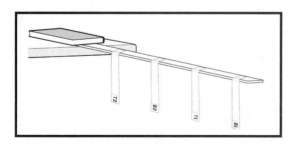

STEP 3: Repeat this process with the other two pieces of tape, labeling them B2 and T2. You should now have four tapes, labeled B1, T1, B2, and T2, hanging from your support stand. The piece of tape stuck to the table should stay there, in case you wish to repeat these effects.

The act of quickly pulling the two pieces of tape apart makes both pieces electrically charged. You will now do some simple experiments to determine some properties of the interaction between these charged tapes.

> **Go through the following steps quickly, but carefully. Electric charge effects sometimes wear off quickly, so if you don't observe any types of interactions you might consider re-charging the tapes (STEPS 2 and 3). If you have difficulty making these observations, your instructor may show you a video of the various steps.**

STEP 4: Carefully remove tapes B1 and T2 from the support stand. Holding both tapes at the top, slowly bring their faces close together and watch carefully.

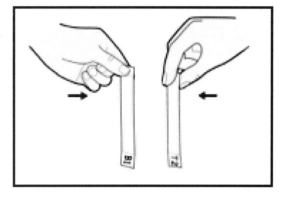

 What happens as B1 and T2 approach each other? Do they attract, repel, or is there no reaction?

 Do the charged tapes exert a force on each other? If so, does the strength of these forces depend on how far apart the tapes are? How do you know?

Try turning B1 around, so that its opposite face is toward T2 as they approach. Next try turning T2 around also. Also try turning the tapes up the other way. (Remember to only touch the handles as you manipulate the tapes.)

Does the same thing always happen or does it depend on which way the tapes are?

STEP 5: Return tape T2 to the stand and carefully remove tape B2. Now bring tapes B1 and B2 together.

 Does the same thing happen as in STEP 4, or does something different happen? If so, what?

 Again, does the reaction you observe depend on which way you hold the tapes?

STEP 6: Next, test tape T1 with tape B2 and then T1 with T2.

 Record the results of all your tests in the Table 1 below. (Enter A for attract, R for repel, or N for no reaction.)

Table 1: Observations with Charged Tapes

	B2	T2
B1		
T1		

 Do the charged tapes exert a force on each other? If so, does the strength of these forces depend on how far apart the tapes are? How do you know?

Draw a force diagram on the picture to the right showing the electric charge force that tape T1 exerts on tape T2, causing T2 to move away from T1. (You can ignore the force that the hand exerts on the tape.)

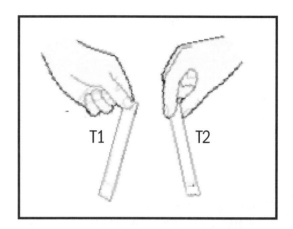

STEP 7: Blow up the balloon. Rub one side vigorously against your hair. (It's best to use a member of your group who has long, straight, and dry hair.)

 After moving the balloon away from your hair, bring the rubbed part of the balloon close to the rubbed part of your hair again. Does anything happen to your hair? If so, what?

 Bring the **rubbed** part of the balloon (**not** an un-rubbed part) close to one of the B tapes (either B1 or B2). What happens to the B tape?

 Bring the same **rubbed** part of the balloon close to one of the T tapes (either T1 or T2). What happens to the T tape?

STEP 8: Answer the following questions based on evidence from these experiments:

 Do the charged tapes have to touch to interact with each other?

In the previous activity you saw that the same two magnets could both attract or repel each other depending on which ends are brought together. Is the same true of two charged pieces of tape or does something else happen?

 What do your observations imply about the electric charge on a tape? Does each tape have only one type of charge all over it, or different charges in different places? How do you know?

As you are no doubt aware, there are two types of electric charge that are called positive and negative. You probably also know that like charges repel each other and unlike charges attract each other.

 After a pair of tapes was charged by quickly pulling them apart, did both tapes have the same type of charge on them, or were the charges different on the two pieces of tape? How do you know?

Consider your observations with the balloon.

 After you rubbed the balloon on your hair, did the rubbed part of the balloon have the same type or a different type of charge as the rubbed part of your hair? How do you know?

Did the rubbed part of the balloon have the same type of charge as the B tape or the T tape? How do you know?

Now consider a system composed of **two** charged tapes as they are brought close together. You have seen that both tapes start moving (and hence the kinetic energy in the system increases) as a result of the electric charge interaction between them.

 How do these observations support the idea that a form of potential energy plays a role in this system?

Since this potential energy is associated with the phenomenon of static electricity we will call it **electrostatic potential energy**[1].

 Complete the I/O energy diagram for a system of two charged tapes[2] when they are close together and moving towards (being attracted to) each other. (You can ignore the fact that you were holding the tapes.)

 Briefly explain how your energy diagram is consistent with your ideas about conservation of energy.

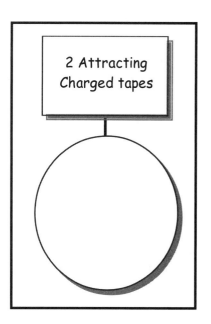

[1]As with magnetic interactions, scientists find the idea of a 'field of influence' around electric charges (which they call an electrostatic field in this case) useful in thinking about electric-charge interactions. The electrostatic field is viewed as a useful idea both in accounting for the observation that electric charges can interact without touching and also as the carrier of electrostatic potential energy in a system of charges.

[2]As with magnets and magnetic fields, we assume implicitly that the electrostatic fields around the charged tapes are part of the system.

A Model for Charges in Materials

To help us explain our observations in the experiment, we will use a model of charges in materials. The model assumes that there are two types of electric charges, which we call positive and negative. Our model assumes that like charges repel and unlike charges attract. Scientists also find it useful to think about all material as containing a very large number of very small charges, both positive and negative. In our model we will assume that these charges cannot be created or destroyed.

It is also useful to imagine that the positive charges in a material **cannot** move, but that the negative charges are free (at least somewhat) to move around.[3] Further, some materials have the property that it is relatively easy to remove some of their negative charges, while other materials have the property that it is relatively easy to add extra negative charges.

Uncharged and charged objects

Although our model assumes that all materials contain large numbers of both positive and negative charges, most objects around us seem to be uncharged. However, when objects do become charged, you can infer that some become negatively charged while others become positively charged. How can the model account for these observations?

 In terms of the model of charges within materials, how could you account for the observation that most objects are uncharged overall?

 How could the model of charges within materials be used to explain why a certain object is negatively charged? What about a positively charged object?

---

[3]Actually, to explain some other phenomena, it is useful to assume that the degree to which the negative charges are free to move is very different in different materials, but the idea that they can move somewhat in all materials is all we need for our model.

All materials have a very large number of positive and negative charges. If the object is uncharged (or electrically "neutral"), the number of positive charges exactly equals the number of negative charges. When an object is "charged" what generally happens is that a very tiny fraction of the negative charges are either removed from the object (making it positively charged) or added to the object (making it negatively charged).

 SIMULATOR EXPLORATION #1: How can a simulator help explain your observations with charged objects?

You can use a special simulator to check your ideas. Using a web browser, access the PhET "Balloons and Static Electricity" simulator.[4] (Your instructor may also demonstrate the simulator for you, or show you a movie taken from it.) In this simulator, charges are represented as +'s (positive charges, colored red) or −'s (negative charges, colored blue).

> **Note: When the simulator first opens it shows a sweater, a balloon, and a wall. We will not be using the wall in this exploration; to get rid of it uncheck the 'Wall' box at the bottom right of the window.**

STEP 1: First consider what happens when the balloon is rubbed against the sweater. (You can also imagine this representing a balloon being rubbed against your hair.) Answer the following questions as you run, or observe, the simulator.

When the simulator is first opened the balloon and sweater are uncharged.

 How does the simulator show that both the sweater and the balloon are initially uncharged overall?

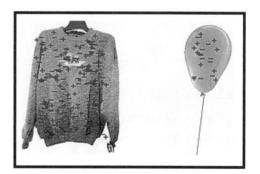

---

[4] This simulation, one of a suite of simulations from the Physics Education Technology (PhET) Project, was developed by a team of researchers and designers at the University of Colorado. You can access this particular simulation at http://phet.colorado.edu. Click on "Go to the Simulations," and then click on "Balloons and Static Electricity."

Now rub the balloon on the sweater by using your computer mouse to 'drag' the balloon around.

 What happens when the balloon is rubbed against the sweater?

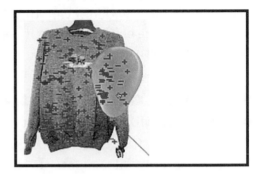

 After rubbing, move the balloon away from the sweater and 'hold' it there. Are the sweater and balloon electrically charged? If so, how are they charged (+ or −), and how do you know?

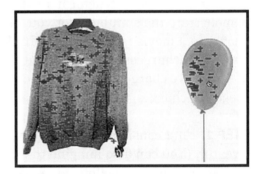

 Now 'release' the balloon, describe what happens, and explain why.

STEP 2: Now check the box at the bottom of the window to add a second, blue-colored balloon. Charge this blue-colored balloon by rubbing it on the sweater also. Now move both balloons away from the sweater and bring the blue-colored balloon close to the yellow-colored balloon.

What happens when the charged blue-colored balloon is brought near the charged yellow-colored balloon? Explain why this happens.

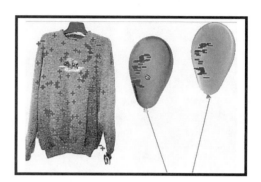

Assuming the real balloon you used in Experiment #1 got charged in the same way (+ or −) as the balloons in the simulator, you should now be able to determine the charges on the top (T) and bottom (B) tapes you used in that experiment.

When you create a pair of charged tapes in the way you did in Experiment #1, which tape (B or T) becomes negatively charged and which becomes positively charged? How do you know?

Summarizing Questions

S1: In Experiment #1 you rubbed a balloon against your hair. Answer the following questions in terms of the model for charges in materials.

(a) After rubbing, what was the type of (excess) charge on the rubbed part of the balloon? What was the type of (excess) charge on the rubbed part of the hair? Explain briefly how the balloon and hair got charged in this way.

After rubbing, if you brought the rubbed part of the balloon near the rubbed part of your hair, you found that the hair was attracted to the balloon.

(b) Draw a force diagram showing the force on the rubbed hair as it was attracted to the rubbed part of the balloon, and explain briefly why the hair was attracted to the balloon.

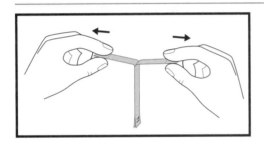

S2: In Experiment #1 you created pairs of charged tapes by ripping them apart very quickly. As you should have inferred earlier, the tapes you labeled B (bottom) became negatively charged in this process, while the tapes you labeled T (top) became positively charged.

Three students were discussing how they thought the model of charges in materials could account for how the two tapes became charged during this process.

I think that when the tapes were pulled apart, the 'sticky' side of the T tape took some positive charges from the B tape. So, the T tape now has extra positive charges and the B tape has some missing.

I disagree. We know only negative charges can move, so the 'sticky' side of the T tape must have pulled some negative charges off of the B tape.

I think that when the tapes were pulled apart, the 'sticky' side of the T tape left some of its negative charges on the B tape. So, the B tape now has more negative charges than it has positive.

Samantha

Victor

Kristen

Do you agree with Samantha, Victor, Kristen, or none of them? Explain your reasoning.

S3: Consider a system consisting of two objects, one positively and one negatively charged

    (a) As these two objects move farther apart, does the strength of the electric charge force increase, decrease, or remain the same? How do you know?

    (b) Does the value of the electrostatic potential energy increase, decrease or remain the same? Explain your reasoning.[5]

---

[5]As you saw in the homework assignment for Activity 1, the behavior of the *magnetic potential energy* in a system of two magnets as they move apart depends on whether they are attracting or repelling. The same is true for *electrostatic potential energy* in a system of charged objects.

S4: Consider a system of two charged tapes that **repel** each other. Draw an I/O energy diagram to describe the situation when the two tapes are close together but are starting to move away from each other. (Ignore the fact that you are holding the ends of the tapes in your diagram.)

S5: In general, in a system that involves a type of potential energy, if there are no energy inputs to or outputs from the system, what happens to that potential energy when the kinetic energy of the system decreases? What about when the kinetic energy increases? Why do you think there is this simple relationship between changes in kinetic energy and changes in potential energy?

 Participate in a whole-class discussion.

Activity 2 Homework 1—Interactions Between Charged and Uncharged Objects
Developing Ideas

Name:_____ Date:_____ Group: _____

Purpose

In Activity 2 you explored what happens when two charged objects are brought near each other. In this homework assignment you will explore what happens when a charged object and an uncharged object are brought near each other.

 How do charged and uncharged objects interact with each other?

Initial Ideas

 In Activity 1 you found that only certain types of metals interacted with magnets. Suppose you conducted a similar experiment, but this time brought different materials (metals and non-metals) near an electrically charged object. Do you think all types of materials would interact with the charged object, or only certain types of materials, or none of them? If only certain types, what types do you think would interact?

 For materials that you think will interact with the charged object, do you think the interaction would always be attraction, always repulsion, or do you think some materials will attract and some will repel? Why do you think so?

CHAPTER 3

EXPLORATION #1: What kinds of materials interact with a charged tape?

STEP 1: Open the movie, *C3Act2_HW_Tapes.mpg* that should be on your *Student Resources DVD*. The person in the movie will bring various uncharged objects near charged B and T tapes.

Stop the movie after each object is brought near the charged tapes, and record your observations (**attract**, **repel**, or **no effect**) in the following table.

Table: Observations with Charged Tape and Materials (from movie)

Material	Reaction with B-tape	Reaction with T-tape
Finger		
Glass rod		
Paper clip		
Paper		
Iron nail		
Polystyrene		
Wood splint		
Aluminum foil		
Foam padding		

STEP 2: Look over the data in the Table.

What materials seem to interact with the charged tapes?

Does the reaction depend on which type of charge is on the tape or not?

Now think about when the person in the movie brought an uncharged object close to the charged tapes. The experiments showed that the tapes were attracted to the uncharged object, so it seems that there can be electric-charge interactions between charged and uncharged objects. How can our model of charges in materials help to explain this phenomenon?

EXPLORATION #2: Interactions Between Charged and Uncharged Objects

STEP 1: If you have access to a balloon, blow it up. Then rub the balloon against a sweater (or your hair) and place the rubbed part of the balloon against a wall. You should observe that the balloon sticks to the wall. (If it is too humid in the room, the balloon may not stick, but you should still observe some attraction between the balloon and the wall.)

In the rest of this exploration, you can either run the "Balloons and Static Electricity" simulator at http://phet.colorado.edu/web-pages/simulations-base.html, or you can watch a movie of the simulator. The movie is on your Student Resources DVD and is called *C3Act2_HW_Balloon_Wall.mpg*. (The simulation was developed by the Physics Education Technology (PhET) Project by a team of researchers and designers at the University of Colorado.)

STEP 2: The simulation shows a sweater, a balloon and part of a wall. If you are running the simulator, the screen should look like this.

Is the wall charged positively, negatively, or is it neutral? How do you know?

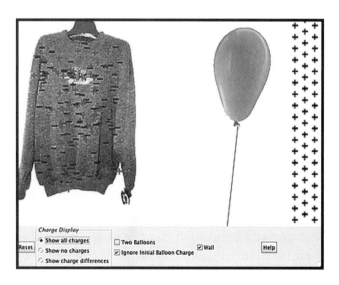

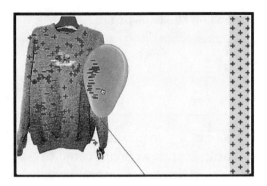

STEP 3: Rub the balloon against the sweater to charge it negatively.

STEP 4: Bring the charged balloon near the wall, but do not touch the wall yet.

 Why do the negative charges in the wall move when the balloon is brought close?

 Why do the positive charges not move?

Remember that according to our model, only negative charges can move within a material; the positive charges stay fixed. Whenever the negative charges in a material are displaced relative to the positive charges, we say the material is electrically *polarized*. In this case, the wall has become electrically polarized in the area close to the balloon. There are still equal numbers of positive and negative charges in the wall, so it is still uncharged overall. However, what has happened is that the distribution of negative charge has changed, so the front surface of the wall closest to the balloon is more positively charged, while the region to the right of the surface is more negatively charged.

STEP 5: Touch the balloon to the wall in the simulator and notice that it sticks, just like your real balloon did.

 With the wall now polarized, are the excess negative charges on the balloon closer to the positive charges in the wall or closer to the negative charges in the wall?

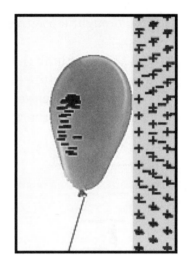

 Which force do you think would be stronger in this case, the attractive force between the negatively charged balloon and the positive charges in the wall, or the repulsive force between the balloon and the negative charges in the wall? Explain your reasoning.

 Once an uncharged object (like the wall) is electrically polarized, do you think it stays polarized forever from then on? What evidence from the simulator supports your answer?

Summarizing Questions

Answer these questions as part of the homework assignment. Be prepared to add any different ideas that may emerge during the whole-class discussion.

S1: In the simulator exploration you brought a negatively charged balloon close to a wall and saw that the wall became electrically polarized. Suppose, instead, you brought a positively charged object near a wall.

(a) Do you think the wall will become electrically polarized in this case? If so, draw a picture and explain how it happens. Indicate whether the surface of the wall close to the object would be more positively charged, or more negatively charged.

(b) If you were to touch the positively charged object to the wall, it would stick. Explain how that happens.

S2: If you rub an inflated balloon against your hair and then bring the rubbed part of the balloon near a pile of tiny pieces of paper, several of the pieces will fly up to the balloon. Using the model of charges in materials, write a scientific explanation for why this happens. (As a hint, consider that each piece of paper becomes electrically polarized when the charged balloon is brought near.)

 EXPLANATION: Why is a small uncharged piece of paper attracted to a charged balloon?

Describe the situation using a diagram: (We suggest drawing two diagrams, one showing how the model would represent the paper before balloon is brought near, the second showing the paper with the balloon nearby.)

CHAPTER 3

Write the narrative: (Use the model of charges in materials to explain what happens to the paper when the balloon is brought close and why the paper is then attracted to the balloon)

S3: The magnetic interaction and the electric-charge interaction have different names; therefore there must be some things different about them (otherwise there would be no reason to call them by different names). Describe some differences between the magnetic interaction and the electric-charge interaction.

Activity 2 Homework 2—Observations and Models
Learning About Learning

Name:_____ Date:_____ Group: _____

Purpose

In the previous activities you have been using models to help you explain observations. In this activity, you will examine how models are used in science to make inferences and how models and inferences differ from observations.

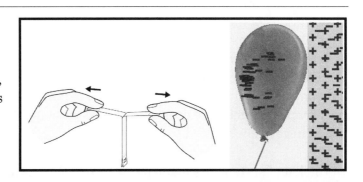

 If a model is a set of related ideas that help explain observations, what is an inference?

Initial Ideas

 1. Consider this conversation between two students discussing the "Balloon and Static Electricity" simulator.

> I think the simulator shows what a balloon and the wall *really* look like if we could magnify them enough.

> I disagree. We don't know if little pluses and minuses *really* exist within the balloon or wall. The simulator illustrates the model that scientists use for thinking about things that we can observe.

Victor

Amara

 Who do you agree with and why?

CHAPTER 3

Interpreting Observational Evidence

In *C3A2* you used a model for charges in materials to help you explain observations of interactions between two pieces of sticky tape. In *C3A2 HW#1* you used the "Balloon and Static Electricity" simulator to help you explain observations of interactions of charged and uncharged materials. Models are built from observations and once built, they can help us understand new observations. When a person comes to a conclusion on the basis of a model, this person has made an *inference*. For example, if a person observes that one balloon sticks to another balloon, she might *infer* that one balloon is positively charged and one balloon is negatively charged. She does not *observe* that one balloon is positively charged and one is negatively charged.

In the list of statements made below, circle the word that best describes whether the statement is most likely an observation or an inference.

Statement	Circle One	
Two different pieces of sticky tape are move towards one another.	observation	inference
A balloon that has been rubbed on someone's hair sticks to the wall.	observation	inference
Two pieces of sticky tape are oppositely charged.	observation	inference
The wall has become electrically polarized in the area closest to the balloon.	observation	inference
Two charged balloons repel from one another.	observation	inference
Only negative charges can move within a material.	observation	inference
Excess negative charges in a balloon are repelled from excess negative charges in another balloon.	observation	inference

What generalization or rule did you use to decide whether each statement was an observation or an inference?

Summarizing Question

S1: The "Balloon and Static Electricity" simulator shows plus and minus symbols inside balloons and walls. Do you think scientists have actually observed these little pluses and minuses inside balloons and walls? If so, what instrument do you think they used? If not, what do you think the pluses and minuses represent?

CHAPTER 3

Purpose

We live in a world where, if not supported, everything seems to want to fall to the ground. Even if we throw a ball straight upward, eventually it reverses direction and falls back down.

In the rest of this cycle you will investigate the cause and characteristics of this seemingly natural tendency of objects to fall.

 Why do objects fall? What energy changes occur when an object falls?

Initial Ideas

Have one of your team hold a pencil about 1m above the table, then release it and let it fall. Discuss these questions with your team.

 While the pencil was falling, what do you think its motion was like? (Constant speed, increasing speed, decreasing speed, or some combination of these?)

Sketch what you think a speed-time graph for the motion of the falling pencil would look like.

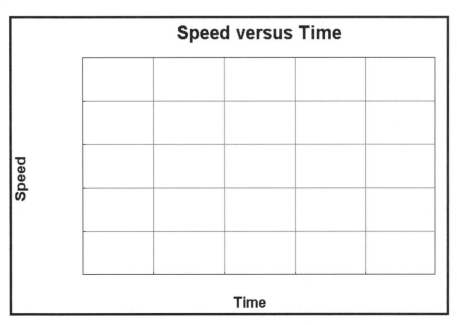

Speed versus Time

Speed

Time

CHAPTER 3

Do you think an interaction caused the pencil to fall? If so, what objects do you think were interacting? If not, explain why you think the pencil fell.

 Participate in a short class discussion about these questions.

Collecting and Interpreting Evidence

 EXPERIMENT: What is the motion of falling objects like?

This experiment may be done as a teacher demonstration.

YOU WILL NEED:

- 1 large ball (such as a soccer ball, or basketball)
- Access to a Motion Sensor connected to a computer
- Stand on which to mount the motion sensor vertically
- Access to the *I&M Computer Simulator*

STEP 1: Mount the Motion Sensor on the stand. Move the stand to the edge of the table, and orient the sensor so that it is pointing down toward the floor, as shown. (Make sure the sensor is at least 1.5 m above the floor.) Open the Motion Sensor data collection file for this activity.

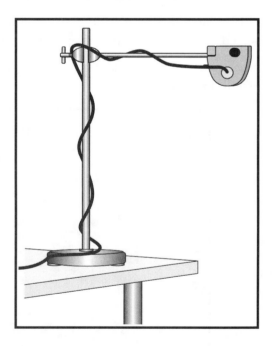

STEP 2: Now hold the ball about 20 cm below the Motion Sensor and start to collect data. As soon as data collection has started let the ball drop to the floor. (The data collection should stop automatically as soon as the ball gets close to the floor.)

Describe the motion of the ball **after** it was released, for the short time shown on the graph.

 Was a force acting on the object while it was falling? What evidence supports your answer?

 What force do you think is responsible for this motion? Draw and label a force diagram for the ball while it was falling.

CHAPTER 3

The experiment with the ball only showed its motion for a short period after it was released.

 If you allowed an object to fall for a longer time, do you think its motion would change significantly? Explain your reasoning.

Simulator Exploration

STEP 3: You can use the *I&M Simulator* to compare your ideas with those of scientists.

Open the simulator setup file for this activity. The simulator shows a baseball that will be released from the top of a building, and will fall for 10 seconds when you click on the start button.

Start the simulator and watch the speed arrow attached to the baseball as it falls.

 Sketch the speed-time graph of the falling baseball and describe its motion below.

 During the time it was falling, does the simulator model show that the baseball was involved in an interaction? How do you know?

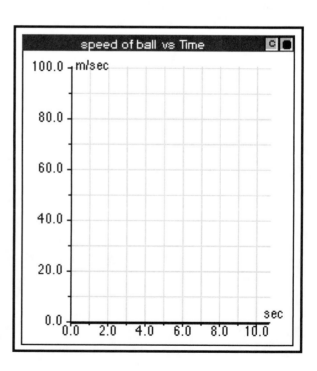

Two students are discussing falling objects. They are not sure about whether a falling object is involved in an interaction with another object, or what that other object involved in the interaction might be:

I know things fall because of gravity but I don't think there is an interaction because there is no other object involved – it's just gravity.

But if there is a force acting on the falling object, it must be interacting with another object somewhere. I'm just not sure what that other object is.

Daryl

Luisa

Do you agree with Daryl, Luisa, or neither of them? Briefly explain your thinking.

What Causes Gravity?

By making several observations of falling objects, the English scientist Sir Isaac Newton constructed a theoretical argument to support the idea that gravity is an interaction (or force) that acts at a distance between **any** two objects that have the property we know as **mass**. In other words, Newton said that all objects with mass attract all other objects with mass even though they are not touching each other.

However, the gravitational interaction between normal everyday objects (such as two people) is extremely weak, and so it is not noticeable. But because the Earth itself is so large, the gravitational interaction between the Earth and every other object near it is large enough to be very noticeable.

Years after Newton, another English scientist named Henry Cavendish conducted an experiment that actually provided evidence to support Newton's *gravity is an interaction* idea. Under carefully controlled conditions, Cavendish brought massive lead balls near, but not touching, objects on a test balance and showed that they attracted the objects on the balance.

A schematic diagram of Cavendish's experimental setup is shown here.

Cavendish observed that when the large lead balls (M) were brought near the small balls (m) as shown, the rod holding the small balls rotated slightly. He observed this rotation by shining a light on the mirror and looking at its reflection on a wall.

Cavendish used this particular arrangement because it is very sensitive to weak forces, allowing the hanging objects to react to those forces without the interference of friction. Even so, Cavendish had to take great care and enclose the moving parts of his apparatus in a sealed box so that they would not be disturbed by even very slight movements of the surrounding air.

Schematic view of the Cavendish apparatus

Energy in Gravitational Interactions

An object falls because of a gravitational interaction between it and the Earth. Consider a system consisting of a falling apple and the Earth.

 While the apple is falling, what happens to the amount of kinetic energy in this system?

 Does the amount by which the kinetic energy in this system changes (by the time the apple reaches the ground) depend on how far apart the apple and the Earth were to start with? How do you know?

Do you think kinetic energy is the only type of energy in this system that changes as the apple falls? If so, how do you reconcile this with your ideas about conservation of energy? If not, what other type of energy do you think changes?

As you have no doubt already deduced, the Earth + apple system exhibits the characteristics of a system that involves another form of potential energy; in this case we call it gravitational potential energy.[1] It is changes in this gravitational potential energy that balance any changes in kinetic energy and so ensures that energy is conserved.

 In the Earth + apple system, as the apple falls towards the ground, does the value of the system's gravitational potential energy increase, decrease, or remain constant? Explain your reasoning.

 Draw what you think would be an appropriate I/O energy diagram for the Earth + apple system as the apple is falling.

---

[1]Again, scientists find it useful to regard gravitational potential energy as being carried by a gravitational field around the objects in the system. This idea also helps to account for the observation that gravitational interactions can occur between two objects without them touching each other ('action at a distance').

Summarizing Questions

S1: A student in a previous class made the following comment:

"When I drop a ball it speeds up as it falls, so its kinetic energy increases. If I look at a system consisting of the Earth and the ball, this means the total energy in this system increases as the ball falls, so energy is not conserved."

Do you agree, or disagree, with this student? Justify your answer.

S2: In many of the situations you examined in previous activities in this cycle, both objects in the system moved as a result of the action at a distance interaction between them. However, in the gravitational interaction between the Earth and a falling object, you see only one of the objects involved move (the one that falls). Do you think the Earth moves too? If so, why don't you observe its motion?

S3: Look at the simulator speed-time graph for the falling baseball. Does the graph suggest that the strength of the gravitational force changes significantly as the baseball falls, or does the strength of the force seem to stay about the same? How does the graph tell you this?[2]

S4: In the past, many people have suggested that the rotation of the Earth might be what causes the gravitational force of the Earth. What evidence from your own experience supports or refutes this idea?

S5: Some people have also suggested that the Earth's magnetism might be the cause of gravity. Again, what evidence can you think of that might support or refute this idea?

 Participate in a whole-class discussion.

---

[2] In fact, the strength of the gravitational force does depend on the distance between the two objects involved, but the relevant distance is that between the **centers** of the objects. As the baseball falls, its distance from the center of the Earth changes by an insignificant amount and so the strength of the gravitational force does not change significantly; hence its speed increases at a constant rate as it falls. You would have to travel several hundreds of miles away from the surface of the Earth to feel a significant change in the strength of the gravitational force.

Name:_____ Date:_____ Group: _____

Purpose

In Chapter 1 you developed a set of ideas about interactions and energy that could be used to explain phenomena involving different types of contact interaction. In Chapter 2 you examined many of the **same** interactions and developed a set of ideas about forces that can be used to explain these phenomena. In the previous two activities of this chapter you have examined the gravitational interaction between the Earth and other objects in terms of both energy and force ideas.

As in Activity 8 of Chapter 2, it should be stressed that these are alternative sets of ideas that can both be used to explain the same situation. Providing the ideas are used correctly, a good scientific explanation could be constructed for the same situation using either set of ideas. In this homework assignment your task will be to use both sets of ideas to explain the same phenomenon.

Explaining the Motion of a Package Tossed Up to a Friend

So far you have only considered objects that are falling toward the Earth. However, objects don't always fall! Suppose you are taking a package to a friend's house and, as you stand at the front door, your friend looks out of a window on the second floor and asks you to toss the package up to her. You toss the package up to her and she catches it.

Describe what you think the motion of the package is like on the way up to your friend, after your hand has lost contact with it, but before she catches it. Do you think it is speeding up, slowing down, or moving at a constant speed? Explain your reasoning.

You can check your idea using the *I&M simulator*. The simulator setup for this assignment shows a package that will be given a quick push upward (to represent your toss) and then continue rising. The simulation will stop when the package is caught by your friend on the second floor.

Run the simulation and sketch the speed-time graph for the package.

Describe the motion of the package, during and **after** the toss.

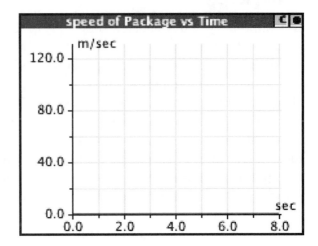

Which part of the graph represents the period when your hand is still in contact with the package, **during** the initial toss? How do you know?

Is the package involved in an interaction **after** the toss, but while it is still rising? How do you know? If so, what kind of interaction do you think it is?

Consider a system consisting of the Earth + package. What is happening to the kinetic energy in this system as the package rises (after the toss). How do you know?

What is happening to the gravitational potential energy in this system as the package rises. Again, how do you know?

Return to the simulator. Click on the blue package to select it, and then place an Energy Bar graph in the setup window.

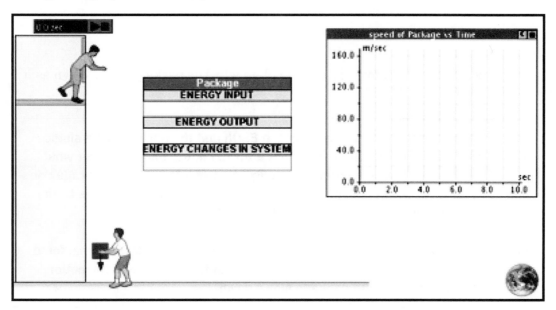

Run the simulation again and observe what happens with the energy bar graph.

 Why is there a mechanical energy input to the system? What does it correspond to?

Do the changes in kinetic and potential energy shown in the energy bar graph match what you described in answering the previous questions?

 Does a force act on the package while it is rising **after** the toss? If so, what force do you think this is, and is it in the same direction as the motion of the package, or in the opposite direction? How can you tell?

Now use both energy and force ideas to explain why the package slows down as it rises up towards your friend.

> **In your energy-based explanation, treat the Earth and the package as a single system that has no energy input or output after the initial toss. Consider what happens to the gravitational potential energy of this system as the package rises and use your ideas about conservation of energy to justify what happens to the kinetic energy, and hence to the speed of the package.**
>
> **In your force-based explanation, consider the direction of the gravitational force of the Earth acting on the package with respect to the direction of its motion and use this to infer why the package slows down.**

 EXPLANATION: Why does the package slow down as it rises?

Describe the situation using a diagram:

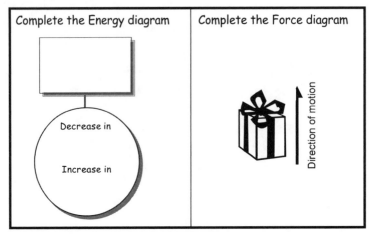

Write the narrative:

Using energy ideas:	Using force ideas:

 Participate in a whole-class discussion about these explanations and make a note of any different ideas that may emerge.

Purpose

In the previous activity you explored how the gravitational force that the Earth exerts on objects makes them fall and speed up as they do so. Do you think that the strength of this gravitational force depends on the mass of the object? For example, does gravity pull with a different strength on a bowling ball and a beach ball? How would this affect the rate at which their speeds increase as they fall, and do any other forces play a role?

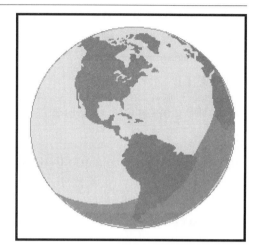

 How does the strength of the gravitational force affect how objects fall? Do any other forces affect falling objects?

Initial Ideas

 If you were to drop a bowling ball and a soccer ball from the same height, which one do you think would reach the floor first? Explain your reasoning.

 Participate in a class discussion about everyone's ideas and make a note of any ideas or reasoning different from your own.

CHAPTER 3

Collecting and Interpreting Evidence

 EXPERIMENT #1: Does the mass of an object affect the strength of the gravitational force of the Earth acting on it?

YOU WILL NEED:

■ A 100-g mass and a 1000-g (1-kg) mass

STEP 1: Have one of your team stand with one arm stretched out horizontally, palm upward. Place the 100-g mass on the palm of the outstretched hand.

 What forces are acting on the mass as your team member holds it? Are these forces balanced or unbalanced? How do you know?

 How does the strength of the force being exerted on the mass by the hand compare with the strength of the gravitational force of the Earth acting on it? Explain your reasoning.

STEP 2: Now have one of your team stand with both their arms stretched out horizontally, palms upward. Place the 100-g mass on one palm, and the 1000-g mass on the other. Your team member should note how much 'effort' it takes to hold up both masses and stop them from falling.

Does it require the same effort to hold up both masses, or is it harder to stop one mass from falling than the other? If so, which one?

 What do you think this implies about the strength of the force each hand has to exert to stop the masses from falling? Are both hands exerting the same strength force, or is a stronger force required to stop one of the masses falling than the other? If so, which one?

 Does your answer to the previous question suggest that the strength of the gravitational force of the Earth pulling downward on both masses is the same, or is it different? Explain your reasoning.

 What does this experiment suggest about how the strength of the gravitational force of the Earth acting on an object depends on that object's mass?

CHAPTER 3

EXPERIMENT #2: Does the mass of an object affect how it falls?

YOU WILL NEED:

- Several objects with different masses (but similar size and shape)
- Hard board (to drop balls onto)

STEP 1: Imagine you held two balls of a similar size, but different mass, at the same height above the ground and released them.

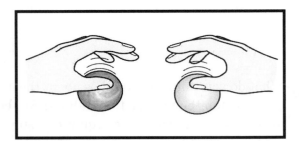

 Which ball do you think would hit the ground first (if either)?

 In the Experiment #1 you developed an idea about how the strength of the gravitational force of the Earth acting on an object depends on its mass (if at all). Explain how your answer to the previous question fits, or does not fit, with this idea.

STEP 2: Lay the hard board on the floor. Select two similarly sized objects of different mass and hold them (one in each hand) at the **same height** (about head high) above the board. Release them at the **same time**. All your team members should **watch** and **listen** carefully as they hit the board.

 Does the more massive object or the less massive one clearly hit the board first, or do they both appear to hit at the same time? (You may want to repeat the experiment to check. Listen to see if they hit the board at the same time, or at a different time.)

Now, repeat the experiment using different pairs of objects, of varying masses.

Describe your observations about which object hits the board first (if either).

Does there seem to be a relationship between the mass of an object and how quickly it falls? What evidence supports your conclusion?

STEP 3: Your responses to the following questions may help you to understand your observations in STEP 2. **The first three questions refer back to the experiments you performed in Activity 6 of Chapter 2, when you added extra mass to a fan-cart and ran a race between two carts on the simulator.**

If two carts with different masses are each acted on by the **same strength** force, which one will speed up more rapidly, the more massive object or the less massive one? Explain your reasoning.

What would you have to do to the strength of the force acting on the more massive cart, to make it speed up at the same rate as the less massive one? Why would this work?

If two fan-carts, with different masses, ended a race in a tie, would this be evidence that the forces acting on them were the same strength, or different strengths?

 In your experiments in this activity you have seen that the same-size objects of different mass all fall at the same rate of increasing speed, and so reach the ground together. What does this result imply about the strength of the force acting on each of them? Is the strength of the force the same on each object, or is it different? Explain your reasoning.

 Is your answer to the previous question consistent with what you found out about the relationship between mass and the strength of the gravitational force in Experiment #1 of this activity?

 How can it be that the gravitational force of the Earth pulling downward on an object with more mass is stronger than the force on a smaller mass object of the same size, yet they both fall at the same rate of increasing speed? (In thinking about this question you may want to look back at the discussion between two students at the end of Activity 6 of Chapter 2.)

EXPERIMENT #3: Does the shape of an object affect how it falls?

YOU WILL NEED:

- A sheet of paper (notebook size)
- A pencil

STEP 1: Do all objects **really** fall together? Suppose you were to drop a bowling ball and a feather from the same height, at the same time.

 Which one do you think would reach the ground first? Explain your reasoning.

STEP 2: Hold the sheet of paper and the pencil (one in each hand) at the same height (about head high) above the ground. Release them at the same time and have all of your team members watch carefully as they fall.

 Does the pencil or the paper hit the floor first? Describe the behavior of the pencil and the paper as they fall.

 Why do you think the result of this experiment is different from what you observed in Experiment #2?

CHAPTER 3

STEP 3: Now scrunch the sheet of paper up into a small ball and repeat the experiment.

 Now, does the pencil or the paper hit the floor first? Describe the behavior of the pencil and the paper as they fall.

 Why do you think the paper behaved differently when you scrunched it up?

 Do you think any other force, apart from the gravitational force of the Earth, acts on objects as they fall? If so, does this force affect all objects equally, or does it affect some more than others?

STEP 4: Suppose you were to drop a heavy object (such as a hammer) and a bird's feather from the same height, at the same time.

 Which do you think would reach the floor first? Briefly explain your reasoning.

Suppose you could take the hammer and feather to a room where there was no air. All other factors being the same, do you think the lack of air would affect the strength of the **gravitational force of the Earth** acting on the hammer and the feather? If so, why?

 Imagine that, in this airless environment, you dropped the hammer and feather from the same height, at the same time? Do you think the result would be different from when you did it in a place where there was air? Explain your reasoning.

Your instructor will show you a demonstration, or a DVD, of two objects falling when there is no air.

 Describe the demonstration (or DVD) and your observations.

 Describe two or three everyday situations in which you think the air is exerting a significant force to oppose the motion of an object. What effect does this force have on the object's motion?

STEP 5: Scientists use the term *'air resistance'* or *'drag'* to refer to the force that the air exerts on an object moving through it.

 Do you think the strength of the force of air resistance acting on an object depends on how fast the object is moving? (In answering this question you may want to think about the force you feel pushing on your hand when you hold it out of the window of a moving car. As the car speeds up, does this force seem to get weaker, stay the same, or get stronger?)

 What would happen to the strength of the force of air resistance acting on an object if its speed was continuously increasing?

Now consider the case of a fan-cart that is released at the end of a very, very, long track. As the cart moves, two forces will act on it: the force of the fan-unit pushing it forward, and the force of air resistance opposing its motion. (We assume the force of friction between the wheels and the track is negligible.) As the fan-cart speeds up we know that the strength of the force from the fan-unit remains constant. However, the force of air resistance starts out as being very weak (because the speed is low) but increases in strength as the cart speeds up.

 During the time the force of air resistance is weaker in strength than the force of the fan-unit, what will happen to the speed of the cart? Will it speed up, slow down, or move at constant speed? Explain your reasoning.

Eventually the speed of the cart will be such that the strength of the force of air resistance will be the same as that of the fan unit. What will happen to the cart's speed now? Again, explain your reasoning.

 In Activity 2 of Chapter 2, Han and Samantha had the following conversation about the motion of a fan-cart. Who do you agree with now? Explain your reasoning.

I think that as long as the fan keeps pushing on it, no matter how long the track is, the cart will keep speeding up.

I agree that the cart will speed up to start with, but I just don't believe it could keep speeding up forever. I think that at some point its speed will become constant.

Han   Samantha

Summarizing Questions

S1: Does the strength of the gravitational force of the Earth pulling an object toward the ground depend on the object's mass? What evidence supports your answer?

S2: What other force, apart from the gravitational force of the Earth, acts on falling objects? What types of object are affected most by this force?

S3: If the force of air resistance is negligible, does the rate at which a falling object's speed increases depend on its mass? Why do you think this is?

S4: When a skydiver jumps out of an aircraft he speeds up at first but eventually, after he has fallen for a while, his speed actually becomes constant. (This is before he opens his parachute.) Use your ideas about the forces acting on the skydiver as he falls to write a scientific explanation for why this happens.

EXPLANATION: Why does a skydiver speed up at first but eventually fall at a constant speed?

Describe the situation using a diagram: (Hint: You may wish to draw two or three force diagrams for this explanation.)

Write the narrative:

 Participate in a whole-class discussion.

Comparing the Class Ideas and Scientists' Ideas

In this chapter you developed some ideas about interactions in systems in which objects exert forces on each other without touching. You also saw how the idea of potential energy is useful in thinking about the behavior of such systems. In addition, you used a model of charges in materials to account for some electric-charge phenomena.

(You will develop you own model to account for magnetic phenomena in Chapter 4.) Your instructor will distribute copies of *Scientists' Ideas: Interactions, Systems, and Potential Energy*. Read through these ideas with your team and make a note of any evidence or examples you have seen that support them.

Explaining Phenomena

In this activity you will use the ideas you have developed to explain phenomena involving the interactions you were introduced to in this chapter.

Remember, when writing an explanation you should first draw a diagram (or more than one, if needed). Depending on the ideas you are using, this could be an I/O energy diagram, a force diagram, or diagrams showing

the distribution of charges in the interacting objects. Then use the information in your diagram(s) to guide your written explanation, making use of your ideas about conservation of energy, or Newton's Laws, or the model of charges in materials, as appropriate. Also make sure you connect these ideas to the original situation you are supposed to be explaining.

Interaction between Repelling Magnet-Carts

In Activity 2 of this chapter you attached magnets to two carts and arranged for those magnets to repel each other. You then held these magnet-carts close together on the track and when you released them, they moved away from each other.

Consider the two magnet-carts as a system for which there are no energy inputs or outputs (meaning any effects of friction can be ignored) and use energy ideas to explain why the magnet-carts started to move after they were released.

EXPLANATION #1: Why did the repelling magnet-carts begin to move after you released them?

Represent the situation using a diagram:
(Complete the I/O energy diagram for the system.)

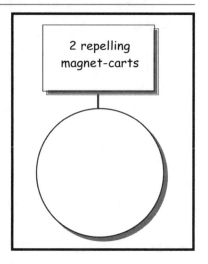

Write the narrative:

Bending a Stream of Water

When a narrow stream of water flows down from a faucet and a charged object is brought near, the stream of water moves toward (is attracted to) the charged object and so the stream 'bends.' (See picture to the right. Your instructor may show you a demonstration or movie of this phenomenon.)

Assuming the water is electrically neutral and the object brought close is a plastic rod with an overall positive charge, use the *model of charges in materials* to explain why the water is attracted to the charged object.

EXPLANATION #2: Why is the stream of water attracted to a positively charged rod?

Represent the situation using a diagram:

Use the pictures below. (The width of the water stream is exaggerated so you can draw charges in it.) First, draw in the charges in the stream of water before the charged rod is brought near. Then draw the charges in the stream of water to show how they are distributed after the charged rod is brought near.

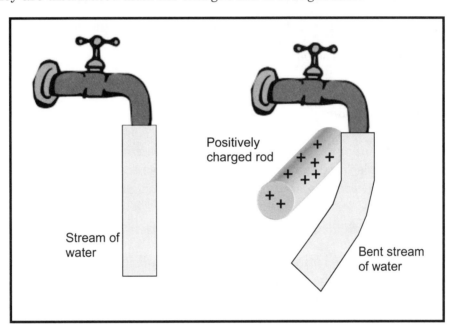

Write the narrative:

(Use the model to explain what happens to the charges in the water and why this leads to the water being attracted to the rod.)

EXPERIMENT #1 Explaining a ball toss.

YOU WILL NEED:

■ A ball (or other small object)

Toss the ball straight up so that it reaches a height of about 1 m above the point where you released it. Let it fall back down and catch it.

It is easier to explain the motion of the ball if you consider it in separate stages:

1) During the toss, while your hand is still in contact with the ball.

2) After the toss, while the ball is still rising.

3) While the ball is falling, before you catch it.

4) While you are catching it.

Now think about the some of these stages, and use *force ideas* to either evaluate or complete someone else's explanation, or write one of your own. Guiding questions are provided in some cases to help you.

During the toss

While you are tossing the ball upward, **before the ball leaves your hand**, does the gravitational force of the Earth act on the ball? Does the hand exert a force on the ball? Explain your reasoning.

Are the forces acting on the ball balanced or unbalanced? How do you know?

Now complete the following explanation for why the ball starts to move upward while you are tossing it.

 EXPLANATION #3: Why does the ball start to move upward when you toss it?

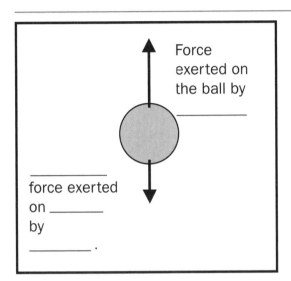

Describe the situation using a diagram: (Complete the force diagram.)

Force exerted on the ball by _____

_____ force exerted on _____ by _____ .

Write the narrative:

The strength of the _____ward force exerted on the ball by

_____ is greater than the strength of the _____ward

_____ force of the _____ acting on the ball.

This _____ combination of forces is equivalent to a single

force acting _____ward on the ball, so the ball begins to

move _____ward, and speeds up as it does so.

CHAPTER 3

Ball rising upward after the toss

Does the gravitational force of the Earth act on the ball while it is rising upward after it has left your hand? Does the hand exert a force on the ball? Explain your reasoning.

Now evaluate this explanation for why the ball slows down as it rises upward **after** the hand has lost contact with it, and eventually starts to fall back down.

EXPLANATION #4: Why does the ball slow down as it is moving upward, and eventually start to fall back down, *after* you toss it?

Describe the situation using a diagram:

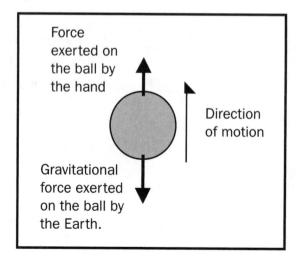

Write the narrative:

> During the toss, the force of the hand is transferred to the ball. But without the hand still pushing it, this force gradually runs out as the ball rises. As the force runs out, the speed of the ball decreases as it rises. When this force runs out completely the gravitational force of the Earth takes over and the ball begins to fall back down.

Evaluate this Explanation: Decide whether this explanation is *good* or *poor* by reviewing each of the following criteria.

Present	Criterion
YES/NO	Complete: All ideas needed are included.
YES/NO	Accurate: All included ideas correspond to established ideas.
YES/NO	Logical reasoning and clarity: Narrative connects ideas to the phenomenon, and is well written.

If you find this to be a good explanation, state your reasons below. If you find it to be a poor explanation, give your reasoning below and correct what is wrong in the explanation above, or write a new explanation below.

Catching the ball

Now consider what happens while you are catching the ball. Thinking about the answers to the following questions should help you in constructing your explanation.

 Which way is the ball moving before you catch it?

While you are catching the ball, does your hand exert a force on it? Does the Earth exert a gravitational force while you are catching it also? How do you know?

 After you have caught it, the ball it is at rest. What must have happened to its speed **while** you were catching it?

 In order for this **change** in speed to take place, would the combination of forces acting on the ball need to be balanced or unbalanced? If unbalanced, in which direction would the strongest force need to be acting—upward or downward?

Now use *force ideas* to write your own explanation below for why the ball slows down while you are catching it.

 EXPLANATION #5: Why does the ball slow down while you are catching it?

Describe the interaction using a diagram: (Draw and label appropriate force arrows on the diagram)

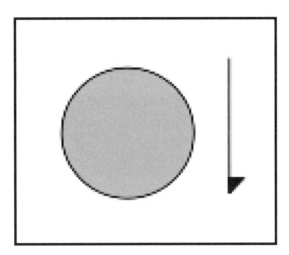

Write the narrative:

 Participate in a whole-class discussion to review the explanations in this activity.

CHAPTER 3

Model of Magnetism

Purpose

In Chapter 3 Activity 1, you studied some properties of the magnetic interaction, in particular how one magnet can affect another magnet. In that activity you discovered that only certain materials (ferromagnetic metals) will interact with a magnet. To remind you of these properties, take a moment to review the *Scientists' Ideas* from that chapter relevant to magnetism.

But what gives a magnet its properties?

Are magnets made of special material and how are they made? What is it about ferromagnetic materials that allows them to interact with magnets? The purpose of this activity is to investigate how you can make a magnet yourself, and to explore in greater depth some additional properties of the magnetic interaction. During the remainder of this chapter you will use this information to construct a model to explain magnetism.

 How can you make a magnet? What are some additional properties of the magnetic interaction?

Initial Ideas

 What material do you think a magnet is made from? Could you make a magnet from any material, only a ferromagnetic material, or can magnets only be made from a different, very special, specific material? Why do you think so?

CHAPTER 4

Collecting and Interpreting Evidence

As a reminder, scientists call materials that are attracted to a magnet ferromagnetic materials. Iron is the most common ferromagnetic material, and objects that include iron in them (like steel) are ferromagnetic. In this activity, you will use iron (or steel) nails to explore some important properties of the magnetic interaction. To start, you will check whether a nail can itself be turned into a magnet.

 EXPERIMENT #1: What happens when a nail is rubbed with a magnet?

YOUR GROUP WILL NEED:

- magnet
- three nails
- small styrene foam float
- aluminum pie tin or Styrofoam® plate
- glass beaker
- water

In this experiment you will distinguish between two types of nails: those that are rubbed with a magnet (called *rubbed*), and those that are not rubbed with a magnet (called *unrubbed*).

> **Keep the magnets far away from the nails. Once you rub a nail, it is no longer unrubbed. Please do *not* rub the nails until you are asked to do so.**

STEP 1: Use the beaker to pour some water into the aluminum pie pan. Lay an **unrubbed** nail on a small, flat piece of styrenefoam and float it in the water. This will give a very sensitive test arrangement. Check that your aluminum pan is not sitting over a piece of metal under the table, and that there are no large metallic objects nearby.

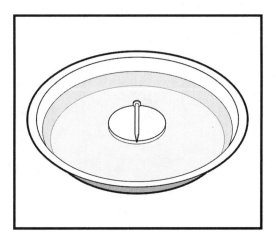

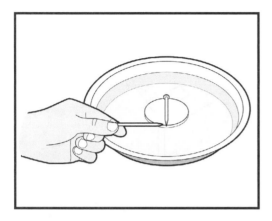

STEP 2: We first want you to investigate whether an unrubbed nail can affect another unrubbed nail. To determine this, take a second unrubbed nail, hold it horizontally, and bring its tip **close to** (but not touching) the floating nail. See picture to the left showing that the held nail should be at right angles to the floating nail. Always test held and floating nails this way. Do not bring the held nail from above (picture below to the left); nor should you bring it parallel to the floating nail (see picture below to the right).

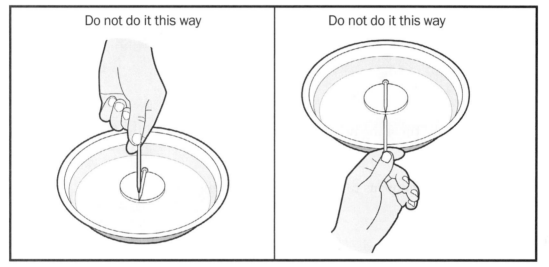

| Do not do it this way | Do not do it this way |

 What, if anything, happens to the floating nail when the held, unrubbed nail is brought nearby?

CHAPTER 4

STEP 3: Make a **rubbed** nail as follows. Place one end of the bar magnet over one end of an unrubbed nail and rub in **one direction only to the other end.** Then lift the magnet away from the nail and repeat the process a few times, always rubbing in the **same** direction.

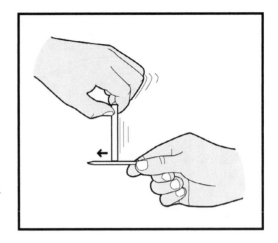

STEP 4: Using the same procedure as described in Step 2, bring the tip of a held **rubbed** nail near the tip of the floating unrubbed nail.

 What, if anything, happens to the tip of the floating unrubbed nail?

STEP 5: Bring the tip of the held rubbed nail near the head of the floating unrubbed nail.

 What, if anything, happens to the head of the floating nail?

STEP 6: Turn the held **rubbed** nail around and bring its head near first the tip and then the head of the floating nail.

 Summarize what, if anything, happens to the tip and head of the floating **unrubbed** nail.

STEP 7: Lay the rubbed nail aside for a moment. *Imagine* that you removed the floating nail, rubbed it with the magnet in the same way you rubbed the other nail, and then floated it again. (Don't do it yet!) You would then have two rubbed nails—one held and one floating.

 Predict what you think would happen if you were to bring the tip of the held **rubbed** nail near the tip of the floating **rubbed** nail.

 Predict what you think would happen if you were to bring the tip of the held **rubbed** nail near the head of the floating **rubbed** nail.

STEP 8: Now remove the floating nail, rub it with the magnet, and replace it on the floater. Then test your predictions.

 What actually happens when you bring the tip of the held rubbed nail near the tip of the floating rubbed nail?

 What actually happens when you bring the tip of the held rubbed nail near the head of the floating rubbed nail?

CHAPTER 4

STEP 9: Repeat Step 8, but this time bring the **head** of the held rubbed nail near the tip and head of the floating rubbed nail.

 What happens?

Summarize your observations in this experiment by answering the following questions:

 What happens when the tip or head of an **unrubbed** nail is brought near the tip or head of another **unrubbed** nail?

 What happens when the tip or head of a **rubbed** nail is brought near the tip or head of an **unrubbed** nail?

What happens when the tip or head of a **rubbed** nail is brought near the tip or head of another **rubbed** nail?

STEP 10: The aim of this experiment was to determine whether a nail (made of ferromagnetic material) could itself be turned into a magnet.

 Based on your observations, would you claim that rubbing a nail in the way you did magnetizes it or does it still behave like a ferromagnetic material that is not itself a magnet? What is your evidence?

Discuss your answer to this question with at least one other group. Add any additional comments below.

 EXPERIMENT #2: Does a rubbed nail interact with anything when there is no other magnet or nail nearby?

In the previous experiment you observed what happens when a rubbed nail is brought near an unrubbed nail or another rubbed nail. You should have discovered that a rubbed nail itself behaves like a magnet. Consider floating a rubbed nail. If you do not bring another nail or magnet nearby, does anything interesting happen to the floating rubbed nail? You will answer that question in this experiment.

CHAPTER 4

STEP 1: Place a **rubbed** nail on the floater, making sure the other rubbed nail and the magnet are far away. Spin the floating rubbed nail gently, and watch it. You should watch the nail for at least half a minute. Repeat this several times.

 Does the floating rubbed nail generally point in different directions after each spin, or does it always seem to end up pointing in the same direction?

STEP 2: Try aiming the floating rubbed nail in different directions, then letting go so it settles into a position. You may have to wait as long as one minute to be sure of what you are seeing.

 What does the nail do?

STEP 3: Compare your observations with that of several (at least five) other groups.

 What is the same (if anything)? What is different (if anything)?

EXPERIMENT #3: How can you rub the nail so it consistently behaves in a particular way?

In the previous experiment you probably discovered that when some groups floated their rubbed nail and let it settle, the *pointed end* ended up pointing towards the geographical north. For other groups, the *head end* of their rubbed nails ended up pointing towards the geographical north.

Whenever a rubbed nail, or any magnet, is allowed to rotate freely, and without another magnet nearby, one end will always end up pointing (approximately) towards the geographical North Pole of the Earth. By mutual agreement, scientists **define** this end of the magnet as the **north pole** of the magnet. The opposite end of the magnet, by definition, is called the **south pole**. Thus, when you rub your nail you produce a magnet with a north pole and a south pole.

STEP 1: Figure out **two different ways** that you can rub your nail with a magnet so that the pointed end becomes the north pole and the head end becomes the south pole.

 Draw some sketches showing how you did it. Also describe what you did in words.

STEP 2: Figure out **two different ways** that you can rub your nail with a magnet so that the head end becomes the north pole and the pointed end becomes the south pole.

 Draw some sketches and describe in words how you did it.

Summarizing Questions

S1: Do both ends of a rubbed nail (magnet) behave similarly or differently when interacting with another rubbed nail? How do you know?

S2: In what ways does a rubbed nail seem to be different from an unrubbed nail when interacting with another rubbed nail?

S3: In the Initial Ideas section of this activity you were asked what material you think magnets are made from. How would you answer that question now? What evidence supports your current answer?

 Participate in a whole-class discussion to review the results of the experiments and the answers to the Summarizing Questions.

CHAPTER 4

Purpose

In the previous activity you discovered that magnet-rubbed nails behave differently from unrubbed nails. Thus, rubbing the nail with a magnet must change the nail in some way. But how does it change the nail? To answer this question you need to develop a model—a picture and description of what you think is going on in the nail.

Scientists construct models all the time to help them understand new phenomena. A good model can do two important things: (1) it can be used to **explain** observations from experiments already done; and (2) it can guide the making of **predictions** about experiments that have not yet been done. After scientists make their predictions based on their model, they (or other scientists) perform the experiments. If the predictions are **confirmed** through the new experiments, the scientists retain their model because it can explain their new observations. However, if the results of the new experiments differ from the predictions, scientists use the new evidence to **modify** their model so it can explain the new set of observations (as well as the previous observations). Then they use their revised model to make new predictions. They develop confidence in their model only after it can be used repeatedly to make predictions that are confirmed in new experiments. The process of science is a process of developing, testing and modifying models.

In this activity you will begin the process of developing a *model for magnetism*.

How can you construct a model of magnetism to explain your observations and guide your predictions?

Initial Ideas

Imagine that an unrubbed nail is rubbed in such a way that its pointed end becomes a north pole. On the next page are two drawings of the nail, representing its state before and after rubbing with a magnet.

Individually, sketch what you think might be different about the nail in these two conditions (unrubbed and rubbed).

Your first individual model:

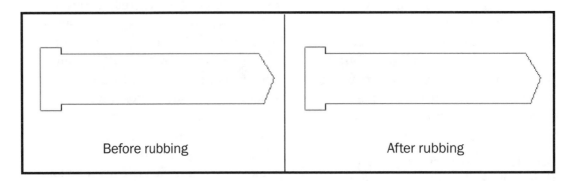

| Before rubbing | After rubbing |

 Describe your initial *model* in words, in particular how the "After rubbing" picture differs from the "Before rubbing" picture. If you are showing some type of entities inside the nails, describe what these entities represent. Your picture and written description is a representation of your own initial model for what happens when a nail is magnetized.

 Write a brief **explanation** to show how your model can account for the following two observations from the previous activity: (1) rubbing an unmagnetized nail with a magnet can *magnetize* it; and (2) the magnetized nail has north and south poles. Your model is good if it can be used to explain these previous observations.

Share your model with other members of your group, listen to them describe their models, then decide on a model that your group feels is best at explaining the two observations already mentioned above. If the group's best model is different from your own, draw a representation of the group's model below, and briefly describe it in words.

Your group's first model:

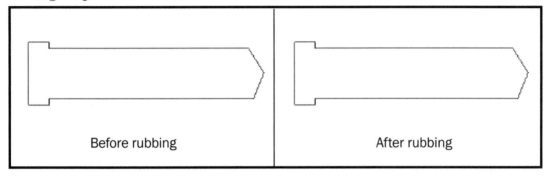

Before rubbing   After rubbing

Description:

 Draw a picture of your group's model on a presentation board. Include a very brief description of what you are representing in the picture.

 Participate in a whole-class discussion. Be prepared to describe your model to the rest of the class, and demonstrate how it can explain the two previous observations.

CHAPTER 4

After listening to the other groups, choose a model that you believe **best** helps you explain the observations with rubbed and unrubbed nails.

Best First Model from Class Discussion:

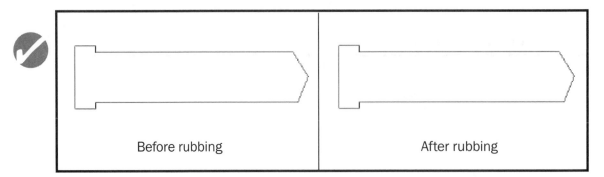

| Before rubbing | After rubbing |

Briefly describe this model in words and indicate why you are most confident in this particular initial model.

Collecting and Interpreting Evidence

In the Initial Ideas section you chose a model that you believe best explains observations you have already made. As stated in the Purpose section, an important criterion of a good model is that it can help you make predictions about new experiments.

> **IMPORTANT: In the remainder of this activity you will make predictions, then test them. In each case, you must base your prediction on your <u>current</u> model. Do not change your model as a result of just thinking about the experiment, because then you are not testing your model. If the outcome of the experiment turns out to be <u>exactly</u> what you had predicted, then don't modify your model. On the other hand, if the outcome is different from your prediction, even in small ways, then you need to consider how to modify your model. Finally, for this process to be useful, the predictions you make should be precise, not vague and general. Only then will the experiment really test your model appropriately.**

EXPERIMENT: What happens when a rubbed nail is cut?

Before doing an experiment, you are going to use your best model from the Initial Ideas section to make a **prediction**. Imagine that you rubbed a nail so that its pointed end was a north pole. Below, sketch again your best model for what is inside the rubbed nail. Label the pointed end as a north pole (use an **N**) and the flat end as a south pole (use an **S**).

After rubbing (best model from Initial Ideas)

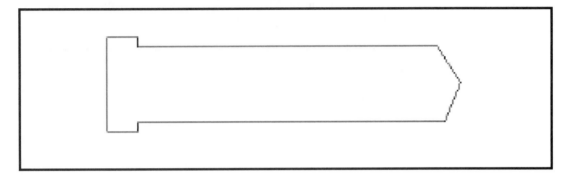

Now imagine you cut the nail in half across the middle.

Draw below what your model above suggests would be inside each of the two halves. Label each end of each piece according to whether it should be a north pole **(N)**, a south pole **(S)** or have no pole **(NoP)**. Remember: do *not* **change your model at this point.**

Model for two halves of nail

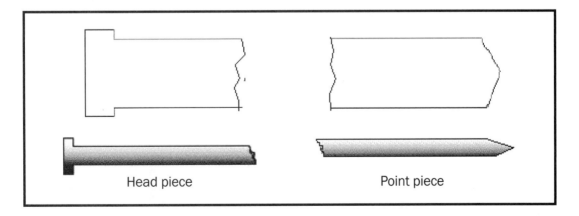

Head piece   Point piece

Suppose you floated each of the nail halves separately on the floater in the aluminum pie pan, as you did in the last activity. If you then rubbed a second uncut nail so its tip was a north pole, and brought that tip near each end of each half of the cut nail, what does your model **predict** would happen: would they attract, repel, or would nothing happen? Write your prediction (*attract*, *repel*, or *nothing*) next to each end of each cut piece on the picture below, and briefly explain why your current model would predict that. (Again, do **not** change your model when using it to make a prediction.)

Prediction: What would happen if the north pole of a rubbed nail was brought near each of these four ends: *attract*, *repel*, or *nothing*.

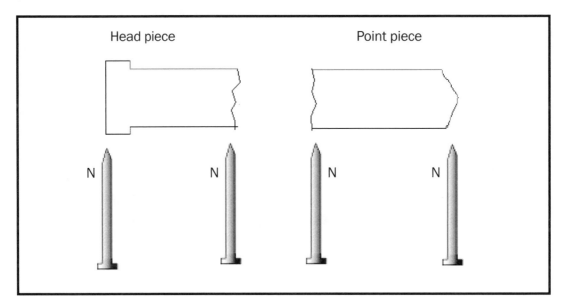

Briefly explain how your current model of the two cut pieces supports your predictions.

Now that you have made your predictions based on your current model, you will test them to see whether your model is fine as is, or whether you need to consider modifying it.

YOU WILL NEED:

- magnet
- three unrubbed nails
- Wire cutter

- aluminum pie tin or Styrofoam® plate
- glass beaker
- water

STEP 1: Rub your two nails with the magnet so that the pointed end of each nail is a north pole. With the magnet and one rubbed nail far away, float the other rubbed nail in the aluminum pie tin to confirm that its pointed end ends up pointing towards the direction of geographical north. Then bring the tip of the rubbed held nail (its north pole) near the tip of the rubbed floating nail (its north pole) and make sure they repel. Then bring the tip of the rubbed held nail near the head of the rubbed floating nail (its south pole), and make sure they attract.

Is the behavior what you expected? If not, repeat the experiment or check with another group or with your instructor.

STEP 2: Take the floating rubbed nail and ask your instructor to cut it in half. *Before* **your instructor cuts the nail, however, you must show him or her how you used your current model to guide your predictions.** After the nail is cut, make sure you keep both halves away from the magnet.

Float the **point piece** all by itself on the floater. After it settles down, does either end point towards the geographical north? If so, which end?

Float the **head piece** all by itself on the floater. Does either end point towards the geographical north? If so, which end?

STEP 3: With the head piece floating, bring the north pole (tip) of the other whole rubbed nail near **each** end of the floating head piece.

 In the picture below, write *attract*, *repel*, or *nothing*, for what you actually observed.

Observation: What actually happened when the north pole of a rubbed nail was brought near each of these ends: *attract*, *repel*, or *nothing*?

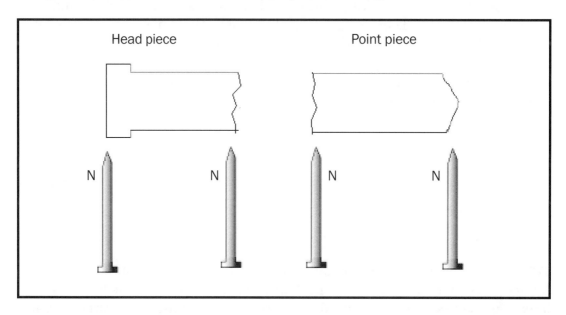

Head piece   Point piece

N   N   N   N

STEP 4: Replace the floating head piece with the point piece and repeat Step 3.

 Record your observations on the picture of the point piece above.

Check your four observations with those of another group to make sure you both agree. If not, check with other groups. If necessary, repeat the experiment and re-record the observations.

 How did **your** observations compare with **your** predictions?

If your observations were exactly the same as your predictions, and if your predictions were based on your current model, you should not change your model at this time. In that case, on the picture below you should re-draw the same representation of your current model. However, if your observations were *different* from your predictions, then you need to consider how you might change your model so it can explain both your new observations **and** your previous observations. Discuss this with your group. Then, on the picture below, sketch your group's new model for what happens when a nail is magnetized. As before, label the pointed end as a north pole (use an **N**) and the flat end as a south pole (use an **S**).

Model of rubbed nail after observations of cutting nail in half

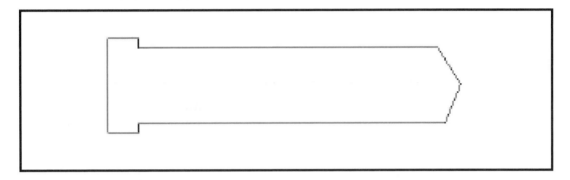

STEP 5: Now, team up with another group. Compare your groups' best models at this time. They may be the same or they may be different.

To help you think further about your model(s), your group and the other group together should consider the following. Suppose the full-length rubbed nail was cut into two pieces of unequal length: say a $\frac{1}{4}$-length piece and a $\frac{3}{4}$-length piece, or a $\frac{1}{3}$-length piece and a $\frac{2}{3}$-length piece.

Using either yours or the other group's model to guide you, predict what would happen when the **north pole of a rubbed nail** was brought near **each end** of each of the cut nails. Write either *attract*, *repel*, or *nothing*.

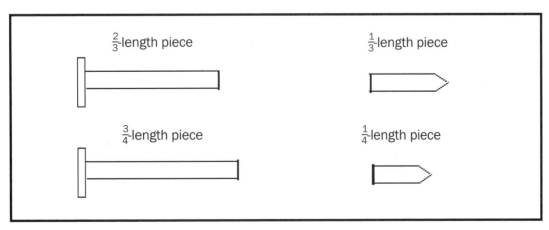

$\frac{2}{3}$-length piece

$\frac{1}{3}$-length piece

$\frac{3}{4}$-length piece

$\frac{1}{4}$-length piece

CHAPTER 4

STEP 6: Each group should test the predictions for one of the cut nails: either the $\frac{1}{3}$–$\frac{2}{3}$ cut or the $\frac{1}{4}$–$\frac{3}{4}$ cut. Your instructor will cut the nails.

Below, summarize your observations. Write either *attract*, *repel*, or *nothing*.

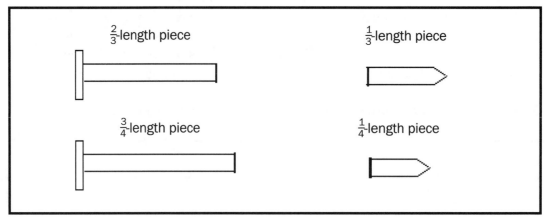

Work again with the other group and try to come up with a model that seems to work best for all your observations (or for as many as you can explain). Sketch the model below and describe how it differs from previous models.

Model of nails after observations of cutting nail at different places

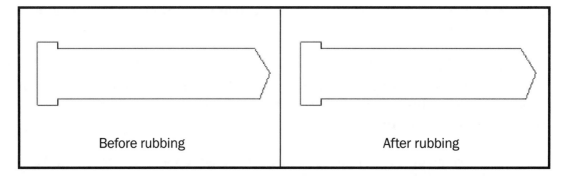

| Before rubbing | After rubbing |

What are the appropriate symbols to use for the entities inside the nail?

It is common for some students to draw plus (+) and minus (–) symbols to represent the entities inside the nail, and for other students to draw north (**N**) and south (**S**) symbols. Is one set of symbols more appropriate than the other set, or does it not make any difference?

Many of you probably realize that plus (+) and minus (–) charges have to do with electric charges. Back in Activity 2 of Chapter 3 you studied the electric-charge interaction, and learned that charged objects can exert either attractive or repulsive forces on each other. Magnets can also exert either attractive or repulsive forces on each other. *But is the interaction between electrically charged objects the same as, or different from, the interaction between magnets?* If the interactions are really the same, but differ only in name, then it probably is not important whether you use plus and minus symbols, or north and south symbols in describing your magnetism model. But if the two interactions are really *different*, then it would be best not to mix up the symbols between the two kinds of interactions.

Imagine that you have two magnets, A and B, and two objects, C and D, that are both electrically charged all over. In answering the following questions, you may wish to review your observations from Activity 2 in Chapter 3.

 Suppose you bring one end of magnet A near one end of magnet B, and observe the two attract each other. What would happen if you then bring the same end of magnet A near the opposite end of magnet B?

 Suppose you bring one side of charged object C near one side of charged object D, and observe the two attract each other. What would happen if you then bring the same side of charged object C near the opposite side of charged object D?

 In the above case, are the effects of the magnetic interaction the same or different than the effects of the electric charge interaction?

Are there other observations you have made that would shed some light on whether the magnetic and electric-charge interactions are the same or different?

As long as there is at least one difference in the effects of the magnetic and electric-charge interactions, then you can claim they are different.

 What conclusion can you draw as to whether the magnetic- and electric-charge interactions are the same or different?

 Therefore, would it be appropriate to use **either N/S** symbols or +/– symbols in your magnetism model, or would it be appropriate to only use **N/S** symbols?

Summarizing Questions

S1: Draw your best model below. Then, list which observations from this activity your model can explain, and which observations (if any) it cannot explain.

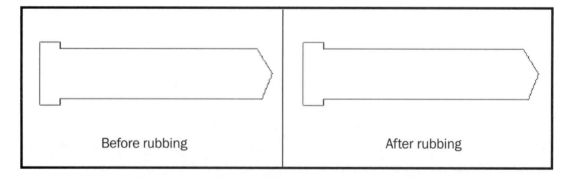

Before rubbing | After rubbing

Observations this model can explain:

Observations this model cannot explain:

Sketch your group's best model on a presentation board and mount it so other groups can see it. Be prepared to describe what your model can and (possibly) cannot explain.

S2: How is your model at the end of the activity different from the model your group proposed at the beginning of the activity?

S3: A group in another class was asked to use their magnetism model to explain why rubbing a nail from head to tip with the north pole of a magnet caused the nail to be magnetized with the tip end a south pole and the head end a north pole. Below is their explanation. Evaluate this explanation in terms of accuracy, completeness and logical reasoning and clarity. Is this a good or a poor explanation? Justify your evaluation.

Draw a diagram:

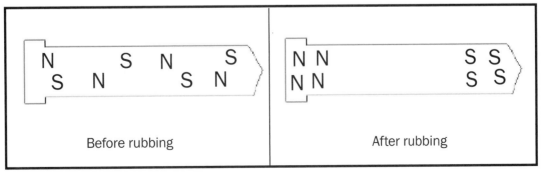

Before rubbing

After rubbing

Write the narrative:

In the unrubbed nail the N's and S's are scattered around the nail, with no particular order. When the north pole of the magnet is dragged from head to tip, it attracts the S's since opposite poles attract. The S's go to the tip, making it the south pole of the nail. The N's are repelled by the north pole of the magnet, and they go to the head end, making it a north pole.

 Participate in a whole-class discussion. After listening to other groups present their models, draw the "best" model below and describe why you think it is best.

Purpose

In the previous activity you proposed your initial model for magnetism, then tested it by performing some experiments cutting nails. Most students probably realized that they needed to modify their initial models. However, you may have found it challenging to modify your model to take into account all the new evidence.

In this activity you will work with both an analogy and a computer simulator model to help you consider additional possible modifications to your model of magnetism. The intent is to modify your model until it can explain a wide range of phenomena.

How can you develop a better model for magnetism?

Collecting and Interpreting Evidence

EXPERIMENT #1: How can a test tube with iron filings serve as an analogy for a magnetized nail?

YOU WILL NEED:

- magnet
- 3 (unrubbed) nails
- test tube partially filled with iron filings and taped shut
- magnetic compass
- piece of masking tape
- access to block of wood and hammer (to be shared with the class)

In Activity 1 you found that a freely floating rubbed nail will orient itself along the north-south direction. In this way, it behaves like a magnetic compass. A commercial magnetic compass consists of a light, thin magnetized needle that can pivot

around a point through its center. Because of its ease of use, we will use a commercial magnetic compass for the two experiments in this activity. In the first few steps we will check the compass needle to make sure it behaves like a magnet.

CHAPTER 4

STEP 1: Lay the magnetic compass on the table and rotate it so the colored tip of the needle points towards the north marking **N**.

STEP 2: Rub one of the nails with the bar magnet so its pointed end becomes a north pole.

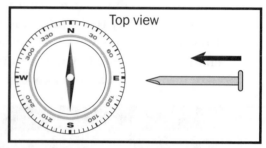

STEP 3: Lay the nail on the table and slide its pointed end towards the end of the colored tip of the compass needle, from the side. See picture. (Do not bring the tip near the middle of the compass needle.)

 What happens to the colored tip of the compass needle? Is it attracted to the nail tip, repelled away from it, or does it remain stationary?

STEP 4: Now turn the nail around and slide its head towards the end of the colored tip of the compass needle, from the side.

 What happens to the tip of the compass needle?

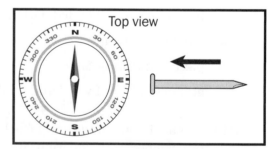

 Assuming that the compass needle is a magnet, is its behavior in Steps 3 and 4 what you expected?

STEP 5: Put away the rubbed nail and pick up one of the unrubbed nails. Repeat Steps 3 and 4.

 Describe what happens to the colored tip of the compass needle in the two cases.

 Is the behavior of the tip of the compass needle in Step 4 what you expected?

If the behavior of the compass needle in Steps 3, 4 and/or 5 is **not** what you expected, check your results with another group or with the instructor before moving on. If the behavior is what you expected, put away the nails for the moment and pick up the test tube with the iron filings.

STEP 6: Shake the test tube a few times and then hold it horizontally so the filings are deposited all along the test tube, as shown here.

Lay the test tube on the table and slide the rounded end slowly towards the end of the colored tip of the magnetic compass, from the side. See picture at right.

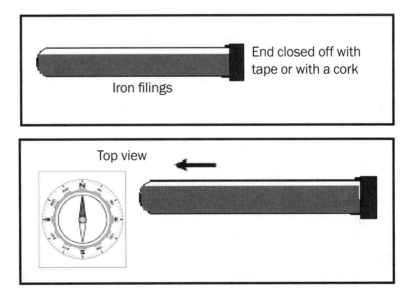

End closed off with tape or with a cork

Iron filings

Top view

CHAPTER 4

Describe what happens, if anything, to the tip of the compass needle.

Turn the test tube around, and slide its taped or corked end towards the end of the colored tip of the compass needle.

 Describe what, if anything, happens to the tip of the compass needle.

 Do your observations suggest that the test tube behaves more like a rubbed nail or more like an unrubbed nail? Why?

STEP 7: Imagine that the rounded end of the test tube is *like* the pointed end of a nail, and the taped end of the test tube is *like* the head of the nail. Rub the test tube in the same way that you would rub a nail when trying to make the pointed end a north pole. Slide the end of the magnet slowly along the test tube as shown, and **carefully observe** what happens to the iron filings. (However, do not do it *so slowly* that the filings rise up and follow the magnet all the way to the other end of the test tube.) Repeat the process a couple of times, then place the magnet far away from your experiment.

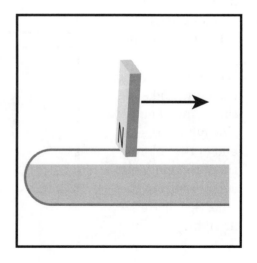

Describe what happens to each of the iron filings near the top as the magnet is dragged across the test tube. Draw a picture to help your description.

STEP 8: Lay the test tube on the table and slide its rounded end towards the colored tip of the magnetic compass, from the side. (Same procedure as in Step 6 above.) Then turn the test tube around and bring its taped or corked end towards the colored tip of the compass needle, from the side.

 Describe what happens to the tip of the compass needle in the two cases.

 Does the *rubbed test tube* behave more like a rubbed nail or more like an unrubbed nail? If it behaves more like a rubbed nail, which end of the test tube behaves like a north pole, and which end behaves like a south pole?

CHAPTER 4

STEP 9: Shake the test tube vigorously. Lay it on the table and repeat Step 8.

 Describe what happens to the tip of the compass needle in the two cases.

 Does the shaken test tube now behave more like a rubbed nail or an unrubbed nail?

STEP 10: Check again to make sure the colored tip of the compass needle is pointing towards 0 degrees (north). Rub one of the unrubbed nails with the magnet so its pointed end becomes a south pole.
Slide the tip of the rubbed nail near the colored tip of the compass needle so the needle turns through a significant number of degrees (say, between 30 degrees and 60 degrees).

Put away the test tube.

 How many degrees does the compass needle turn towards the tip of the rubbed nail?

Place a piece of tape next to the tip of the rubbed nail and mark the exact position of the tip.

Turn the rubbed nail around and place its head end at the exact same position the tip was previously.

How many degrees does the compass needle turn away from the tip of the rubbed nail?

The number of degrees the compass needle turns is a rough indication of the magnetic strength of the rubbed nail. The greater the number of degrees the compass needle turns, the greater is the magnetic strength of the rubbed nail.

STEP 11: *Imagine* that you hammered the rubbed nail into a block of wood, and then removed the nail from the wood with the claw end of the hammer.

Predict whether the *hammered* nail would then behave more like a rubbed nail or an unrubbed nail. Why do you think so?

STEP 12: To **test** your prediction, hammer the rubbed nail into a block of wood. Hammer it in as far as you can, while still being able to remove it with the claw end of the hammer. After removing the nail, lay it on the table near the compass so its tip is at the same position it was before.

How many degrees does the compass needle turn towards the tip of the hammered nail?

Turn the hammered nail around and place the head end at the same position. Is the colored compass needle tip attracted toward or repelled from the head of the nail, or does nothing happen? If it is attracted or repelled, through how many degrees does it turn?

CHAPTER 4

Does the *hammered* nail behave more like a rubbed nail with the same magnetic strength it had before, a weakened rubbed nail, or an unrubbed nail?

 Consider all the observations you made in Steps 6-12. How might your observations of what happens inside the test tube when you rub it with a magnet *suggest* what might be happening inside the nail when you rub it with a magnet?

The test tube with iron filings can serve as an analogy for the nail. An analogy can serve as a tool to help you think about how you might modify your own model of the magnetized nail.

SIMULATOR EXPLORATION

Another tool to help you think about your model of the nail is the computer simulator. As stated before, the computer simulator was programmed to be a representation of a scientist's model. You can manipulate different objects in the simulator and compare their behavior with your own experimental observations and with predictions you make with your own model. Here we introduce you to a special simulator that lets you manipulate objects that behave like magnets.

Go to the *PET* simulators web page and open up Chapter 4 Activity 3 setup.

STEP 13: There is a magnet whose north pole is just above the left side of a dashed line. Below the dashed line are two magnets that can only rotate around a pivot through their centers.

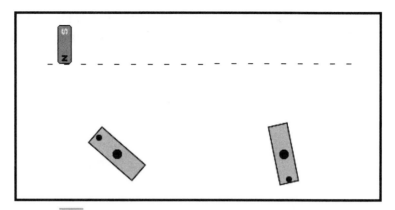

STEP 14: Press the RUN button to turn on the simulator, and observe what happens to the two pivoted magnets. Then slowly drag the magnet to the right, keeping the north pole just above the dashed line. **Stop** dragging the magnet (but **don't** turn off the simulator) after it moves a few dashes to observe what happens to the two pivoted magnets. Repeat dragging the magnet another few dashes and observe what happens to the pivoted magnets. Repeat until the magnet is dragged all the way to the right, just above the dashed line.

 Describe what happens to the two pivoted magnets as the magnet is dragged across the dashed line.

 Is the small dot at the end of each pivoted magnet a north pole or a south pole? How do you know?

 How is the behavior of each pivoting magnet **similar** to the behavior of each iron filing in the test tube when you dragged the magnet across the test tube?

CHAPTER 4

How do your observations with the test tube and computer simulator help you think about what the entities inside the nail might be like?

In this activity, and in the previous two activities, you created a magnetized nail by rubbing its surface with a magnet. When you did the test tube experiment, however, the magnet did not touch the iron filings, yet all the filings were affected by the magnet. Does that mean that you might be able to magnetize a nail without actually rubbing its surface? The purpose of the next experiment is to help you investigate that question.

 EXPERIMENT #2: Can you magnetize a nail without touching it?

YOU WILL NEED:

- A magnet (keep away from the unrubbed nails until instructed to use it)
- 3 nails (unrubbed)
- A magnetic compass

STEP 1: Imagine that you hold the north pole of the bar magnet about 0.5 cm away from the **head** of an unrubbed nail for about 5 seconds, as shown. The magnet and nail **do not** touch. Then you remove the magnet and put it away.

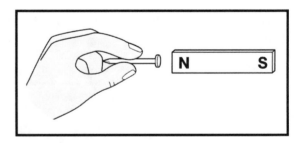

 Would the nail remain like an unrubbed nail, or would it now behave like a rubbed nail? If the latter, would its head end be a north pole or a south pole?

STEP 2: Try it. Make sure you hold the nail so it doesn't move towards and touch the magnet. If it touches, start over with another unrubbed nail. After putting the magnet away, test the nail by bringing its head near the colored tip of the compass needle, from the side. Then bring its tip near the colored tip of the compass needle.

Describe what happens to the compass needle in the two cases.

Does the nail behave like a rubbed nail or an unrubbed nail? If it behaves like a rubbed nail, is its head end a north pole or a south pole?

Imagine that you took the same nail you just used, and held its **tip** about 0.5 cm away from the north pole of the bar magnet for 5 seconds. After removing the magnet, would you expect the nail to behave as an unrubbed nail or as a rubbed nail? If you think it would behave as a rubbed nail, which end (tip or head) would be the north pole?

CHAPTER 4

STEP 3: Try it, and then test the nail with the colored end of the compass needle.

 Describe what happens.

 Is this result consistent with what you had expected?

 Can you magnetize a nail without touching it?

 Once a nail becomes magnetized can you re-magnetize it and switch its poles?

Summarizing Questions

S1: Sketch your best **current model** for an unrubbed and a rubbed nail.

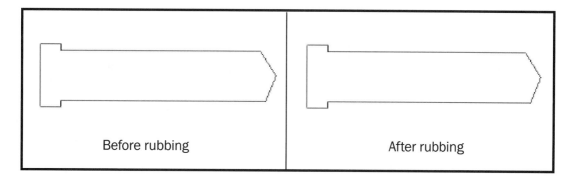

Before rubbing

After rubbing

(a) What do the **entities** inside the nail represent?

(b) What is **different** about the arrangement of entities in the unrubbed and rubbed nail?

(c) **Why** does the arrangement of the entities inside the nail seem to change when the magnet is rubbed across it?

CHAPTER 4

(d) How did your observations with the test tube (with iron filings) and the computer simulator either **support** your previous model (from the last activity) or help you think about how to **modify** your previous model?

Draw your best current model on the presentation board and be prepared to describe it to the class.

S2: Using your best current model for magnetism, write a **scientific explanation** for why the magnetized nail became unmagnetized (or much less magnetized) when it was hammered into the block of wood.

Draw pictures of the nail before being hammered and after being hammered:

Write the narrative:

S3: Describe, by drawing pictures, what you think happens to the entities inside the unrubbed nail when a bar magnet is held **near** it (but without touching it).

 Participate in a whole-class discussion.

CHAPTER 4

Name:_____ Date:_____ Group: _____

Purpose

We know that an unmagnetized (unrubbed) nail does not interact with another unmagnetized nail. We also know that a magnetized (rubbed) nail does interact with another magnetized or unmagnetized nail, even when they don't touch. This suggests that a magnetized nail produces a magnetic field in its surrounding region, whereas an unmagnetized nail does not produce a magnetic field in its surrounding region.

In the previous activity you performed an experiment with a test tube containing a large number of individual iron filings and a magnetic compass. Rubbing the magnet across the test tube from one end to the other appeared to "line up" the filings. In that case, when you brought the test tube near the compass, you found that it behaved like a magnetized (rubbed) nail. Shaking the test tube seemed to cause the set of filings to lose their alignment. Then the test tube behaved like an unmagnetized (un-rubbed) nail. You also used the computer simulator model to observe what happens when a magnet was moved near other magnets that were free to rotate.

The observations with the test tube and simulator might have suggested the following model for the inside of a nail: that it behaves as if it contains a large number of entities, each of which behaves like a little magnet (with its own north and south poles). If we imagine the inside of a nail to contain a large collection of little magnets, can this model *explain* the behavior of both unmagnetized and magnetized nails? For example, can this model explain one important difference between a magnetized and unmagnetized nail: that the magnetized nail produces a large magnetic field, whereas the unmagnetized nail produces essentially no magnetic field?

In this homework you will use a computer-based simulator model to examine what might happen when you arrange a collection of magnets in different ways. The simulator model contains a magnetic field meter that will allow you to measure the strength of the magnetic field produced by a collection of magnets.

CHAPTER 4

SIMULATOR EXPLORATION: How does a collection of magnets behave?

STEP 1: Open up **Chapter 4 Activity 3 Homework 1 Setup**. There is a bar magnet in the center of a dashed box. In the simulator model, the dashed box represents the boundary of a nail. On the right side of the setup area is a **magnetic field meter**. The little circle above the field meter is the sensitive part. When the simulator is turned on, the meter reading gives the strength of the magnetic field at the position of the small circle.

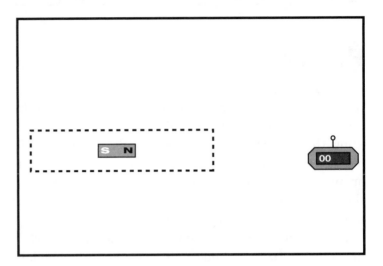

STEP 2. Turn on the simulator. Notice the reading on the magnetic field meter. The "T" on the meter stands for Tesla, the unit of magnetic field strength. The unit is named in honor of Nikola Tesla (1857-1943), the Croatian-born American electrical engineer who did pioneering work with magnetism and alternating current (AC) electricity.

 What is the strength of the magnetic field at the position of the meter?

STEP 3: Click the bar magnet tool in the palette and paste a second magnet inside the dashed rectangle. Click the Select tool, then drag the magnets so they lie one above the other as in the picture at right.

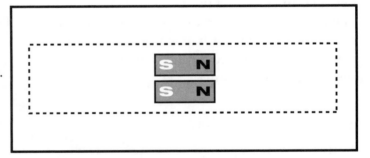

 What is the value of the magnetic field strength at the position of the meter?

STEP 4: Next, rotate the lower magnet so its poles point in the opposite direction. To do that, first click the magnet to select it, then place the cursor on the double arrow at the lower right. (See picture below to the left.) Drag the cursor to the left (see middle picture), then upwards. End up with the lower magnet pointing exactly in the opposite direction to the top magnet. (See picture below to right).

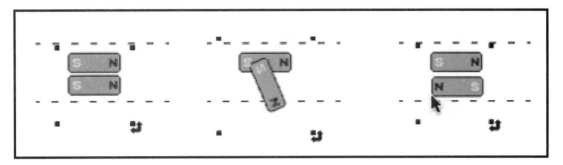

 What is the value of the magnetic field strength at the position of the meter?

 Does a combination of two magnets oriented in the **same direction** (north pole above north pole) produce a greater or weaker magnetic field strength in the area outside the magnets than a single magnet by itself? Or is the strength the same?

 Does a combination of two magnets oriented in **opposite directions** (north pole above south pole) produce a greater or weaker magnetic field in the area outside the magnets than a single magnet by itself? Or is the strength the same?

STEP 5: Add eight more bar magnets to the setup area (making a total of ten). **All magnets must be placed inside the dashed rectangle and they cannot overlap.** Arrange the magnets (rotating any if necessary) so the collection of ten magnets produces the largest possible value for the magnetic field strength at the position of the meter.

Sketch the arrangements of the ten bar magnets inside the dashed rectangle. Record the value of the (maximum) magnetic field strength.

 Why do you think this works? That is, why do you think this arrangement of magnets combines to produce a very large magnetic field (at the position of the meter)?

STEP 6: Change the orientation of one or more of the ten bar magnets so that when they are all inside the dashed box the magnetic field strength at the meter position is as **small** as possible (as close to zero as possible). You may find it convenient to drag a magnet away from the other magnets, rotate it, and then drag it back inside the dashed box. Do not overlap any of the magnets.

Sketch the arrangements of the ten bar magnets inside the dashed rectangle and record the (minimum) magnetic field strength.

 Why do you think this works? That is, why does this arrangement of the collection of magnets produce a very small magnetic field (at the position of the meter)?

Summarizing Questions

At the beginning of this homework we suggested a model that assumed that the inside of the nail was like a collection of small magnets. Let's call this the "small magnets model" of the nail.

S1: The "small magnets model" assumes there are a large number of small magnets inside a nail (or any piece of iron). Let's focus our attention on only one of the *small magnets* inside the nail, as shown in the first picture below. The next several pictures show the north pole of a bar magnet being dragged across the nail. Draw in the *small magnet* and show what happens to it in the sequence of pictures.

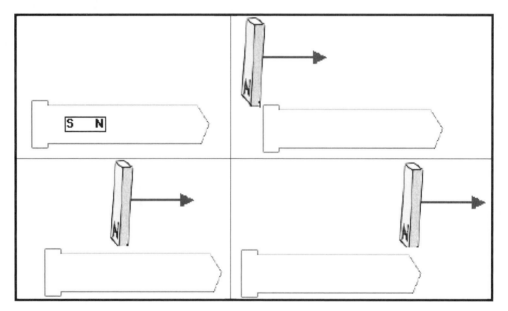

S2: How does the small magnets model account for why a magnetized nail produces a strong magnetic field?

S3: How does the small magnets model account for why an unmagnetized nail produces no magnetic field (or perhaps a very weak one)?

S4: Using the small magnets model, write a **scientific explanation** for why rubbing a nail from head to tip with the north pole of a bar magnet causes the tip of the nail to become a south pole.

Draw a diagram or diagrams:

Write the narrative:

S5: A good model not only helps explain known observations, but it also guides new predictions. Imagine you magnetized a nail and measured the strength of the magnetic field it produces (for example, by observing how many degrees a compass needle deflects when the tip of the nail is held nearby). If you were to cut the nail in half, do you predict the magnetic field of the cut nail would be stronger than, weaker than, or the same strength as the whole nail? Use the small magnets model to justify your prediction.

Comparing the Class Ideas and Scientists' Ideas

Scientists spent many years developing models for magnetism. You worked on it for a much shorter period of time. However, through a careful set of experiments you were able to modify your model until you felt reasonably satisfied that it could account for all (or at least most of) your observations. How does your model compare with one that seems satisfactory to scientists? Your teacher will distribute a copy of *Scientists' Ideas: The Magnetic Interaction*. Review the ideas and the magnetism model described in this handout to see how they compare with the ideas and model you developed. Add evidence from the experiments you did that would support each of the idea statements. This handout introduces the domain model for magnetism, which is very similar to the small magnets model introduced in the homework for Activity 3. This handout also supplements and extends the magnetism-interaction ideas introduced earlier in the *Scientists' Ideas* in Chapter 3.

Explaining Magnetism Phenomena

From now on you should use the domain model to help guide your explanations. The diagrams you draw in your explanations should include pictures of the domains inside the nail or piece of iron. Your written narrative should include a description of what happens to the domains in the given situation. As always, your explanation should be accurate, complete, logically consistent and written clearly.

 EXPLANATION #1: Explain why a magnet attracts an unmagnetized paper clip.

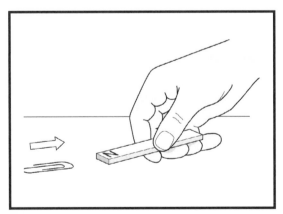

> You can think of the paper clip as similar to the unrubbed nail you studied in Activity 3.

CHAPTER 4

Draw diagrams before the magnet is brought near the paper clip, and after the magnet is near the paper clip:

Write the narrative:

EXPLANATION #2: Explain why the middle and ends of a bar magnet compare the way they do in strength.

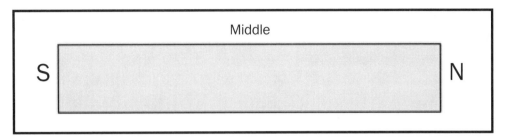

Make a prediction. Is the middle of a bar magnet weaker or stronger than the ends, or do the middle and ends have about the same strength? Write an explanation to support your prediction.

Draw a diagram:

Write the narrative that supports your prediction:

CHAPTER 4

Design an experiment to find out whether the middle of the magnet is stronger, weaker, or equally as strong as the ends. State what you did and describe your results.

If your observations are different from your original prediction, then write a new explanation below to account for your results.

Draw a diagram:

Write the narrative that supports your observation:

EXPLANATION #3: (Optional) Explain why a refrigerator magnet sticks on one side, but not the other.

You are familiar with refrigerator magnets. They tend to be thin, with designs on them, and they easily stick to the refrigerator. The refrigerator is a ferromagnetic material that is not, itself, a magnet. So it would seem that the explanation for why the refrigerator magnet sticks to the refrigerator is similar to why a magnet would stick to a paper clip (except that the refrigerator is so massive that it wouldn't move towards the magnet.) However, there is something different here, because if you flip the refrigerator magnet around, front to back, *it no longer sticks to the refrigerator* (or it sticks very weakly). So it seems that the refrigerator magnet only works on one side, but not the other! How can this happen?

Last year a student was trying to figure out how the magnetic domains inside the refrigerator magnet might be arranged in order to produce the kind of behavior that was observed: that the magnet sticks to the refrigerator on one side, but not on the other. He came up with four possible models to consider. These are shown

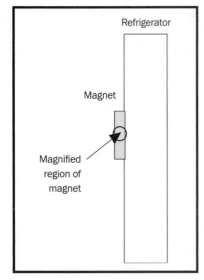

Refrigerator

Magnet

Magnified region of magnet

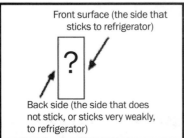

Front surface (the side that sticks to refrigerator)

?

Back side (the side that does not stick, or sticks very weakly, to refrigerator)

on the next two pages, and each represents a side-view diagram of what a tiny magnified cross-sectional region of the refrigerator magnet might look like in terms of the domain model. In each case, a single domain is represented as an arrow: the arrowhead represents the north pole of the entity.

Consider each of these four models. Decide which **one** of these four seems to best account for the observed behavior of the refrigerator magnet; that the front surface sticks to the refrigerator, and the back surface does not (or does so very weakly). Briefly explain why. Also, briefly explain why the other three are less accurate models to explain the behavior of the refrigerator magnet. (You do not need to do an analysis. Just apply the domain model to this new situation. As a hint, you may wish to think about the arrangement of domains in a horseshoe-shaped magnet, and what happens when several horseshoe magnets are placed side-by-side.)

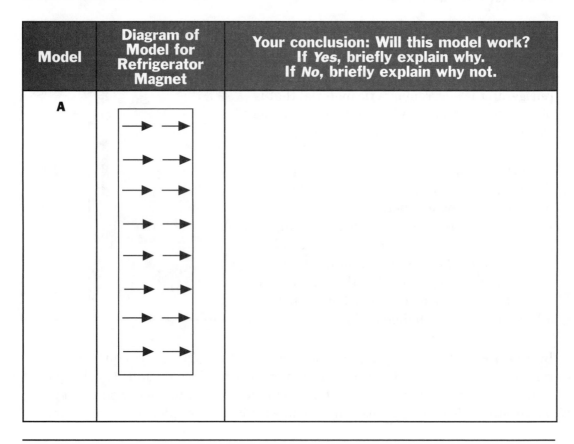

Model	Diagram of Model for Refrigerator Magnet	Your conclusion: Will this model work? If *Yes*, briefly explain why. If *No*, briefly explain why not.
A		

Model	Diagram of Model for Refrigerator Magnet	Your conclusion: Will this model work? If *Yes*, briefly explain why. If *No*, briefly explain why not.
B	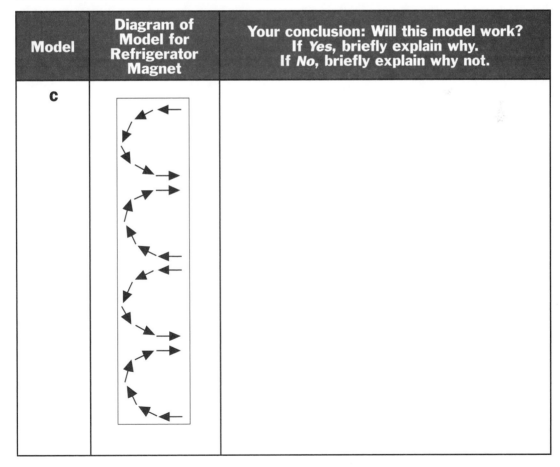	

Model	Diagram of Model for Refrigerator Magnet	Your conclusion: Will this model work? If *Yes*, briefly explain why. If *No*, briefly explain why not.
C		

CHAPTER 4

Model	Diagram of Model for Refrigerator Magnet	Your conclusion: Will this model work? If *Yes*, briefly explain why. If *No*, briefly explain why not.
D		

 Participate in a whole-class discussion to go over the explanations.

PET

Name:_____ Date:_____ Group: _____

Your Ideas about Science Knowledge

In this chapter you created and agreed upon a model of magnetism that is useful for explaining your observations. In the article *Ideas and Myths about the Nature of Science*, several common ideas or "myths" about how scientists create explanations for their observations are discussed. Fill out the table below by providing examples from your own experiences learning physics in *PET* class to **debunk** these myths. *Please refer to the article for elaborations on each myth and the scientists' ideas associated with each myth.* The article is attached at the end of this homework.

Myth about Science Knowledge	Below, describe an experience from *PET* class that can help debunk the idea on the left.
As long as experiments are done correctly, they will be able to prove a theory to be correct.	
Developing new science knowledge involves following careful procedures, rather than being creative.	
A hypothesis is an educated guess.	

CHAPTER 4

Myth about Science Knowledge	Below, describe an experience from *PET* class that can help debunk the idea on the left.
Once accepted by the scientific community, scientific ideas are considered fact.	
Scientists are particularly objective. They are not influenced by their personal experiences or beliefs when they do science.	
If a new idea is supported by scientific evidence, other scientists usually accept it with little resistance.	
Science ideas are usually generated by a scientist working alone, with little collaboration with other people.	

Please bring the article, *Common Ideas and Myths about the Nature of Science* with you to the next class session. Your instructor will also distribute *Scientists' Ideas: The Nature of Science*, which summarizes some of the important values and methods that scientists use in developing new knowledge.

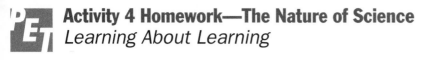

Name:_____ Date:_____ Group: _____

Common Ideas and Myths About the Nature of Science

Most adults have taken a science class at some time in their lives. Many people are aware of the periodic table, Darwin's theory of evolution, plate tectonics, and Newton's laws. Fewer people are aware of how this knowledge came about and the processes that the scientific community actually went through to arrive at ideas that are accepted as scientific knowledge and are reported in science textbooks.

The *Scientists' Ideas* sheets describe many historical episodes that illustrate the process that scientists have gone through to arrive at ideas. The purpose of this paper is to summarize relevant common ideas about the nature of science that adults and children develop throughout their lives and through schooling. All of the common ideas discussed here have been described as "myths of science" in other articles (McComas, 1997). McComas referred to these common ideas as "myths" because they are pervasive within our society and they paint a picture of science that is very different from what scientists actually believe about the nature of science.

While all scientists and science educators may not agree on the exact definition of the "nature of science," there is general consensus regarding the ideas discussed here. The nature of science has been defined as "a way

of knowing, or the values and beliefs inherent to the development of scientific knowledge" (Lederman, 1998).

This paper is organized in sections that first present a common idea or myth that adults and children tend to hold. This is followed by a brief discussion about how scientists' views differ from these common ideas.

Common Idea (Myth) 1: Evidence Accumulated Carefully will Result in Sure Knowledge

Scientific investigations rely heavily on the careful accumulation of evidence. People often believe that this means that science and its methods will provide absolute proof of an idea, theory, or hypothesis. The problem is that when dealing with observations it is impossible to accumulate enough evidence to conclude for sure that a particular idea will *always* hold true. McComas (1997) offers a useful example: On the basis of extensive observations, a scientist may hypothesize that all swans are white. She may search the world and observe only white swans. She may then predict that the next swan she sees will also be white, and find that she was correct. Many other scientists may then be convinced by the observational data and they may all agree that the white swan idea is a good one. However, only one black swan needs to be discovered in order to prove the whole idea wrong. But if this black swan is not seen or reported, people may go on thinking that the white swan idea holds true. Scientists typically believe that their ideas or theories may have great predictive power, that is, they are very useful for predicting future events. However, scientists understand that theories may or may not consist of the full truth of reality. Science ideas are useful to the extent that they can help scientists predict future events and explain observable events.

Science ideas are taken as useful and accepted by the scientific community not only on the basis that available evidence supports the idea, but also on the basis of consensus among scientists that the idea is useful and that no better idea has emerged. In fact, it is quite common for scientists to meet at conferences to present data and argue which of several ideas has more predictive and explanatory power.

Common Idea (Myth) 2: A Hypothesis is an Educated Guess

The term "hypothesis" is often thought of as having the same meaning as the term "prediction," and both are often thought of as an "educated guess." However, in science, a "hypothesis" and a "prediction" are two different things, although they may be closely related.

A prediction (or what might be called an educated guess) is a statement about what you think will be the specific outcome of a situation or an *experiment*. A prediction should be based on (guided by) one or more ideas or a model. If the prediction turns out to be correct, then the idea(s) on which it is based need not be changed.

A hypothesis, on the other hand, is a much more general idea, or model, that is used to *design* situations in which predictions can be made. A hypothesis is used for choosing what data to pay attention to, what additional data to seek, and to guide the interpretation of data (AAAS, 1993). For example, children are often required to state their hypotheses in science fair projects. This is because it can help them design an experiment to test predictions. Consider a child who has seen his dad use bug spray to get rid of bugs. The child has also noticed that flies in the house seem to disappear whenever his dad cleans the bathroom and sprays air freshener. The child hypothesizes that there is something in the air freshener that acts like bug spray. He then designs an experiment to test this hypothesis. He gets a shoe box, puts a cardboard divider in the middle of the box and cuts a hole in the divider. He captures several flies, puts them in one side of the box, and closes the lid. He makes the *prediction* that if he sprays air freshener in the side of the box with the flies, the flies will go through the small hole in the divider to the other side of the box to get away from the chemical. If the child found that his prediction was correct, he would have collected some evidence to support his hypothesis. However, he found that his prediction was incorrect. The flies just flew around in the box as they did before he sprayed the air freshener.

Sticking to his hypothesis, he decided that there was something wrong with his experiment, so he performed the same experiment, this time with the bug spray. He found that indeed, the flies did go through the little hole to the other side of the box. He concluded that because his prediction about the air freshener was wrong, there must be a problem with his initial hypothesis. So, he generated a new hypothesis. This time he hypothesized that it is another cleaning agent that his dad uses when cleaning the bathroom that acts like bug spray. Things to think about: what experiment(s) could he design to test this hypothesis, and what predictions would it lead to? What other hypotheses might he have generated?

A prediction can be shown to be correct or incorrect. A hypothesis, like a model, cannot be proven to be true, although substantial evidence can be collected to support it. A hypothesis can, however, be proven incorrect if it leads to incorrect predictions. If scientists find that a hypothesis continues to lead to accurate predictions, and is consistent with accepted theories, they might accept the hypothesis as a useful model for explaining some aspect of the world. While a hypothesis can be used to make predictions, it is not the prediction itself. A scientific prediction is based on a hypothesis or model.

Common Idea (Myth) 3: Science is Procedural More Than Creative

Many people believe that as long as scientists use sound procedures, the evidence speaks for itself and would lead all people to the same conclusion or explanation. Assuming that procedures and methods are considered to be sound, scientists often do agree on what the evidence *is*. However, there is more controversy over what the evidence *means*. For example, when a magnet is cut in half, experimental evidence shows that each piece of the magnet now has two poles that behave differently. There is little disagreement on this repeatable experimental result. What this result means is subject to the informed creativity of the person interpreting the evidence. In the history of science there have been many attempts to explain what experiments like this might mean and several clever and creative ideas have emerged. Explanations have ranged from the 17th century idea that an invisible substance flows through magnets in a specific direction, to the currently held idea that tiny magnets exist within the magnet and these tiny magnets align themselves with the surrounding magnetic field (the domain model of magnetism). Both of these ideas were supported by available evidence but they are only two of many possible explanations of how magnets might work. Scientists have come to a consensus on the domain model of magnetism because it has predictive power, it explains all the evidence that is available at this time, and it is consistent with other accepted theories of matter.

CHAPTER 4

Procedures are important in science but human creativity and imagination also play a significant role in explaining the meaning of the evidence that results from careful procedures. The common idea that science is procedural more than creative gives rise to the common idea that scientists' ideas are absolute.

Common Idea (Myth) 4: Scientists' Ideas are Absolute

People of all ages often view science knowledge as "fact" or as absolute truth. When we understand that many of the science ideas that end up in textbooks are creative models that were consistent with all of the evidence available at the time, we can begin to see the tentative nature of these ideas. As new instruments are developed and more precise measurements are made possible, scientists gain access to evidence that was not previously available. In addition, development of theory in other areas often leads to questions that were not previously asked. When scientists ask new questions, they develop experiments that have not been done before. This also leads to new evidence. As more evidence becomes available, ideas that were once accepted by the scientific community become subject to change. This is clear in the history of science.

In the 4th century to the 17th century, the science idea that an object can maintain a constant speed only if a constant force is applied was accepted by most people. The associated idea that objects slow down and stop because of their *natural motion* was also believed to be true. It was not until the 17th century that people began to ask new questions, perform new experiments, and collect new evidence about the motion of objects. As a result of the new evidence, science ideas began to change to what we now know as Newton's laws of motion. Newton's laws of motion were challenged in the 20th century as a result of advances in theory, instrumentation, and creative thought.

Common Idea (Myth) 5: Scientists are Particularly Objective

The common idea that scientists are particularly objective is related to Common Idea 1, that evidence accumulated carefully will result in sure knowledge. It was stated earlier that, often, most scientists agree on what the evidence *is*. However, it must be understood that this agreement takes place within a culture and community that is accustomed to a particular way of thinking and is guided by particular theories that exist at a given time.

For example, from the 16th until the late 19th century, scientists utilized the concept of "ether," an invisible substance that transmitted just about everything from magnetic influence to light. Since scientists perceived the world through this lens, the observations they made led them to "see" evidence that was closely associated with this theory of an invisible substance. When scientists make observations, certain features are deemed unimportant or are not seen at all, depending on the scientists theoretical perspective. In addition, the theoretical perspective that is used by a scientific community leads scientists to ask only a limited set of questions closely associated with the theory. This, in effect, limits the total set of answers and explanations that can be made.

For example, in a famous experiment in the late 19th century, scientists Albert Michelson and Edward Morley asked a question about how the motion of the Earth through the invisible substance called ether affected the speed of light. This question was driven by the assumption and belief that there existed such a thing as ether. Michelson and Morley made careful observations that led to the conclusion that the speed of light was always the same! It did not depend on the invisible substance! This finding opened up the possibility of a whole new set of questions, experiments, and observations that no longer involved the concept of ether.

This experiment became famous partly because it challenged the prior knowledge that most scientists were using to guide their observations, experiments, and explanations. Scientists, like all people, approach a situation with a rich set of prior knowledge and they use this prior knowledge to design experiments and interpret results. The experiments they design, and therefore the observations they make, are tied to their way of viewing the world. It is impossible to remove ourselves entirely from the theories and ideas that implicitly guide our thinking. These theories and ideas are often part of a larger culture that is accustomed to a particular way of viewing the world. Although we may try

very hard to be objective, it is important to recognize that observations are situated in a larger social context.

Common Idea (Myth) 6: Acceptance of Science Knowledge is Straightforward

This common idea is associated with the belief that the scientific community immediately adopts a new way of thinking when new evidence contradicts their old way of thinking. The acceptance of evidence that contradicts the contemporary way of thinking is usually not quite so straightforward and is often met with a large amount of resistance. For example, when Michelson and Morley performed their famous experiment discussed above, most scientists (even they themselves) did not believe it. Scientists repeated the experiments over and over and they examined the experimental apparatus for problems to convince themselves that there was something wrong with the experiment. This way they could preserve their current scientific way of thinking in terms of ether.

It took time for the scientific community to abandon the ether model and to begin to think of new ways to explain magnetism, light, and action at a distance. Some historians of science argue that many scientists never abandon their old way of thinking because they are so attached to it, and because their careers are based on it. Science historian and philosopher, Thomas Kuhn (1962) argues that in some cases, scientists who have refused to adopt new ways of thinking simply have to die off and make way for new scientists with new ideas. The idea of *fields* which is now used to explain things like action at a distance, magnetism, electricity and other phenomena did not gain acceptance until many years after the Michelson-Morley experiment. It took time, accumulated evidence, and much theoretical, mathematical, and conceptual argumentation before the idea was accepted.

The fact that people's ideas are resistant to change can also be seen in the science classroom. Students have ideas about how the world works when they come into the science classroom. Even in the face of experimental evidence, they often have difficulty accepting evidence that contradicts their current beliefs. It usually takes some time, accumulated evidence, and argumentation in order for new ideas to gain acceptance, and old ideas to become modified by students.

Common Idea (Myth) 7: Science is a Solitary Pursuit

When people think about how science knowledge is developed, they often picture a scientist in a white lab coat, isolated from society, working for hours and hours alone in a lab. We often think about a very intelligent person with messy hair who suddenly "discovers" something new all by himself. It should be evident from the discussion in this paper that this is not always the case. While scientists do work for hours and hours in labs and in the natural environment, science ideas are not

simply discovered and immediately accepted by the scientific community. Instead, consensus plays a very large role in the adoption and acceptance of what we know as scientists' ideas. An idea must not only be consistent with evidence but also the entire scientific community must be convinced that the idea is a useful idea. The scientific community then uses these ideas to guide their research, to ask new questions, and to design experiments.

The development of a scientific idea is often done through collaboration. It usually involves the contributions of many different scientists as well as people from industry, technology, and other fields. Scientists work together and share their ideas through journals, conferences and personal communication. They draw on the ideas of others to collaboratively construct knowledge. As we have seen throughout this paper, scientists' ideas are subject to change and are not always accepted in a straightforward way. Many people are involved in what is studied, how it is studied, and the answers we end up with. Science does not happen in isolation and is influenced by the larger social and political context of society.

Conclusions

Scientists are learners just as students in a physics classroom are learners. They have prior knowledge about how the world works and they use that knowledge as they ask questions, construct investigations, and interpret their results. Much of scientists prior knowledge is based on theories and perspectives that exist within the scientific culture and community. This prior knowledge, like the prior knowledge of students in the classroom, may come into conflict with evidence and often needs to be changed. This process of learning takes time. It takes time for the learner or the scientist to make sense of his or her observations and it takes time to achieve consensus within the scientific community.

The Nature of Science is very similar to the nature of learning. Scientists are in the business of learning so it should not be surprising that the processes they go through to arrive at an acceptable idea are similar to the processes that students can go through in constructing new understandings of how the world works.

References

American Association for the Advancement of Science AAAS (1993) *Benchmarks for Scientific Literacy.* Oxford: Oxford University Press.

Kuhn, T. S. (1962/1996). *The Structure of Scientific Revolutions.* (1996). Chicago: University of Chicago Press.

Lederman, N.G. (1998). *The State of Science Education: Subject Matter Without Context, The Electronic Journal of Science Education,* 3(2).

McComas, W. F. (1997). *15 Myths of Science: Lessons of Misconceptions and Misunderstandings from a Science Educator. Skeptic* 5(2), 88-95.

CHAPTER 4

Purpose

In a previous activity you made some decisions about which *model of magnetism* was the most useful for accounting for all available evidence. In this activity, you will examine how models have developed in the history of science and how models differ from things that we can actually observe with our senses.

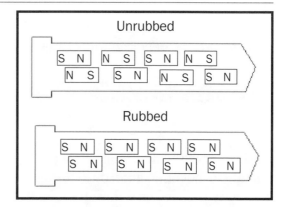

> **What is a "model" in science? Do models change over time? If so, why?**

Initial Ideas

What role do you think observations play in the development of models? Provide an example.

Collecting and Interpreting Evidence

The next few pages of this activity contain a brief historical account of how the domain model of magnetism was ultimately developed within the scientific community. Read through the article and then answer the Summarizing Questions at the end of this activity.

READING: The Development of a Model of Magnetism

"...the meaning of the experiments does not become apparent until theory makes it so."

Albert Einstein and
Leopold Infeld (1966)

This reading is a brief summary of the history of the development of the domain model of magnetism. This summary is based on Johnson's (1999) historical analysis.

The Story

William Gilbert's Harmony and Discord Model

By the end of the 17th century, William Gilbert had identified two different poles of a magnet and observed that one end of a magnet was attracted to one end of another magnet and repelled from the other end. He described attraction in terms of "harmony" and repulsion in terms of "discord." According to this model, when two magnets were in harmony, they attracted to one another and when they were in discord, they repelled one another. While Gilbert's *harmony* and *discord* model could explain why magnets attracted and repelled other magnets, the *harmony* and *discord* model could not really account for two different poles and it could not explain why magnets attracted iron. In addition to attraction and repulsion, Gilbert also observed that when he cut a magnet in half, the two pieces actually acted like two individual magnets. His *harmony* and *discord* model could not explain this either.

René Descartes' Particles and Pores Model

In 1644 René Descartes published an influential work that outlined his own model for magnetism. Descartes, following the work of other scientists who were trying to explain electricity, described magnetism in terms of an invisible substance or fluid that exists everywhere and consists of very small spiral particles that are always in motion. According to his model, a magnet was a special type of matter because it had several pores or channels through which the spiral particles in the substance passed. Descartes' model could explain why the two ends of a magnet acted differently. He proposed that inside the walls of the pores or channels in a magnet there were many hairs or teeth that resisted the flow of the substance, therefore the substance could flow only in the preferred direction through the magnet. This idea helped to explain the existence of two poles of a magnet, one into which the substance flowed and the other out of which the substance emerged. Since the substance could only move in one direction through the magnet, attraction was easily explained by the idea that if magnets were aligned correctly (north to south pole) the substance would flow out of one and into the other magnet, creating a continuous flow-attraction. When the magnets were not aligned correctly (e.g., north pole to north pole), the fluid flowed in opposite directions and emerged from the two interacting ends of both magnets, therefore the magnets repelled.

In addition to accounting for the two different poles of a magnet, Descartes' model could explain why a magnet was attracted to iron. In Descartes' model, the holes or pores in the *iron* were not aligned like they were in the magnet, so there was no preferred direction for the substance to flow through in iron. The invisible substance could still flow through the pores but not as easily as it does through magnets. According to Descartes' model, when a magnet is brought into the presence of iron, the spiral particles of substance pushed the holes in the iron into alignment, so the iron could behave like a magnet during an interaction with a magnet.

Franz Aepinus' Magnetic Fluid Model

In 1756, Franz Aepinus published a book explaining his own model for magnetism. According to Aepinus' model, there exists a "magnetic fluid" which moves around through the air and gets stuck in iron. The magnetic fluid was similar to the "electric fluid" which was earlier introduced by Benjamin Franklin and was a popular idea at the time for explaining observations with electricity. According to Aepinus' *magnetic fluid* model, all iron contains a magnetic fluid. A magnet was simply a piece of iron in which the magnetic fluid was stuck at one end. This left the piece of iron with an excess of fluid on one end and a deficit of fluid on the other end. This model could explain the two-ended nature of the magnet (north and south poles—one end has fluid and the other does not), and could explain why a magnet was attracted to iron (iron contained a very small amount of

magnetic fluid which would shift during an interaction with a magnet). The magnetic fluid model could also explain the observation that when a magnet is cut in half, the two halves still act like individual magnets; according to Aepinus, when the magnet is cut in half, some of the magnetic fluid "evaporates" from one end of each half, leaving one end of each half with an excess of fluid and the other end of each half of the magnet with a deficit of fluid. Aepinus introduced another addition to magnetic theory. He introduced a set of mathematical calculations that could support his model. The practice of supporting models with mathematical calculations was quickly becoming commonplace in science. One of the problems with Aepinus' model is that it was not quite clear how the fluid moved around within a half of a broken magnet, and exactly how the evaporation process took place.

Charles Coulomb's Magnetic Entities Model

In the late 18th century, Charles Coulomb introduced the idea of "magnetic entities" which pre-exist within the magnet. According to this model, each *entity* contained magnetic fluid and entities could not be broken apart. The fluid could move around within each entity but could not move between entities (for example, an entity would act like a tiny magnet if the fluid was stuck at one end, as is the case in Aepinus' model). Coulomb took special care to provide evidence that could support his model, to provide mathematical support for his model, and to make his model consistent with other models of action-at-a-distance that were accepted by the scientific community at the time (such as Newton's model for gravity). Coulomb's model eventually led to the modern domain model of magnetism.

References

Johnson, A. (1999). Students' Development of Models of Magnetic Materials, Patterns of Group Activity, and Social Norms in a Physics Classroom, Unpublished dissertation, University of California, San Diego and San Diego State University.

Meyer, H. (1971). *A History of Electricity and Magnetism*. Cambridge, MA: MIT Press.

Einstein, A. & Infeld, L. (1966). *The Evolution of Physics*. New York: Simon & Schuster, Inc.

Summarizing Questions

S1: How would you know if a model is a good model? What criteria would you use to decide between several models of the same observations?

S2: In the table below, the models that were discussed in the article are listed in rows and the observations that people made with magnets are listed in columns. For each observation, write an "**X**" for each of the models that explains that observation.

Observation / Model	Attraction and Repulsion	North and South Poles	Attraction to Iron	Cutting the Magnet Yields Two Magnets
Gilbert's Harmony and Discord Model				
Descartes' Particles and Pores Model				
Aepinus' Magnetic Fluid Model				
Coulomb's Magnetic Entities Model				

S3: Why do you think that people in history felt the need to generate new models of magnetism even though other models such as the "harmony and discord" model and the "particles and pores" model already existed to explain observations with magnets?

CHAPTER 4

S4: What do you think are some reasons that Coulomb's model was the one that ended up being accepted (in a slightly modified form) by the scientific community?

S5: In what ways do you think models are different from observations?

Activity 5 Homework–Children's Ideas about Magnetism
Learning about Learning

Name:_____ Date:_____ Group:_____

Purpose

Throughout Chapter 4 you developed and modified your model for magnetism. In this activity you will have the opportunity to listen to 2nd and 3rd grade students describe their models of magnetism. The purpose of this activity is for you to determine which parts of students' ideas may be useful and how ideas at a given point in time reflect learning (even though the ideas students express may not look like scientists' ideas).

🔑 **Why do elementary students' models about magnetism make sense?**

Initial Ideas

Movies for this activity can be found on your *PET DVD* in the Student Resources folder for Chapter 4. The folder contains video clips of 2nd and 3rd grade students investigating properties of magnets.

> **Use headphones when viewing videos and make certain that the volume on your computer is at its maximum setting.**

Open *C4Act5_HW_Pred_Obs* and watch the movie. In this movie, 2nd and 3rd grade students predict whether a variety of different materials will be attracted to a magnet. They then make observations to compare with their predictions.

At the end of the activity shown in the movie *C4Act5_HW_Pred_Obs*, the class arrives at the following class consensus ideas:

- Some metals are attracted to magnets.
- A magnet has two different ends.
- Different (north vs. south) ends of two magnets pull each other.
- Similar ends of two magnets push each other.
- Some magnets are stronger than others.

 Imagine that just after the activity, students were asked to draw pictures to show what they think is happening inside a magnet that makes the magnet special. Do you think these students would generate models of magnetism similar to the ones our *PET* class came up with? If so, why? If not, how do you think they would be different?

Collecting and Interpreting Evidence

Video Clip 2: Models of Magnetism

Near the end of the magnetism unit, the teacher asked students to draw pictures to show what they think is happening inside a magnet that makes the magnet special.

 Open *C4Act5_HW_Mag_models.mpg* and watch the movie.

Also open the document *Models_Pix.pdf* or *Models_Pix.doc* and take a close look at the pictures that students are referring to in the movie.

 1. All of the students' models shown in the pictures attempted in some way to connect explanations with observations (or to their class consensus ideas). One might categorize the elementary students' models in the following way:

- **Explanatory/Predictive:** Models that not only provide potentially realistic explanations for observations but could also be used to predict outcomes of future experiments. These models could be tested by a clever experiment.

- **Analogical/Imaginative:** Models that use imaginative and analogical schemes to illustrate how the child is making sense of his or her observations.

(a) Try to find at least one example of each of these types of models from the pictures of students' models. Use evidence from the transcript and from the pictures to support your claims.

CHAPTER 4

(b) Discuss the advantages and/or limitations of each category for students' further learning about magnetism and the nature of science. Use examples from the transcript and pictures.

Summarizing Questions

The following questions will be discussed in class. Take a moment to prepare your own reflections on these questions to share with your group.

S1: Pick one of your favorite models from the set of elementary students' pictures. Electronically cut and paste a copy of the model into your answer below. Describe your interpretation of the model (what is this student thinking)? Why is this model your favorite?

(a) How does this model attempt to incorporate observational evidence? Is it *consistent* with evidence?

(b) What is incomplete or problematic about this model?

(c) Is this model explanatory/predictive or analogical/imaginary? Justify your decision that the model you discussed is explanatory/predictive or analogical/imaginative.

CHAPTER 4

S2: Which of the children's models do you think is the **best** model?

S3: What are your criteria for "best" model? Are these the same criteria you apply to your own models in your *PET* class? Why or why not?

 Participate in a whole-class discussion to share your answers to these questions and challenge or support the answers of others.

C4Act5_HW_Pred_Obs.mpg

00:05:20	Katie	This one next. This one will attract.
09:24	Kevin	Yeah, that will attract.
00:13:02	Adrianna	It's over here.
00:14:05	Katie	Skyler.
00:19:06	Katie	Steel wool...I don't think it will attract.
00:24:29	Kevin	Steel wool...It's steel! It's steel!
00:31:05	Adrianna	(now looking at a broken cassette tape) I don't think because it, because it doesn't have metal outside. That's why.
00:36:23	Teacher	How about you Kevin, Kevin what do you think it will ...?
00:40:01	Adrianna	Because I think that only the metal will.
00:43:05	Kevin	I think, I think it will because it's metal inside.
00:53:27	Kevin	We thought the (glass) marble would stick but it didn't.
00:58:25	Teacher	Why did you think it would stick?
00:59:28	Kevin	Because, because (he describes the magnetic marbles the students played with on the first day of class).
01:03:03	Kevin	Who, who said yes on this, this one?
01:05:22	Skyler	I did.
01:07:03	Kevin	It doesn't.
01:07:22	Teacher	It doesn't? Okay write it down.
01:10:02	Adrianna	And I, and with the pencil, I noticed that this is magnet (pointing to the metal end of a pencil) but, wait, let me, the metal, it will stick but when you do it with the eraser it kind of will but it does with the metal. And if you do it with the wood, I think it won't stick.
01:34:06	Kevin	It doesn't work on the wood.
01:35:17	Teacher	Did you write that down?
01:40:27	Teacher	Okay, now on the back you guys need to think of a rule for what attracts and what doesn't. What kinds of things always attract to magnets?
01:49:08	Skyler	Metal things.
01:50:08	Teacher	All metal things, though?
01:51:28	Katie	No.
01:52:05	Kevin	Yeah, yeah.
01:52:28	Adrianna	I think metal things that, I think.
01:55:26	Kevin	No, no, not all metal things, this is metal and it doesn't.
01:58:29	Teacher	Okay, so what kind of metal?
02:00:28	Adrianna	I think the metal things that, these metal things that are gold, the pencils that's metal...
02:08:25	Teacher	So what can we say for a rule? What do you think Katie?
02:15:09	Katie	I'm thinking. Some metal things attract to magnets.

02:30:22	Researcher	What are you writing down there?
02:32:13	Felix	Our...
02:33:28	Jacqueline	That almost all metal sticks to magnets.
02:39:18	Researcher	Ooh. But not all of them?
02:40:24	Jacqueline	No.
02:42:03	Researcher	Does anything that's not metal stick to magnets?
02:45:17	Felix	Um, no. Only the things that have metal in them stick to magnets.
02:54:16	Jacqueline	This one didn't, this one didn't.
02:56:16	Researcher	Which one, can you show us which one you're pointing to? That one did not.
03:09:16	Harley	Almost every metal sticks–
03:11:29	Felix	Sticks to magnets.
03:13:22	Researcher	Okay, does it have to be a metal to stick?
03:16:20	Felix	No.
03:16:26	Researcher	It doesn't have to be a metal? What else can it be if it wants to stick?
03:21:30	Felix	It could be.
03:24:14	Harley	Some type of plastic (shows the researcher that tape within the cassette was attracted).
03:31:27	Researcher	Oh, look at that. What is that?
03:39:09	Harley	(?) little pieces of metal in it.
03:41:14	Researcher	You think it has little pieces of metal?
03:42:17	Harley	Yeah cause, I think it has little pieces of metal in this to make the sound.
03:50:07	Researcher	Oh, in order to make the sound. I see.
03:52:12	Jacqueline	And the inside of a compass like attracts to a magnet.
03:56:20	Researcher	What do you think the inside of the compass is made out of?
04:00:29	Felix/Harley	Metal.
04:02:06	Researcher	Why?
04:04:03	Felix	Because it sticks to the magnets.
04:08:19	Harley	It sticks and it's just cer– it's just one kind of the metal that the magnets attract to.
04:18:14	Teacher	Boys and girls we are almost out of time but we need to find out, we need to find out what you discovered. We need to find out what you observed. Did anybody observe something that was different from what you predicted?
04:35:05	Kevin	Yes.
04:35:28	Teacher	Kevin what did you observe that was different from what you predicted?
04:39:13	Kevin	Um, we thought it, um the steel wool wouldn't and it did.

04:45:12	Teacher	You thought it would not stick and it did stick. Felix, did you have a surprise?
04:49:24	Felix	Um that the, that the compass and the middle, and the middle part it was sticking to the magnet.
05:11:06	Teacher	Oh and you predicted that the compass would not stick.
05:13:16	Felix	Yeah.
05:14:03	Teacher	But the middle part did stick and that was a surprise. Anybody else, any other group have a surprise?
05:21:13	Student	A lot of surprises.
05:23:22	Teacher	You had a lot of surprises, Georgina did your group have a surprise?
05:25:14	Georgina	We thought that the penny and the dime would stick but it won't.
05:30:12	Teacher	But it didn't. And then one group hasn't shared yet, which group, Harley--
05:36:02	Harley	I was with this group but I got a good one!
05:37:29	Teacher	Charlie's group you guys share. What was a surprise you found?
05:44:05	Kaitlen	We thought the bread tie wouldn't work but it did.
05:48:25	Teacher	Now listen to see if your rule is alike or different than the group that's sharing.
05:56:05	Jacqueline	Almost all metal sticks to magnets.
06:00:20	Teacher	Say it one more time Jacqueline.
06:02:29	Jacqueline	Almost all metal sticks to magnets.
06:06:02	Charlie	That's kind of like ours.
06:07:14	Teacher	Almost all metal–
06:08:22	Kevin	That's kind of like ours too.
06:11:10	Teacher	Almost all metal sticks to magnets.
06:13:11	Charlie	That's kind of like ours.
06:14:17	Teacher	Let's listen to all of them. Okay, Lupe you want to go?
06:21:21	Katie	Some metal things stick to magnets.
06:25:25	Teacher	Some metal things, hmm that sounded like
06:29:22	Harley	The first group
06:31:08	Felix	My, my idea.
06:32:12	Student	Almost all.
06:33:02	Teacher	Oh, almost all and some.
06:36:24	Charlie	Certain kinds of metal attracts a magnet. I think it should say "to magnets."
06:45:19	Teacher	Anybody want to try to put all the rules together into one rule that we could all believe is true? Give it a shot Harley.

CHAPTER 4

| Teacher | Anybody want to try to put all the rules together into one rule that we could all believe is true? Give it a shot Harley. | |

C4Act5_HW_Mag_Models.mpg

00:05:28	Teacher	Imagine that you have a really big magnet; we want you to draw a picture and show what you imagine or think or predict is happening inside the magnet that makes a magnet special.
00:14:30	Interviewer	You think there's what?
00:15:13	Georgina	Magnets, inside the magnet because it's like, like almost like electricity.
00:31:22	Interviewer	Uh huh. And so is this one big magnet or is it a bunch of magnets?
00:37:02	Georgina	A magnet.
00:38:20	Interviewer	And what are all these little things?
00:40:27	Georgina	I think that this is what it would be inside of a magnet.
00:45:08	Interviewer	Oh okay, so you're gonna point to these things and tell us what they are?
00:48:03	Georgina	Yeah.
00:48:26	Interviewer	Alright!
00:49:26	Interviewer	And how does your magnet work?
00:52:02	Charlie	I think that it's like a person that like loves chocolate and they, they want to grab the chocolate so much and like these likes to grab the, the right kind of metal that's why it like sticks to it. Cause it like, it's like a person that loves chocolate that like really wants to grab it bad.
01:13:11	Interviewer	So does that explain when the red and the red push from each other?
01:18:09	Charlie	Uh...Oh I know how to say that.
01:22:12	Interviewer	Um hum, so think about that one for–
01:24:05	Charlie	I know that one too.
01:25:03	Interviewer	What do you think?
01:26:15	Charlie	That it's like, I hate that kind of chocolate and I won't have it and they push away.
01:33:30	Nestor	The little ball that's inside of the orb, and the electricity comes out from the little ball inside the orb and causes it to stick to any kind of metal.

01:52:07	Adrianna	I think that inside the magnet there's some, there's metal.
01:58:22	Interviewer	Is it just regular metal?
02:01:05	Adrianna	There's like black metal.
02:03:07	Interviewer	Is it the same as the metal that's inside a nail?
02:07:16	Adrianna	Umm, no.
02:13:10	Interviewer	Why not?
02:15:01	Adrianna	Because the, the, cause the nails, the metal it's not the one that could stick to a magnet.
02:30:28	Interviewer	It's not the right kind?
02:32:05	Adrianna	Yeah.
02:32:19	Interviewer	Ah, it's like the kind in a nickel or a penny?
02:36:17	Adrianna	Yeah.
02:36:21	Interviewer	Oh, and then the magnet, what kind is it?
02:41:26	Adrianna	I think there is some black metal. The right kind.
02:52:10	Elizabeth	I think that both sides are different because one side pulls and another pushes. I think they're different chemicals that they put in each side.
03:03:26	Interviewer	Oh, and do you have a picture that shows that?
03:06:14	Elizabeth	Yeah.
03:06:20	Interviewer	Can I, will you show me on the picture? Okay so, where's the magnet?
03:09:26	Elizabeth	There (pointing to her picture).
03:13:28	Interviewer	Okay and where's the different sides?
03:18:10	Elizabeth	Well this is a side and this is another side.
03:21:03	Interviewer	Oh okay, so this is all one magnet?
03:25:07	Elizabeth	Ah, mmm, no, it's because these are different chemicals and first you put one side a different chemical and another a different one.
03:39:17	Interviewer	Ah, and so that's why they do different things?
03:42:09	Elizabeth	Um hum.
03:43:14	Jacqueline	The force is from where the magnet's getting stronger.
03:48:29	Teacher	Is the force (Jacqueline had the word "Forz" written on the page) coming from here or is it coming from...
03:51:07	Jaqueline	Where? I don't understand.
03:53:24	Teacher	The force.
03:55:24	Jacqueline	From here (pointing to an area between magnets drawn on the page).
03:57:09	Teacher	Between the magnets? Okay.
03:59:12	Jacqueline	But we can't, we can't actually see it.
04:02:08	Teacher	Okay, it's invisible really?
04:04:15	Jacqueline	But we could feel it.

CHAPTER 4

04:06:18	Teacher	How could you feel it?
04:08:03	Jacqueline	By, if you have like two magnets and they don't stick together you can feel how it's pushing each other.
04:15:25	Teacher	What does it feel like?
04:17:24	Jacqueline	Like if you have, ah, if you are trying to pull it hard and it doesn't stick together.
04:25:00	Teacher	Okay.
04:27:01	Teacher	How do you think you can make a magnet stronger?
04:29:11	Jacqueline	By putting a lot of magnets together?
04:38:19	Interviewer	Can you explain your, your, your idea?
04:41:13	Skyler	Um the (inaudible) and its metal.
04:49:22	Interviewer	Which one?
04:50:20	Skyler	This.
04:51:22	Interviewer	Is that the magnet?
04:52:21	Skyler	Uh huh.
04:53:17	Interviewer	Alright, so here it is. And which is really strong?
05:00:02	Skyler	That one.
05:01:10	Interviewer	Yeah. So what is these thingies?
05:04:00	Skyler	The electricity.
05:05:13	Interviewer	Oh, so let me read it, or do you want to read it?
05:09:28	Skyler	No you can read it.
05:10:28	Interviewer	Why don't you read it.
05:11:30	Skyler	'Kay. The little magnets sticks together and it makes it strong and it, the little magnet picks up the chair.
05:22:02	Interviewer	Uh huh. And what is inside this? if you had special glasses what would you see?
05:28:25	Skyler	Uh, metal?
05:30:22	Interviewer	Metal inside. Is that what that is?
05:33:14	Skyler	Yeah.
05:34:20	Interviewer	So how does your magnet work?
05:36:23	Silvester	He has thunder out of his hand–that's where it sticks, and this is where they fight and if they bump, that's where it doesn't stick because they bump and it makes it shake and it make it fall.
05:50:22	Interviewer	Okay, so this is where it sticks to what?
05:53:30	Silvester	To um, metal.
05:55:26	Interviewer	And this side doesn't stick to metal?
05:57:25	Silvester	No, because they fight and the– they bump and then they– um, it shakes and then they fall.
06:06:02	Interviewer	And if they fall, what does that mean?
06:08:05	Silvester	The metal falls.
06:10:01	Interviewer	Oh, the metal falls off, I see. And here the lightning bolt keeps it on?

06:15:10	Silvester	Um hum.
06:17:03	Silvester	This one's the bad side and this one's the good side.
06:19:05	Interviewer	Ah, why does it have two sides?
06:21:08	Silvester	It's like this one, because this one makes the um erases (he has the metal and eraser part of a pencil shown attracting to one side and repelling from the other side. Attraction and repulsion are shown by arrows towards and away from the magnet) and this one makes it go and it's locked and the bug helps it.
06:39:05	Interviewer	Oh, this one has a bug too?
06:40:09	Silvester	But it, it, (?) because some, a lot of people hold it from this side and he's helping it push it away because this one's not locked and every–if it comes this way it might bump it too hard and it might open it so he's trying to hold it and they bump it and it shakes and that falls off.
07:05:28	Interviewer	And then this side?
07:08:05	Silvester	It, it, helps. And this is the night time and this is the, this is the morning but I didn't get to do it and this is the emergency door and if something happens they have to get out but they have to do– they have to go out and no one has to see them because they're magic and they don't want anybody to see and they have to run to another magnet.
07:38:07	Interviewer	Oh, which, who's they?
07:39:16	Silvester	Those peoples.
07:41:14	Interviewer	Oh and what do the people do?
07:43:19	Silvester	They just help the magnet?
07:45:11	Interviewer	What do they help?
07:46:21	Silvester	They don't, because they have something secret in this and this one's fine but they just–this one just, this side is the good side and it's happy they play, and this one is bad because cause they have to be bad so, so if, if it connects and they play this would come down and it would see the secret stuff and he's trying to help because–and they fight because if this comes and put it down, he he bumps and this shakes and he falls off.
08:23:20	Interviewer	So do you think this model is at all like this one? Or are they both very different from each other?
08:29:24	Silvester	These parts and this part is the same but they don't have to climb up.
08:35:12	Interviewer	Oh! I see, very cool, very good.
08:38:15	Silvester	And this one's the circle magnet and this one's the one–
08:42:04	Interviewer	I see this one's the horseshoe magnet and is one of these.
08:51:17	Kevin	It's like um, ah, ah, well bright and yellow and it makes the magnet stick.
09:03:12	Interviewer	Oh, that, and so what are these?

CHAPTER 4

09:06:04	Kevin	That's the electricity inside.
09:08:09	Interviewer	Ah! Now is it the same on both sides?
09:13:06	Kevin	Ah, some, sometimes it could be bigger? And sometimes it could be smaller.
09:20:04	Interviewer	Alright, thank you.
09:22:28	Katie	I think there's a person in the magnet to tell the magnet what to do because there might be a TV in the magnet and a little radio and a wire.
09:41:20	Lupe	What does the TV do really?
09:44:03	Katie	It tells the, it says something and then it goes through the wire to the speaker and it says– the speaker tells the magnet what to do.
09:57:18	Lupe	Oh.
10:01:23	Harley	So if there's metal right there the TV will show it and then it will come through her and it will say, "there's metal up here, come stick to me."
10:10:20	Katie	No. It will say "Push" and if the magnet hears that it will push and if it hears "do not push" the magnet won't push.
10:20:04	Harley	Oh. It will stick?
10:21:16	Katie	Felix?
10:23:13	Felix	Can I go next.
10:27:10	Lupe	How come you can't hear the magnet talk?
10:31:20	Katie	Maybe because it only lets magnets hear and um maybe it talks in a whisper voice even though the volume's up high.
10:53:19	Felix	I think there are metal inside a refrigerator and metal inside a magnet and that's how they stick.
11:12:10	Teacher	Tell them your really interesting question you thought of too Felix. Before you raise your hand listen to this question he has about magnets.
11:18:18	Felix	Why do magnets stick only to some metal and not all metal?
11:35:25	Kaitlen	I think that a magnet will be able to stick to a refrigerator. The refrigerator has the magnet have some special thing inside of it. Know how it on the refrigerator it has some white stuff over it? Well I think inside that white stuff over the refrigerator there is a magnet inside of it. You know what I mean? So if you put a magnet on a refrigerator it will stick. I think that you have to put different things together to make a magnet. I think you have to fire it so it will stick. If we could look inside a magnet, I think that would be fun. How are magnets made because I think it would be interesting to know.
12:30:02	Harley	Um, um, I don't think, well you might think this but, I think that there might not be a magnet inside the fridge that it's just metal because the magnets already here and if there's a magnet right there it might push, I mean what if it accidentally push the other way and they push? No for real. I mean, I'm not joking.
12:57:17	Teacher	Have you thought about that Kaitlen?

| 12:58:29 | Kaitlen | Hum um... |

CHAPTER 4

Name:_____ Date:_____ Group:_____

Georgina's Model

Charlie's Model

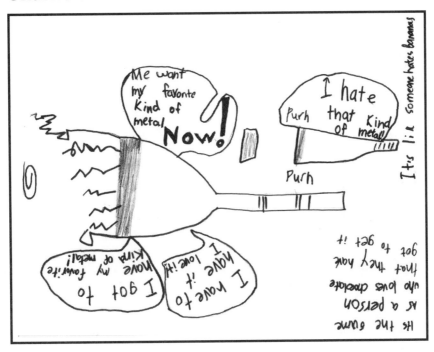

Nestor's Model

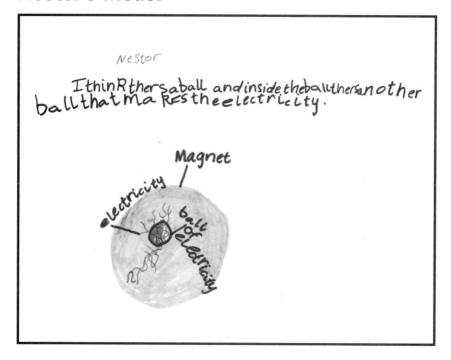

Adrianna's Model

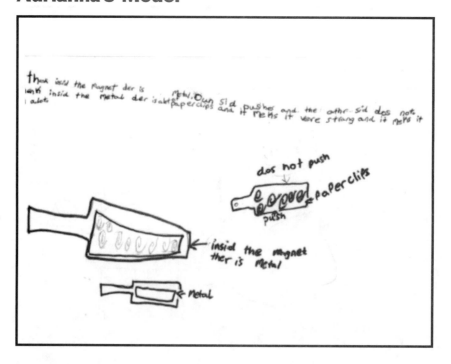

Elizabeth's Model

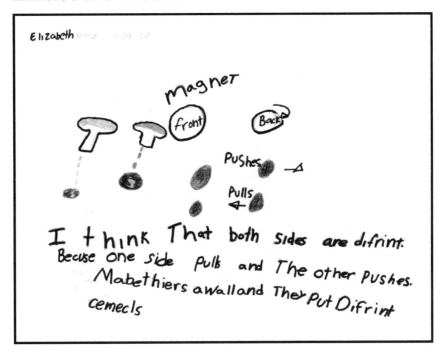

Jacqueline's Model

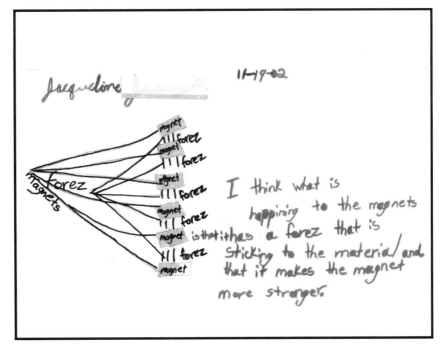

CHAPTER 4

Skyler's Model

Harley's Model (not shown in video)

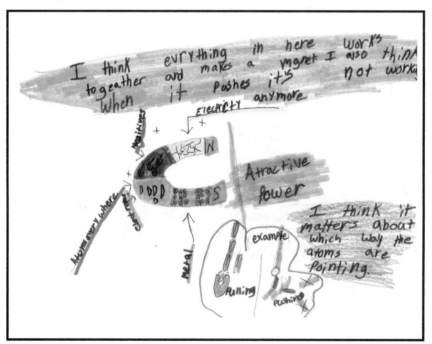

Silvester's Model #1

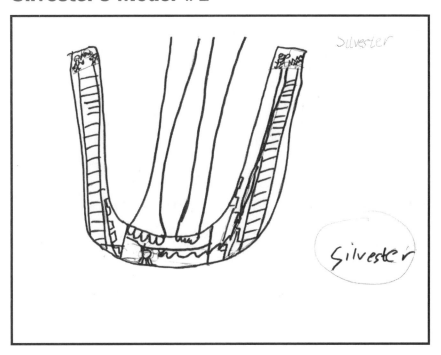

Silvester's Model #2

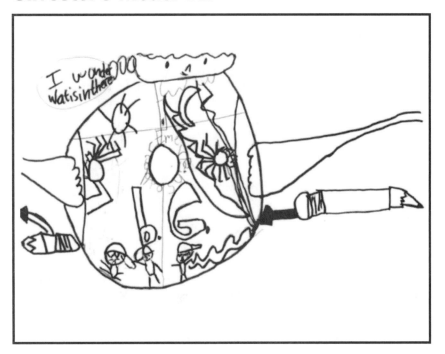

CHAPTER 4

Kevin's Model

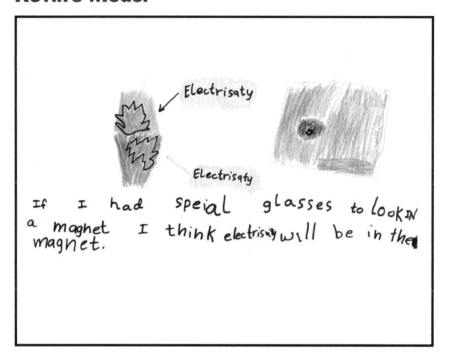

If I had speial glasses to look IN a magnet I think electrisity will be in the magnet.

Katie's Model

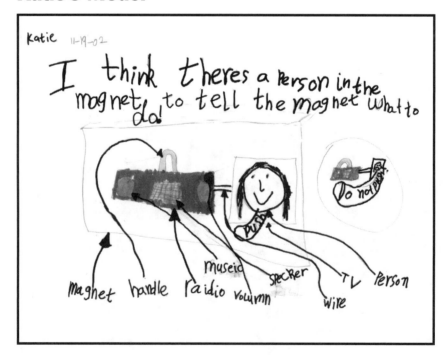

Katie 11-19-02

I think theres a person in the magnet to tell the magnet what to do!

Felix's Model

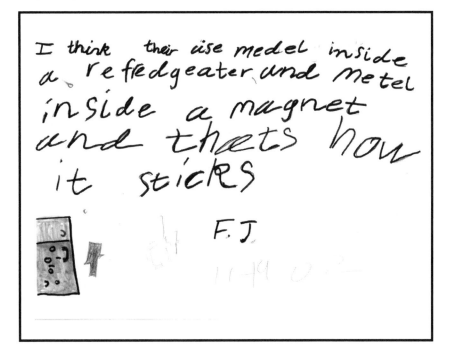

I think their use medel inside
a refredgeater and metel
inside a magnet
and thets how
it sticks

F.J

Kaitlen's Model

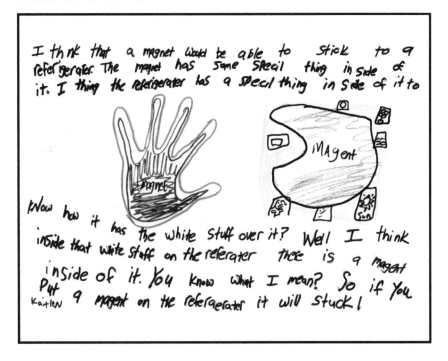

I think that a magnet would be able to stick to a referigerator. The magnet has some specail thing inside of it. I thing the refeigerater has a specil thing inside of it to

Now how it has the white stuff over it? Well I think inside that white stuff on the referater thee is a magat inside of it. You know what I mean? So if you Put a magat on the referaerater it will stuck!

Kaitlen

CHAPTER 4

Electric-Circuit Interactions

Purpose

Many practical devices work because of electricity. In this first activity of the Chapter you will first focus your attention on a simple circuit, consisting of a battery and a bulb. When the bulb is connected to the battery and it lights, we say that there is an *electric-circuit interaction* between the battery and bulb. For the bulb to light, however, does it make any difference *how* the battery is connected to the bulb? Does it make any difference what *kinds of materials* are used to connect the battery and bulb? As you work through this activity, you will investigate the simple electric-circuit and develop answers to these questions. Then you will take apart a flashlight to see how it works.

> **What conditions are necessary for an electric-circuit to work?**

Initial Ideas

Imagine that you had a battery, a small bulb and some wires. You were curious about what arrangements would cause the bulb to light. On the following page are pictures of six possible arrangements, with brief descriptions of how the wires are connected in each case. Look at each arrangement carefully and **predict** whether that particular arrangement would cause the bulb to light. **Do this individually at first before discussing it with your group.**

Write "YES" next to **Pred:** for each arrangement that you think would light the bulb. Write "NO" next to **Pred:** for each arrangement that you think would not light the bulb.

#1

The tip of the bulb touches the negative end of the battery. A wire touches the negative end of the battery and the positive end of the battery.

Pred: Obs:

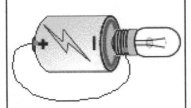

#2

The tip of the bulb touches the negative end of the battery. A wire touches the positive end of the battery and the metal side of the bulb.

Pred: Obs:

#3

One wire touches the positive end of the battery and the tip of the bulb. A second wire touches the negative end of the battery and the tip of the bulb.

Pred: Obs:

#4

The tip of the bulb touches the positive end of the battery (but not the knob in the middle). A wire touches the metal side of the bulb and the negative end of the battery.

Pred: Obs:

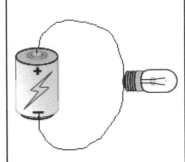

#5

A single wire touches the positive end of the battery and the negative end of the battery. The tip of the bulb touches the middle of this wire.

Pred: Obs:

#6

The metal side of the bulb touches the positive end of the battery. A wire touches the tip of the bulb and the negative end of the battery.

Pred: Obs:

What criteria were you using in making your decisions? That is, what did you think was necessary for the bulb to light?

Discuss your answers and reasons with your group members. If you change your mind, do not erase your original answer, but instead just add the opposite answer alongside your original answer.

Collecting and Interpreting Evidence

 EXPERIMENT #1: What conditions are necessary to light the bulb?

EACH STUDENT WILL NEED:

■ One battery

■ One bulb

■ Two bare copper wires

■ Other items (switch, bulb holder, battery holder and three hook-up wires) to be picked up during Step 4 below

STEP 1: Try each of the six arrangements pictured on the previous pages. In some cases you will need another group member to assist you to hold all the pieces together.

 Write "YES" next to **Obs** (for Observation) for each arrangement that actually lights the bulb, and write "NO" next to **Obs** for each arrangement that does not light the bulb.

 Which of the setups use a battery, bulb and a *single* wire to make the bulb light?

CHAPTER 5

STEP 2: Figure out one more *different* arrangement of battery, bulb and a single wire that lights the bulb.

 Draw a sketch of your new successful arrangement.

STEP 3: Figure out an arrangement using the battery, bulb and *two* wires that light the bulb.

 Draw the circuit below.

In which of the setups from the Initial Ideas question does a wire directly go from the positive to the negative end of the battery without touching the two parts of the bulb?

Did the bulb light in any of those cases?

In those cases did you notice if the wire got warm?

 Look over all the arrangements that allow the bulb to light, and answer the following questions:

Which part or parts of the **battery** need to be part of the connections?

Does a wire or part of a bulb need to touch the positive end of the battery only where the knob is, or can it touch any place on the positive end of the battery away from the knob?

Which part or parts of the **bulb** must be touched to make the bulb light?

CHAPTER 5

STEP 4: It is awkward to hold the battery, wires and bulb together to build circuits. To make things easier, there are special holders for the battery and for the bulbs, and special hook-up wires that have ends that are easy to attach. There is also a switch to make it easier to open and close the circuit.

Get a battery holder, bulb holder, switch and three hook-up wires with small alligator clips on their ends. Snap the battery into its holder, and screw the bulb into the bulb holder. Use the three hook-up wires and connect the circuit together with the switch.

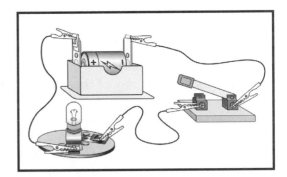

With the handle of the switch down between the clip, the bulb should light. The circuit is said to be "closed." When the handle is lifted up, the bulb should stop glowing, and the circuit is "open."

 EXPERIMENT #2: How do the two ends of the battery need to be connected to the two sides of the bulb?

The evidence from Experiment #1 suggests that one side of the bulb needs to be connected to the positive end of the battery, and the other side of the bulb needs to be connected to the negative end of the battery.

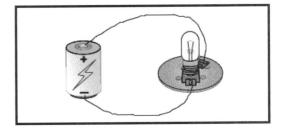

But do the two sides of the bulb need to be connected to the positive and negative ends of the **same** battery? Consider the following arrangement:

 Do you think the bulb in the above arrangement will light? Explain your reasons.

Get two batteries, two hook-up wires and a bulb in a socket. Hook up the arrangement shown above.

 Does the bulb glow?

 Do the two ends of the bulb need to be connected to the two ends of the **same** battery for the circuit to work?

 EXPERIMENT #3: What kinds of materials are necessary for an electric-circuit to work?

In the previous experiment you used copper wires to connect the battery and bulb together. (At first you just used bare copper wires. Then, to make it easier to connect things, you used special copper wires with a surrounding plastic sheath and metallic alligator clips at its ends.) Does it make a difference what kinds of materials you use to connect the battery with the bulb? Will anything work to allow the bulb to light? You will try to answer those questions in this experiment.

YOUR GROUP WILL NEED:

- One battery in battery holder
- One bulb in bulb holder
- Switch
- Four hook-up wires
- Bulb with glass removed

- Various items made of different materials, like an iron nail, wood stick, glass rod, aluminum foil, copper strip, steel nut, etc.
- Magnifier

STEP 1: Construct a circuit similar to the one shown in the picture. The iron nail is placed in the circuit. At the start the switch handle is up. Close the switch.

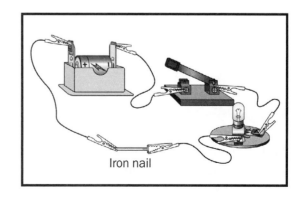
Iron nail

CHAPTER 5

Does the bulb light? Record your observation in the Table on the next page.

STEP 2: Open the switch and remove the iron nail. Replace it with another item from the bag. Attach the two free alligator clips to the two ends of the item. Then close the switch.

 Record your observations in the Table on the next page about whether the bulb does or does not light.

STEP 3: Repeat step 2 for all of the other items that you gathered.

 Record your observations in the Table.

STEP 4: Try two or three additional items to see whether they will allow the bulb to light.

 Add your observations to the Table.

 What seems to be common about the types of materials that need to be included in the loop of an electric-circuit so the bulb will light?

Materials that can be included in a circuit to light the bulb are called **conductors**. Materials that do not allow the bulb to light when included in a circuit are called **insulators**.

Materials that allow the bulb to light

Item and material	Does the bulb light? (YES or NO)
iron nail	
wood stick	
glass rod	
aluminum foil	
copper strip	
steel nut	

STEP 5: Hook up the circuit with the battery and bulb. Close the switch so the bulb glows. Look closely at the bulb through the magnifier.

Which **part** of the bulb is actually glowing? (See picture on next page for the names of the various parts.)

Below is a sketch showing the various parts of a bulb, and whether each part is a conductor or an insulator.

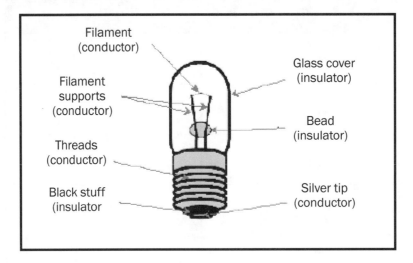

Filament
(conductor)

Glass cover
(insulator)

Filament
supports
(conductor)

Bead
(insulator)

Threads
(conductor)

Black stuff
(insulator

Silver tip
(conductor)

STEP 6: Look closely inside a bulb that has its glass cover removed. Use the magnifier if necessary. Play particular attention to what happens to the two filament support wires in the base of the bulb.

To the right is a picture of a battery, bare bulb (cutout view) and two wires. By connecting lines, show how the two filament support wires are connected to the two wires from the battery.

Starting at one end of the battery, describe in words the sequence of parts (both outside and inside the bulb) that form a continuous pathway of conductors from one end of the battery to the other. Use terms like *wire, filament support wire, filament, side of bulb* and *bottom tip of bulb.*

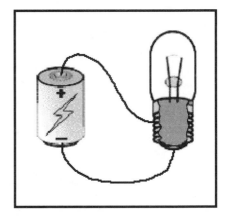

EXPERIMENT #4: What are two ways of connecting two bulbs to a battery?

YOU GROUP WILL NEED:

- One battery in battery holder
- Two bulbs in bulb holders
- Switch
- Four hook-up wires

Your task is to figure out two different ways of connecting two bulbs to a battery, subject to the following conditions:

1. In the first arrangement, the two bulbs glow equally as bright as a single bulb connected to a single battery. Furthermore, when either of the two bulbs is unscrewed from its socket, the other bulb remains lit at the same brightness.

2. In the second arrangement, the two bulbs glow equally, but each is much less bright than when a single bulb is connected to a single battery. Furthermore, when either of the two bulbs is unscrewed from its socket, the other bulb goes out (it no longer glows).

After you are successful at constructing each of these two arrangements, sketch diagrams of them below.

The first arrangement is called a **parallel** (or multiloop) circuit, and the second arrangement is called a **series** (or single loop) circuit.

EXPERIMENT #5: (Optional) How does a flashlight work?

YOU WILL NEED:

- Flashlight that can be taken apart–the flashlight may have either a plastic or metal casing.

- Two batteries, one bare bulb and one bare copper wire.

STEP 1: Two members of your group should work together to connect two batteries, a bulb and a bare copper wire as shown to the right.

 What do you need to do to make the bulb light?

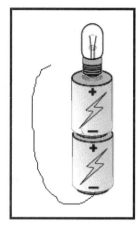

This arrangement can be thought of as a very simple flashlight. However, to turn this flashlight on and off requires you to alternately touch the free wire to the side of the bulb and then pull it away. That's not very convenient. A regular flashlight does this in a clever way.

STEP 2: Examine the regular flashlight with your group. Take it apart and figure out how it works.

 Draw a picture of the various electrical parts of the flashlight and show how they are connected together. Use a different colored pencil to trace the path of conductors around the entire circuit. Write a few sentences to explain how the flashlight works– that is, what actually happens when you slide the switch and the light goes on.

Draw your sketch on a discussion board and mount it so other groups can see it. When they are ready, walk around the room and look at the other groups' drawings. If you find a diagram much different from your own, discuss those differences with the other group(s).

Summarizing Questions

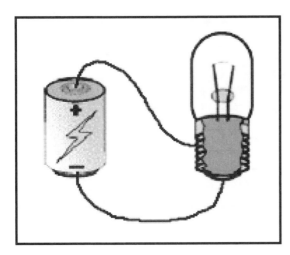

S1: Draw a continuous line that shows the pathway of conductors from one end of the battery, through the bulb, to the other end of the battery. As you did in Step 6 of Experiment #3, be able to describe in words the different parts of the pathway.

S2: The pictures below represent three different ways of putting together a battery bulb and one or more wires. In each case indicate whether the bulb will light or not light. Justify your choice in terms of the ideas developed in this activity (i.e., the conditions necessary to light a bulb).

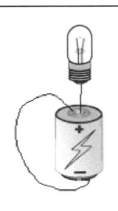  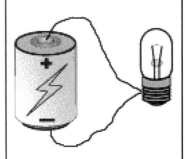

(a) One wire touches the positive end of the battery and the tip of the bulb. A second wire touches the positive end of the battery (not the knob in the middle) and the negative end of the battery.	**(b)** One wire touches the negative end of the battery and the metal side of the bulb. A second wire touches the positive end of the battery and the tip of the bulb.	**(c)** One wire touches the positive end of the battery and the metal side of the bulb. The other wire touches the negative end of the battery and the metal side of the bulb.

CHAPTER 5

S3: Below are pictures of a battery holder, bulb holder and switch. Several parts of these components are identified. Indicate whether you think each part is a **conductor** or an **insulator**. Justify your answers.

(a)

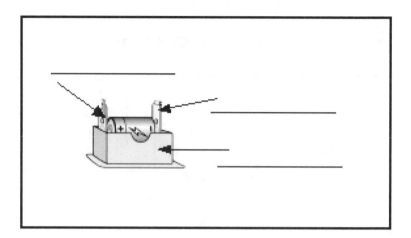

(b)

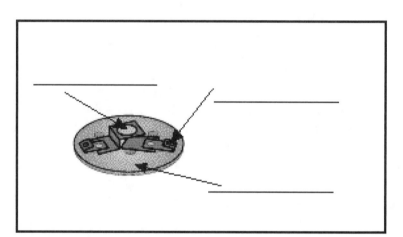

(c)

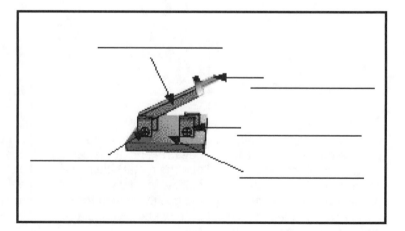

S4: In Experiment #4 you constructed two different circuits, each with a battery and two bulbs. Assume that each bulb is in a bulb socket.

Redraw the two circuits below, but make the bulb and socket large enough in each case to explicitly show the different parts of the socket and the filament support wires and filament in each bulb. Using a different color pen or pencil, trace a conducting path (or paths) from each end of the battery, to each socket, through the inside of each bulb, and then to the other end of the battery.

CHAPTER 5

S5: Consider the same two circuits you drew. **Write a scientific explanation for why (a) in one case, when a bulb is unscrewed from its socket, the other bulb remains lit. Also explain why (b) in the other case, when a bulb is unscrewed from its socket, the other bulb goes out.** For each case, your explanation should include a diagram of the circuit with one bulb unscrewed from its socket, and a written narrative for why the other bulb either continues to be lit or goes out. Your diagrams should be large, like the ones you drew in S4.

 Participate in a whole-class discussion about answers to the above questions.

Purpose

In the previous activity you developed criteria for how circuit components should be connected together to make a bulb light. When the battery is connected to the bulb, there is an **electric-circuit interaction**. In terms of energy, during the electric-circuit interaction *electrical energy* is transferred from the battery to the bulb, causing it to light. When this happens, there is a decrease in chemical potential energy inside the battery and an increase in thermal energy inside the bulb. (The bulb's temperature increases so much that it glows.) In Chapter 1 you learned how to describe an interaction between two objects in terms of a source/receiver energy diagram. For the electric-circuit interaction between the battery and bulb, the S/R energy diagram is drawn as follows:

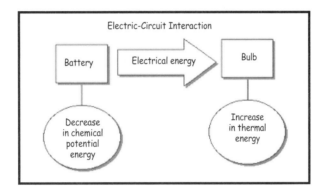

At the end of this activity there is an *Interactions* Chart and an *Energy of Object / System* Chart. These charts summarize the various types of interactions, energy transfers and energy changes that you have studied (and will be studying) in this course. Take a few minutes now to review the charts, as you will probably want to refer to them throughout this activity.

In Chapters 1 and 3 you also learned that an input/output energy diagram is a convenient way of describing a situation when an object or system is interacting with more than one other object. The general form of the I/O energy diagram looks like this.

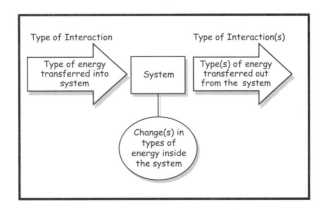

In this activity you will examine electric circuits with different components and learn how to describe how they work in terms of energy transfers and energy changes.

How can we describe an electric-circuit interaction in terms of energy?

Initial Ideas

Plug in a 120-volt bulb in a socket. Touch the bulb momentarily after it is lit.

Draw an input/output energy diagram for the bulb. Include all the energy transfers and changes that you think are relevant.

Participate in a whole-class discussion.

Collecting and Interpreting Evidence

 SIMULATOR EXPLORATION #1: What are the energy transfers and changes in a simple battery and bulb circuit?

You can use a special computer simulator to check your I/O energy diagram from the Initial Ideas section. The following steps tell you how to open the simulator and set up the appropriate circuit.

STEP 1: To start, open *Chapter 5 Act. 2 Setup 1*. You will see a large setup area, and to the right is the tools palette.

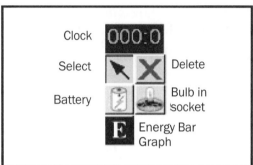

STEP 2: Place a battery and bulb in the setup window by first clicking on each device in the palette, then clicking in the setup area.

STEP 3: For the circuit to work, the battery must be wired to the bulb. To draw a wire between the battery and bulb holder, place the cursor arrow at one end of the battery, then click and start dragging the cursor towards one end of the bulb.

As you get near, the clip will "flash" a small yellow rectangle.

At that point, you can let go of the cursor and the wire will connect.

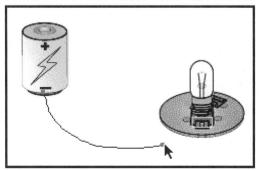

CHAPTER 5

STEP 4: Wire together the rest of the circuit as shown here.

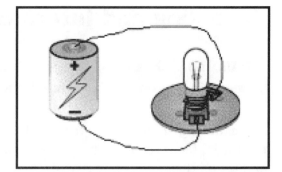

STEP 5: RUN the simulator by clicking on the Run (Play) button. The bulb should light.

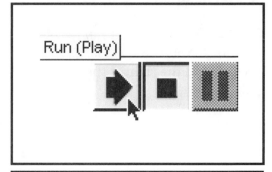

STEP 6: Then STOP the simulator.

We now want to add an **energy bar graph** to find out what types and how much energy is transferred into and out of the bulb, and how much energy changes in the bulb as the circuit is working.

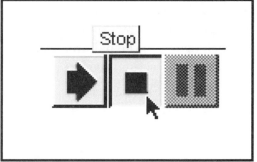

STEP 7: Click on the bulb to Select it. (You can tell it is selected when there are four small black rectangles surrounding it.)

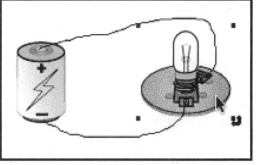

STEP 8: Move the cursor over to the palette and click on the Energy bar graph tool.

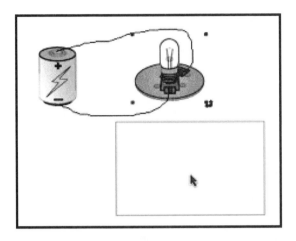

STEP 9: Then (without holding down the mouse button) drag the mouse cursor into the setup area. You will see a rectangle appear. Drag the rectangle so it is below the bulb.

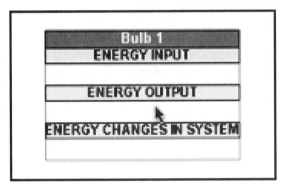

STEP 10: Click the mouse button on the rectangle, and it will turn into an energy chart. Since the simulator is not yet running, there are no types or values of energy yet. But wait....

STEP 11: Click Run, then PAUSE the simulator after 10 seconds.

Below, fill in the types and amounts of energy for the bulb. All energies are measured in joules. (Remember that lifting a 1–kg mass up a distance of 1–m requires #10 joules of energy.) After recording the data, you can stop the simulator, but do not close it.

Bulb (10 seconds)	
ENERGY INPUT	
Type of Energy =	Amount =
ENERGY OUTPUT	
Type of Energy =	Amount =
Type of Energy =	Amount =
ENERGY CHANGES IN SYSTEM	
Type of Energy =	Amount =

CHAPTER 5

How do the types of energy inputs, outputs and changes from the simulator compare with the I/O energy diagram you drew in the Initial Ideas section?

Now let's consider the battery. Inside a common dry cell battery there is a carbon rod connected to the positive terminal. The outside casing is made from zinc. Between the carbon and zinc is an acidic paste. When the battery is connected to a bulb (or any other electrical device), a chemical interaction occurs between different chemicals inside the battery. This interaction causes the chemical potential energy of the battery to decrease, and the battery to warm up. Since there is a fixed amount of chemical potential energy to begin with, eventually the chemical potential energy will decrease so much that the battery will no longer function properly; the battery *dies*.

 Draw an input/output energy diagram for the battery.

STEP 12: Return to the simulator and add an Energy bar graph below the battery (using a similar procedure that you used for the bulb). If the Energy bar graphs for the battery and bulb overlap, you need to separate them by clicking on the Select button and dragging one of the Energy bar graphs away from the other.

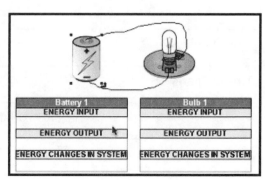

STEP 13: Click Run, then PAUSE the simulator after 10 seconds.

 Fill in the types and amounts of energy for the battery and for the bulb. (The data for the bulb should be very similar to the data already collected, but here we want to make sure that you are collecting data for both the battery and the bulb for the exact same amount of time.) After recording data, you may stop the simulator.

Battery (10 seconds)	
ENERGY INPUT	
Type of Energy =	Amount =
ENERGY OUTPUT	
Type of Energy =	Amount =
Type of Energy =	Amount =
ENERGY CHANGES IN SYSTEM	
Type of Energy =	Amount =
Type of Energy =	Amount =

Bulb (10 seconds)	
ENERGY INPUT	
Type of Energy =	Amount =
ENERGY OUTPUT	
Type of Energy =	Amount =
Type of Energy =	Amount =
ENERGY CHANGES IN SYSTEM	
Type of Energy =	Amount =

CHAPTER 5

Compare the types of energy outputs and changes for the battery with the I/O energy diagram you drew. Redraw the I/O diagram, if necessary, to ensure that your diagram shows all the types of transfers and changes.

 How does the simulator indicate that the chemical potential energy inside the battery **decreases** with time?

 How does the electrical energy transferred out from the battery compare to the electrical energy transferred into the bulb, during the 10–second period?

 Does that make sense?

Recall that the Law of Conservation of energy can be stated in the following form: Energy Input = Energy Changes + Energy Output. Using this equation, check to see if energy is conserved in the bulb. (The simulator rounds off energy values to the nearest 0.01 joule, so if two numbers are within 0.01 joules of each other, you can claim that they are equal.)

 Use the same equation to check to see if energy is conserved in the battery.

 Some people claim that electrical energy is "used up" in the bulb. Others claim that the energy is not used up, but instead is transformed into a different type (or different types) of energy. Which claim makes the most sense to you, and why?

There must be a complete circuit in order for the battery to transfer electrical energy to the bulb, causing it to glow. If the wires connecting the battery to the bulb were disconnected, no electrical energy would be transferred and the bulb would not glow.

 When a battery is connected to a bulb, does the bulb light up immediately, or does it take some time before it lights up? What does this imply about how quickly energy is transferred from the battery to the bulb?

CHAPTER 5

SIMULATOR EXPLORATION #2: What are the energy transfers and changes in a space heater? Do the energy changes within the system continue to change as the circuit continues to run?

Many people use small space heaters to warm up their rooms on cold days and nights. Imagine you have connected your space heater to a source of electrical energy (like a battery). When you turn the space heater on, the coils warm up and as they do, they emit infrared radiation to the surroundings and also warm up the air in contact with the coils. The warmed air then moves away from the heater and spreads to other parts of the room. The warmth you feel from the heater is caused both by the IR radiation and the air that was warmed by being in contact with the coils.

Draw an I/O energy diagram for the space heater when it is turned on.

The simulator has a tool that behaves like a space heater. Open *Chapter 5 Act. 2 Setup 2* and you will see the following setup:

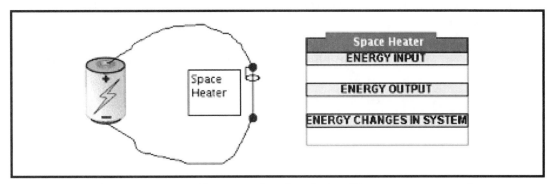

 **STEP 1:** Turn on the simulator. Keep your eye on the energy bar graph and also on the clock above the palette on the right. Run the simulator for about 10 seconds, and then pause it.

 Record the types and amounts of energy input, output, and changes in the table below. All energies are measured in joules.

Space Heater (10 seconds)	
ENERGY INPUT	
Type of Energy =	Amount =
ENERGY OUTPUT	
Type of Energy =	Amount =
ENERGY CHANGES IN SYSTEM	
Type of Energy =	Amount =

 Compare the energy types with those you drew in your I/O energy diagram. If they don't match, re-draw the I/O diagram below.

CHAPTER 5

STEP 2: Restart the simulator and run it for about 30 seconds and pay attention if the electrical energy, heat energy and thermal energy continue to increase during the entire 30-second period, or whether at some point one or more of the energies stops increasing.

 Do the electrical energy input and heat energy output values continue to increase?

 Does the thermal energy continue to increase during the 30-second period? If not, at approximately what time does it stop increasing?

Since an increase in temperature is associated with an increase in thermal energy, as long as the temperature of the space heater coils increases, so will its thermal energy. The period of time during which the temperature increases is called the *transient state*.

 Why do you think the thermal energy stops increasing after about 20 seconds?

For many systems that warm up, like the space heater, the temperature reaches a certain maximum value known as the operating temperature. Beyond this point, the increase in thermal energy that results from electrical energy being transferred into the space heater is exactly balanced by the decrease in thermal energy resulting when heat energy is transferred out from the space heater. (The situation is similar to what happened in Chapter 1, Activity 5 when hot water was poured into a glass. In that case, the increase in thermal energy of the glass resulting from hot water being poured into it is exactly balanced by the decrease in thermal energy resulting when heat energy was transferred out from the glass.) When this balance is reached, the thermal energy no longer changes and the temperature of the system remains constant. This situation is called the *equilibrium state*.

Do you think a similar thing happens with a bulb? That is, does the filament heat up (transient state) to a certain temperature and then remain the same (equilibrium state)? If so, do you think the filament reaches its operating temperature much more quickly than the space heater, much less quickly, or do you think it would take approximately the same amount of time? Why do you think so?

STEP 3: You can check your idea by returning to the simulator. Delete the battery and space heater. Set up the same circuit as in Simulator Exploration #1 (battery connected to a bulb), and place an Energy bar graph for the bulb.

Run the simulator and pay careful attention to the thermal energy in the bulb (filament). Does it stop increasing, and if so, when does it seem to stop increasing?

The filament of the bulb gets very hot, like the space heater, but as you can see it happens very quickly. The filament is made of special material (tungsten) that can get hot enough to glow brightly. The regular copper wires that make up most of the rest of the circuit do not generally get very hot, and they do not glow.

SIMULATOR EXPLORATION #3: What are the energy transfers and changes in a generator and bulb circuit?

Generators, like batteries, are sources of electrical energy. Large ones provide sufficient power for parts of an entire city. A small, hand-cranked generator provides sufficient power to light a flashlight bulb.

CHAPTER 5

Your instructor may have small hand-operated generators to distribute to the class. If so, you can connect one to a bulb and turn the handle slowly. (If you turn it too fast, the bulb will burn out. Because these bulbs are not inexpensive, you should try to be careful.)

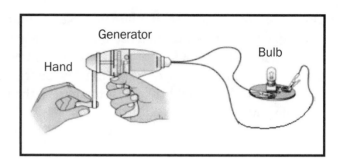

 Draw an I/O energy diagram for the generator.

The simulator has a generator tool, which allows you to explore its use and to check your I/O energy diagram.

STEP 1: Open *Chapter 5 Act. 2 Setup 3*, and then construct the generator-bulb circuit shown here. (The simulator image does not show a hand turning the handle, but you can assume it's there.)

STEP 2: RUN the simulator and observe what happens. Then stop the simulator.

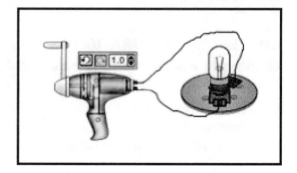

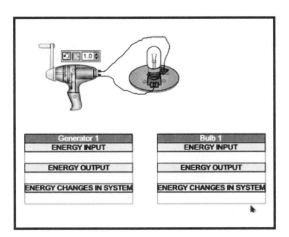

STEP 3: To add an energy bar graph, click the generator to select it. Then click the energy bar tool in the palette, drag the rectangle to beneath the generator, and click it in place. Repeat this procedure to add an Energy bar graph for the bulb. Your setup window should look similar to the picture on the left.

STEP 4: RUN the simulator for 10 seconds, and then PAUSE it.

 How does the electrical energy output from the generator compare to the electrical energy input to the bulb? Does this make sense?

 Copy the types and values of the energies from the Generator Energy bar graph into the table below.

GENERATOR (10 seconds)	
ENERGY INPUT	
Type of Energy =	Amount =
ENERGY OUTPUT	
Type of Energy =	Amount =
ENERGY CHANGES IN SYSTEM	
Type of Energy =	Amount =

CHAPTER 5

How do the energy types displayed in the table compare with the I/O energy diagram you drew above? If different, re-draw the I/O energy diagram below.

 Was energy conserved during the 10-second period when the generator was operating? How do you know?

The **rate of energy transfer** is the amount of energy transferred from the generator to the bulb in one second.

 Calculate the rate of electrical energy transfer from the generator to the bulb by dividing the electrical energy transferred during 10 seconds by 10.

The rate of electrical energy transfer is measured in energy units divided by time units, in this case joules/sec. By definition, a joule/sec is also called a **watt**. A 100-watt bulb has 100 joules of electrical energy transferred into it each second. A 60-watt bulb has 60 joules of electrical energy transferred into it each second.

Using data you collected in Simulator Exploration #1, calculate the wattage of the small bulb in the simulator.

Suppose you were able to increase the rate at which the generator transferred electrical energy to the bulb. What do you think would happen to the brightness of the bulb?

In the simulator, you can increase the rate at which electrical energy is transferred from the generator to the bulb by increasing the speed at which the handle is turned. The simulator also displays a number alongside the bulb, which is called the brightness number. Larger brightness numbers correspond to brighter bulbs.

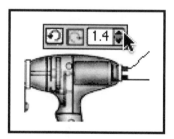

STEP 5: Run the simulator and click the cursor on the small upward arrow in the panel above the generator. This increases the speed at which the handle turns. Keep clicking until you reach the maximum speed (2.6).

What happens to the brightness of the bulb as the handle turns faster and faster?

Stop the simulator, and then run it again for 10 seconds with the generator turning at its maximum speed. What is the value of the electrical energy transferred into the bulb in 10 seconds?

Calculate the rate of electrical energy transferred into the bulb (in units of watts).

Higher wattage bulbs have a greater rate of electrical energy transferred into them, and are brighter, than lower wattage bulbs.

Electric companies use large generators to produce electrical energy, which they then sell to you. The generators are always turned at the same speed so bulbs in your homes don't change brightness!

Summarizing Questions

S1: Victor and Amara are debating their answer to the question: In a circuit, what happens to the energy provided by the battery?

I dont think energy is used up in the circuit. Instead it is just changed into another type of energy.

I don't agree. Since the battery eventually dies, then I think energy must be used up in the circuit.

Victor

Amara

Do you agree with Victor, with Amara, or with neither one? If you agree with either one, or if you suggest an alternative answer, support your answer with what you learned in this activity.

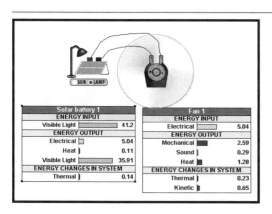

Solar battery 1	
ENERGY INPUT	
Visible Light	41.2
ENERGY OUTPUT	
Electrical	5.04
Heat	0.11
Visible Light	35.91
ENERGY CHANGES IN SYSTEM	
Thermal	0.14

Fan 1	
ENERGY INPUT	
Electrical	5.04
ENERGY OUTPUT	
Mechanical	2.59
Sound	0.29
Heat	1.28
ENERGY CHANGES IN SYSTEM	
Thermal	0.23
Kinetic	0.65

S2: A solar battery can be an energy source for an electric-circuit. On the left is a picture from the computer simulator, where a solar cell is connected to a motor (with fan blades attached). The input light energy for the solar battery comes from the table lamp. Energy bar graphs are shown for both the solar battery and the motor. The simulator is run for 10 seconds and then paused. The large amount of visible light energy output from the solar battery is due to the large fraction of the light striking the battery that is reflected from the surface.

(a) Draw an I/O energy diagram for the solar battery.

(b) Draw an I/O energy diagram for the motor (with fan blades).

CHAPTER 5

S3: A battery is connected to two bulbs in a parallel circuit. A student uses the simulator to help describe the interactions involving the battery in terms of energy. She runs the simulator for 10 seconds and records the following information for the **battery**.

- No Energy Input

- Change in thermal energy = 0.07 joules

- Change in chemical potential energy = – 1.38 joules

- Electrical energy output = 1.28 joules

What type of energy is missing from this list of energy types, and what is the amount of energy that is missing? Write a scientific explanation to justify your decision about what type of energy is missing and how much energy is missing. (In this case you should draw an energy diagram. In your written explanation, justify why you included all the types of energy in your diagram, especially the type of energy that is missing from the student's list. Then use the Law of Conservation of Energy.)

 Participate in a whole-class discussion about answers to the above questions.

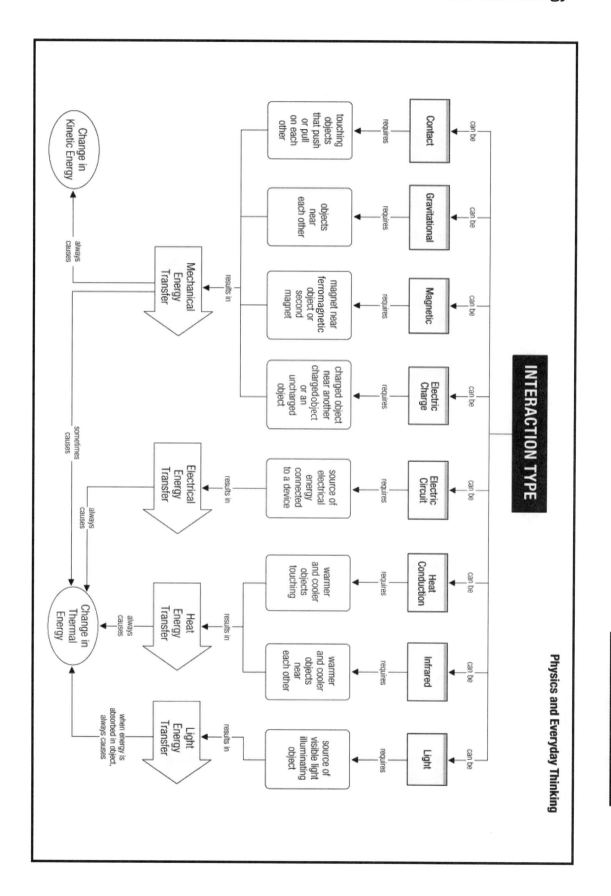

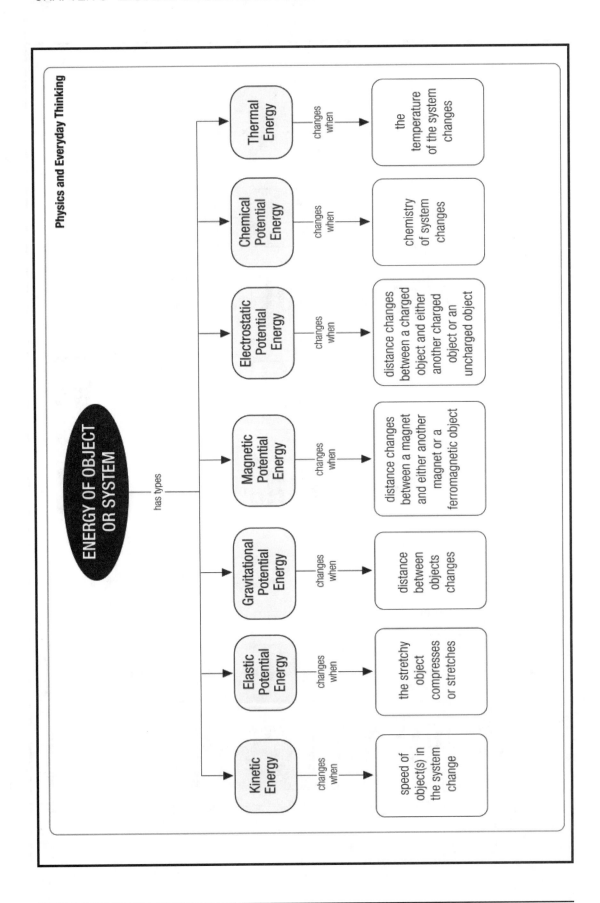

Physics and Everyday Thinking

Name:_____ Date:_____ Group: _____

Purpose

In Activity 2 you analyzed a simple circuit with one battery and one bulb in terms of energy. At right is a snapshot from the simulator, showing the circuit and the Energy bar graphs for the battery and bulb. The simulator was run for 10 seconds.

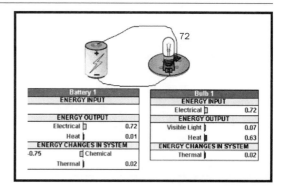

The **rate** at which electrical energy is transferred out from the battery is the total electrical energy transferred divided by the time (10 seconds). It is measured in units of watts. So,

Rate = 0.72 J/10 s = 0.072 watts.

In Activity 1 you constructed two different circuits with one battery and more than one bulb. One was a single loop or series circuit and one was a multi-loop, or parallel circuit. In this homework we want to analyze series and parallel circuits in terms of energy.

Initial Ideas

To the right is a series circuit consisting of one battery and three bulbs. Suppose this circuit were run for 10 seconds.

Predict whether you think the **rate** of electrical energy output from the battery would be greater than the rate in the one-bulb circuit, equal to the rate, or less than the rate. Why do you think so?

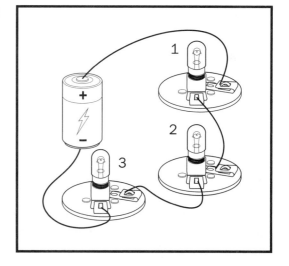

Predict how you think the total electrical energy transferred out from the battery in ten seconds is divided among the three bulbs in the series circuit. Does each bulb receive the same total amount of electrical energy transferred out from the battery, or does each bulb receive only a percentage of the total electrical energy from the battery (and, if so, what percentage)? Why do you think so?

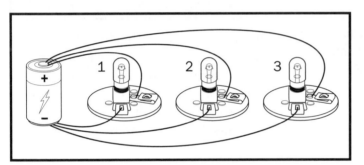

To the left is a parallel circuit consisting of one battery and three bulbs. Suppose this circuit were run for 10 seconds.

 Predict whether you think the rate of electrical energy output from the battery would be greater than the rate in the one-bulb circuit, equal to the rate, or less than the rate. Why do you think so?

 Predict how you think the total electrical energy transferred out from the battery in 10 seconds is divided among the three bulbs in the parallel circuit. Does each bulb receive the same total amount of electrical energy transferred out from the battery, or does each bulb receive only a percentage of the total electrical energy from the battery (and, if so, what percentage)? Why do you think so?

Collecting and Interpreting Evidence

To check your predictions, open *Chapter 5 Activity 2 Homework Setup*. Construct the circuit as shown here and set out Energy bar graphs for each of the three bulbs and the battery. (You may need to readjust the position of the Energy bar graphs after running the simulator so they don't overlap too much.)

Run the simulator for 10 seconds, and then pause it.

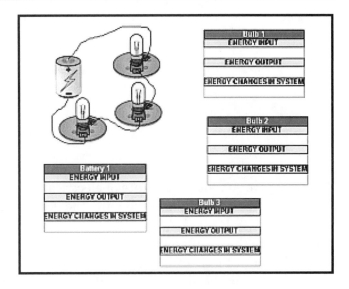

 What is the electrical energy output from the battery? How does that compare with the output for the one-bulb circuit?

 How does the amount of the electrical energy input to each of the three bulbs compare to each other? How does each compare to the total electrical energy output from the battery?

CHAPTER 5

Calculate in watts the rate of electrical energy transferred from the battery and the rate of electrical energy transferred to **each** bulb. (For each bulb, the rate in watts equals electrical energy divided by time, in this case 10 seconds.)

As you saw in Activity 2, the rate of electrical energy transferred into a bulb determines the brightness of the bulb: the greater the rate, the brighter the bulb.

Returning to the simulator, delete everything and then construct the three-bulb parallel circuit. Place an Energy bar graph for the battery and one for each of the three bulbs. Run the simulator for 10 seconds, and then pause it.

 What is the electrical-energy output from the battery? How does that compare with the output for the one-bulb circuit?

 How does the amount of electrical energy input to each of the three bulbs compare to each other. How does each compare to the total electrical energy output from the battery?

 Calculate in watts the rate of electrical energy transferred from the battery and the rate of electrical energy transferred to each bulb.

Summarizing Questions

Compare the three-bulb parallel circuit with the three-bulb series circuit by answering these questions:

S1: For both series and parallel circuits, how is the total electrical energy from the battery divided among the bulbs in the circuit?

S2: Does a battery transfer electrical energy at a greater rate in a parallel or a series circuit? What is your evidence?

CHAPTER 5

S3: In which circuit, the parallel or series, would the battery *die* first? Explain your reasoning.

S4: In terms of the rate of electrical energy transferred, why is each bulb in the parallel circuit just as bright as the bulb in the one-bulb circuit, but each bulb in the series circuit is much dimmer?

Purpose

In Chapters 1 and 2 you learned that there are two ways that scientists describe interactions: either in terms of energy transfer and energy changes, or in terms of forces. When thinking about an electric-circuit interaction, there are also two ways of describing it. In the previous activity, you learned how to describe the interaction in terms of the transfer of electrical energy from the battery (or other source) to the receiver. In this activity you will learn another way to describe what happens in an electric-circuit–in terms of *electric-current*.

> ## How can we describe an electric-circuit interaction in terms of electric current?

Initial Ideas

To the right is a diagram of an electric-circuit with a battery and two bulbs.

In terms of your initial ideas about electric current, do you think the value of the electric current is the same at points A, B and C, or do you think it is different. Why do you think so?

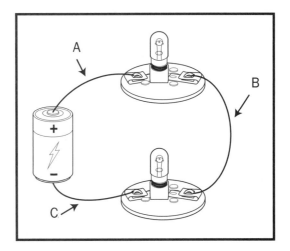

 Participate in a whole-class discussion.

CHAPTER 5

Beginning to Think About Electric Current

Consider a battery, bulb and some wires. For the moment, assume the circuit is not connected together, as shown below to the left. Scientists believe that inside the conducting wires (and all other conducting parts of the circuit) there are electrically charged particles that move in *random* directions—just as many electric charges move in one direction as move in the opposite direction. In this situation there is no net movement of the electric charges in any particular direction. (This is illustrated below to the left in the blowup of a tiny section of the wire.)

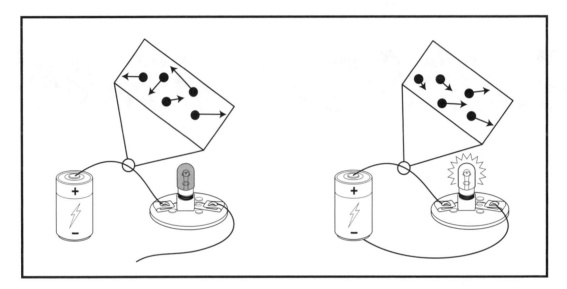

However, when the circuit is connected together so the bulb glows, there is an electric-circuit interaction and the battery exerts a force on each and every electric charge in the circuit. The force on all the charges causes them to move around the circuit, from one end of the battery to the other. (This is illustrated in the picture above to the right[1].) As electric charges enter one end of the battery, an equal number of electric charges leave the other end of the battery. All the conductors in the circuit are always full of moving charges. **The amount of electric charge moving past any point in the circuit in one second is defined as the value of the *electric current* at that point.** So, if the number of electric charges passing by a point in one second increases, the value of the electric current will increase in a corresponding way. Since the electric force can be *felt* almost instantaneously by all charges in the circuit as soon as the circuit is connected, an electric current exists almost simultaneously at **all** places in the circuit – inside all wires, inside the filament of a bulb, inside the battery, and inside any other electric component connected to the circuit.

---

[1] Scientists have performed experiments that prove that in an actual circuit only the negative charges move, so when the circuit is connected together there is a movement of negative charges around the circuit from the negative end of the battery to the positive end. However, before scientists knew this, they had *assumed* positive charges moved from the positive towards the negative end of the battery, as depicted in the pictures. Most science textbooks still describe current in electric circuits *as if* the positive charges are the ones that move.

It is convenient to think of the electric force that the battery exerts on all the charges as a sort of *push* on the charges. The strength of the push by the battery on the charges is called the **battery voltage**, and is measured in units of volts. A 9-volt battery provides six times the push on the charges as a 1.5-volt battery (since 9 = 6 x 1.5).

Back in Chapter 2 you learned that the rate of change of speed of an object (also known as acceleration) depends on two factors: the strength of the unbalanced force acting on it and its mass. Although an electric-circuit is a much more complicated system than just a single object acted on by a force, it is helpful to think about an electric-circuit in a somewhat similar way. The push provided by the battery on the charges is analogous to the force acting on the object. The value of the electric current in the circuit is analogous to the rate of change of speed of the object. The property of a bulb that is analogous to the mass of the object is called the *resistance* of the bulb.

In the remainder of this activity you will develop and test ideas about the relationships between the **voltage of the battery**, the amount of **resistance** of the bulb, and the value of the **electric current** in the electric-circuit. You will also investigate the relationship between the electric current and the brightness of the bulb.

Collecting and Interpreting Evidence

We defined the value of electric current in the previous section. In the Initial Ideas section you were asked to use your own intuitive understanding of what electric current means and to compare the value of the electric current at different points around a circuit. To test your prediction from the Initial Ideas section, you can use the computer simulator and a special device, called an **ammeter** that measures the value of electric current. The simulated ammeter measures electric current in units of milli-amperes, or mA.

 SIMULATION EXPLORATION #1: How does the value of the electric current compare at different points around a single-loop circuit?

Open *Chapter 5 Activity 3 Setup 1* and set up the circuit shown to the right. Ammeter A reads the current in the circuit at a point between the positive end of the battery and the top bulb. Ammeter B reads the current at a point in the wire between the two bulbs. Ammeter C reads the value of the current at a point between the lower bulb and the negative end of the battery. Turn on the simulator.

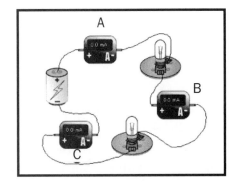

CHAPTER 5

Record the values of the three ammeter readings.

Ammeter A = _____; Ammeter B = _____; Ammeter C = _____

 How do the three readings compare?

 How do these results compare with your prediction in the Initial Ideas section?

 As mentioned earlier, electric current is the amount of electric charge that flows past each point in the circuit each second. Which of the following two claims is supported by the simulator results:

Claim 1: Electric current is used up in the circuit.
Claim 2: Electric current is not used up in the circuit.

 Explain how the simulator result supports your claim.

In the next exploration you will study the relationship between the strength of the push from the battery (the battery voltage) and the value of the electric current. You will also investigate the relationship between the brightness of the bulb and the value of the electric current.

SIMULATION EXPLORATION #2: What is the relationship between the value of the electric current and the battery voltage? What is the relationship between the brightness of the bulb and the value of the electric current?

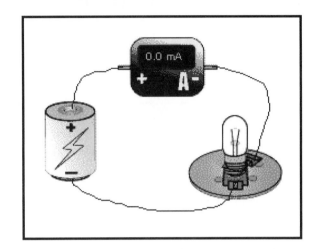

STEP 1: Delete the battery, two bulbs and ammeters from the previous simulator exploration. Set up the circuit shown to the right. The battery voltage is 1.5-volts.

Turn on the simulator and record the value of the ammeter and the brightness (the number alongside the bulb) in the third row of the Table on the next page. Then turn off the simulator.

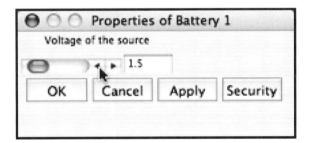

STEP 2: The simulator allows you easily to change the battery voltage. Double-click on the battery to open its Property box. Click on the left arrow to lower the voltage to 1.0 volts. Click OK to close the box.

(We should mention that with a real battery you couldn't change the voltage. Instead you would need to stack two or more batteries so their voltages add.)

Turn on the simulator and record values in the table.

STEP 3: Repeat Steps 1 and 2 for the remaining battery voltages in the table.

CHAPTER 5

Table 1: Battery Voltage, Electric Current and Bulb Brightness

Battery Voltage (volts)	Electric Current (mA)	Brightness Number
1.0		
1.5		
2.0		
2.5		
3.0		
3.5		
4.0		
4.5		
5.0		
5.5		
6.0		

STEP 4: Plot Current versus Voltage, using the top graph on the next page. Draw a line through the data points.

STEP 5: Plot Brightness versus Current, using the bottom graph on the next page. Draw a line through the data points.

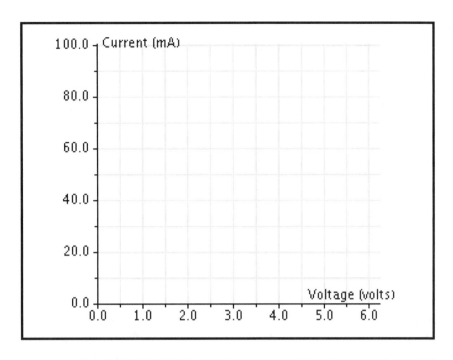

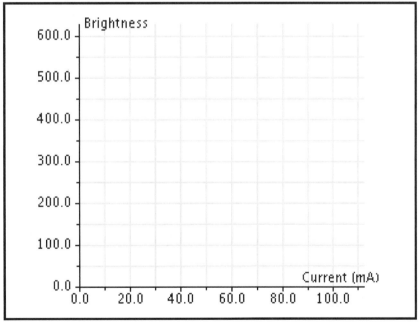

Your graph of Current versus Voltage should be a straight line (or very nearly so). This straight-line graph means that the current is *proportional* to the voltage; that is, that as the voltage increases, the current also increases in the same way. Thus, if the voltage doubles, the current becomes twice as great; if the voltage increases three-fold, then the current becomes three times as great. This proportional relationship can be written mathematically as follows:

Current ~ Voltage

This is read "current is proportional to voltage," or "current varies directly with voltage." Later in this activity we will be able to write an exact equation, rather than just a proportional relationship.

 Is the Brightness versus Current graph a straight line, is it an upward curved line, or is it something else (describe what)?

If the graph is a straight line, then you can claim the brightness is proportional to the current. If the graph is an upward curved line, then you can only claim that brightness increases with increasing current, but not proportionally. (Thus, if the current doubles then the brightness increases more than twice as much.) If the graph is neither, your claim depends on the shape of the graph.

 What claim can you make about the relationship between brightness and current?

 EXPERIMENT #1: How can an analogy help us make sense of electric circuits?

EACH PERSON WILL NEED:

- Three coffee stirrers and one straw
- Tape
- Scissors

STEP 1: A simple analogy for an electric-circuit involves blowing air through a stirrer. Each member of your team should hold one end of the stirrer in your mouth and hold the palm of your hand near the other end.

Blow through the stirrer and observe the effect on your palm. By feeling the moving air pushing against your palm you get a sense of the amount of air coming out of the end of the stirrer each second, which we will call the *air current*.

The air current in the stirrer is analogous to the electric current in the electric-circuit. However, this analogy is not perfect, in part because in a circuit the wire doesn't end but is connected to the other end of the battery. But even though this analogy (like all analogies) is not perfect, we can still use it to help us make sense of some properties of electric current and circuits. We will call this the **blowing-through-straw** analogy for an electric-circuit.

STEP 2: Blow harder and harder through the stirrer.

 Does the value of the air current increase, decrease or remain constant?

 Why does the value of the air current change when you blow harder and harder through the straw?

CHAPTER 5

The following table summarizes how different aspects of blowing through a straw (stirrer) are analogous to different aspects of an electric-circuit.

Analogy between Electric-circuit and Blowing through Straws

Electric-circuit	Blowing through Straws Analogy
Battery	Lungs and mouth
Battery voltage (strength of battery push, measured in volts)	Strength of blowing through straw
Light bulb filament	Straw (or stirrer)
Electric charges in battery, bulb, ammeter and connecting wires	Air in lungs, mouth and straw
Electric current is rate of flow of electric charges	Air current is the rate of flow of air
Ammeter measures value of electric current	You get a qualitative measure of the air current as the air hits the palm of your hand

In Simulator Exploration #2 you found that the greater the battery voltage, the greater the value of the electric current. How did blowing harder and harder through the stirrer provide results that are analogous to the electric-circuit results?

STEP 3: Now let's consider what happens to the value of the air current if you change the length or thickness of the stirrer.

 If you blow through the end of the stirrer with the same strength, but make the stirrer longer, what do you think will happen to the value of the air current? Why?

 If, instead, you made the stirrer have a larger diameter (larger opening), but kept it the same length and blew with the same strength, what do you think would happen to the value of the air current? Why?

STEP 4: Make a double-length stirrer by carefully taping the ends together, making sure that the openings at the two ends align with each other. Blow through the two stirrers using the same blowing strength as before. Feel the air hitting your palm at the other end. (You may need to also blow through a single stirrer to remind yourself how the air hitting your palm felt before.)

 Even though you try to blow with the same strength, is it easier or more difficult to blow through the two-stirrer combination compared to the single stirrer?

 With the same blowing strength, how does the air current in the two-stirrer combination seem to compare with the air current in the single stirrer?

CHAPTER 5

STEP 5: Cut the straw so it's the same length as the single stirrer. The diameter of the straw should be several times larger than the diameter of the stirrer. Alternately blow with the *same strength* through one end of the straw and then one end of the stirrer. Keep your palm the same distance from the end of each.

 Is it easier, harder, or equally difficult, to blow through the straw compared to the stirrer?

 How does the air current in the straw compare to the air current in the stirrer?

 Let's summarize your findings. Fill in the following:

For the same blowing strength, the longer the stirrer/straw, the _____ (higher, lower) the value of the air current.

For the same blowing strength, the thicker the stirrer/straw, the _____ (higher, lower) the value of the air current.

 Do these results make sense to you? Why or why not?

Scientists use the term straw ***resistance*** to refer to the property of the stirrer/straw that determines how difficult it is to blow air through it. The resistance of the stirrer/straw depends on its length and diameter.

Fill in the following:

For the same blowing strength, the longer the stirrer/straw, the _____ (greater, smaller) its resistance to the flow of air though it.

For the same blowing strength, the thicker the stirrer/straw, the _____ (greater, smaller) its resistance to the flow of air though it.

 Do these results make sense to you? Why or why not?

Before proceeding, it's important that your observations and conclusions are similar to those of other groups in the class. Check your answers to the two previous sets of fill-in-the-blanks questions with at least one other group.

In Simulator Exploration #2 you varied the battery voltage (the strength of battery push) and observed what happened to the value of the electric current in the circuit. As you had seen in Activity 1, it is the filament wire in the bulb that actually glows. The filament wire provides resistance to the flow of electric charges through it just like the stirrer/straw provides resistance to the flow of air through it. You have already seen what happens to the value of the air current if you change the resistance of the stirrer/straw (by changing its length or diameter). In Simulator Exploration #2 you used the same bulb (same filament wire) to collect your data. What would happen to the value of the electric current if you were able to change the resistance of the filament wire in the bulb? The purpose of the next Simulator Exploration is to help you answer that question.

SIMULATOR EXPLORATION #3: How does the value of the electric current in a circuit depend on the properties of the bulb filament?

Consider a circuit with a 1.5-volt battery, an ammeter and a special bulb. The bulb is special because you will be able to change the resistance of its filament (making it higher or lower).

 If you kept the battery voltage constant, but you increased the value of the resistance of the bulb filament, do you think the value of the electric current in this circuit would increase, decrease or remain the same? Use the blowing-through-straw analogy to help justify your prediction.

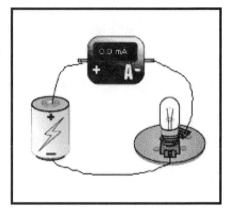

STEP 1: On the *PET* Simulator Index page open ***Chapter 5 Act. 3 Setup 2.*** There should be two circuits, each with a battery, ammeter and bulb.

STEP 2: If you double-click on one of the bulbs, you will open its property window. The default resistance of the bulb is listed as 30 ohms. (The **ohm** is the unit of resistance.) Close the bulb property box. Then open the other one and notice that its resistance is also set at 30 ohms.

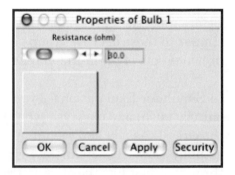

 Turn on the simulator and record the value of the electric current in the table on the next page in the row for 30 ohms. (Both bulbs are the same, so the electric currents in each circuit should be the same.)

The resistance of the bulb filament depends on its length and thickness (and also the materials out of which it is made). In the simulator, however, you change the value of the bulb's resistance in its property box. The simulator doesn't allow you to separately change the length or diameter of the filament wire, or the material out of which it is made.

STEP 3: Turn the simulator off, open the property box for one of the bulbs and change the resistance to one of the values in the Table below. Close that property box, then open the other bulb's property box and change its resistance to another value in the Table.

Turn on the simulator and record the values of the electric current and resistances for the two circuits in the Table.

Table 2: Electric Current versus Bulb Filament Resistance (Simulator); Battery Voltage = 1.5 Volts

Bulb Filament Resistance (ohms)	Electric Current (mA)
14	
16	
18	
20	
25	
30	
40	
50	
60	
70	
80	
90	
100	

CHAPTER 5

STEP 4: Repeat Step 3 until you fill the entire table with data. (You should choose two additional resistance values not listed in the table and record data for them. They can have higher or lower resistances than those already listed in the table. Note: If the electric current gets too high the simulator is programmed for the bulb to *burn out*. In that case, delete the burned out bulb and replace it with a new bulb from the palette to the right of the setup area.)

Use your data to plot a graph of Current versus Resistance.

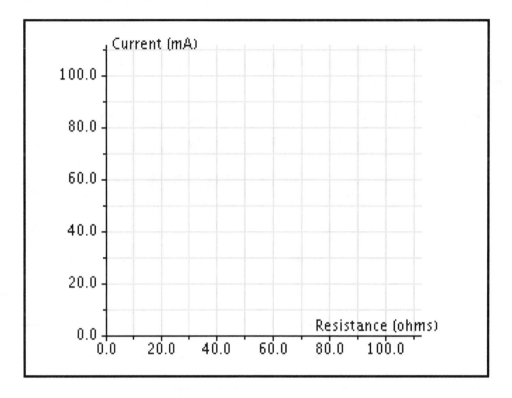

 Sketch a smooth line through the points.

As the resistance of the bulb filament increases, does the value of the electric current in the circuit increase, decrease, or remain essentially constant? How does this result from the simulator compare with your prediction?

Your graph of Current versus Resistance should be a smooth curve that shows that the current decreases as the resistance increases (for a constant battery voltage). This type of curve suggests that the current is *inversely proportional* to the resistance. (That is, if the resistance doubles, then the current becomes one-half as much; if the resistance increases three-fold, then the current becomes one-third as much.) This relationship can be written mathematically as follows:

$$Current \sim \frac{1}{Resistance}$$

This relationship is read "current is inversely proportional to resistance," or "current varies indirectly with resistance." The relationship assumes the battery voltage remains the same. In Simulator Exploration #2 you found that if the bulb doesn't change, then Current ~ Battery Voltage. In that case, since the bulb remained the same, then its resistance remained the same. It turns out that the proportional relationship between current and battery voltage, and the inversely proportional relationship between current and resistance, can be combined into the following single equation:

$$Current = \frac{Battery\ Voltage}{Resistance}$$

This relationship is known as **Ohm's Law**. It not only applies to the simple case of a single battery and a single bulb, but it also applies to more complicated circuits. The "resistance" in the above equation actually refers to the value of the resistance of the entire circuit, both the bulb and all the connecting wires. However, because the connecting wires, usually made of copper, have very little resistance compared to the resistance of the bulb (actually the filament of the bulb, made of tungsten), we usually ignore the resistance of the connecting wires when using the relationship above. However, there is a special case when we cannot ignore the resistance of the connecting wires. This special situation is called a short circuit, and you will study it in the next activity.

Resistance and Thermal Energy

Why do materials like bulb filaments have a certain amount of resistance to the flow of electric charges? We will try to provide a reasonably simple answer to this question.[2]

---

[2] Scientists have other, more sophisticated models to help explain the concept of resistance. They are based on ideas beyond what we have been learning in this course, so we will not discuss those more sophisticated models here.

In Chapter 2 you learned that whenever an object slides over a surface, there is a friction force that opposes the motion of the object and tends to slow the object down. In the case of an electric-circuit we can imagine that when the battery pushes electric charges through the metal filament of the bulb, a similar thing happens. There are friction-like interactions between the moving electric charges and the atoms that make up the material of the filament wire. These interactions tend to decrease the amount of electric charge that flows through the filament each second. This is the origin of the *resistance* of the wire. The actual amount of resistance will depend not only on the strength of the friction-like interactions, but also on the length and thickness of the wire.

First, consider the length and thickness of the wire. In Experiment #1 you used stirrers and straws to determine that the resistance of a stirrer/straw increases if the stirrer/straw becomes longer or thinner. By analogy, we can assume that the amount of resistance of a wire in an electric-circuit becomes greater if the wires become longer or thinner.

Next, consider the friction-like interactions. The strength of the friction-like interactions between the moving electric charges and the atoms of the material depends both on the temperature of the material and the type of material. Consider the temperature effect first. For the same type of material, the strength of the interactions, and hence the amount of resistance, increases when the wire gets hotter. Tungsten filaments are used in bulbs because tungsten can get white-hot without melting. When a bulb is first turned on, the resistance of its filament changes drastically as it heats up from room temperature (low resistance) to its working temperature (high resistance).

Next, let's consider an example of how the strength of the friction-like interactions (and hence the resistance) depends on the type of material. The heater elements of most toasters are made from a special nickel-chromium alloy called "nichrome." You would rarely find heater elements to be made of copper. The reason is that the structure of copper is very different from the structure of nichrome. The consequence of this difference in structure is that the friction-like interactions occurring when electric charges move through copper is much, much weaker than the friction-like interactions occurring when the electric charges move through the nichrome alloy. This means that the amount of resistance of a copper wire is much smaller than the amount of resistance of a nichrome wire of the same length, thickness and temperature. This is why the heater elements of a toaster get hot enough to glow, while the copper power cord hardly warms up at all.

Returning to a light bulb, why does the bulb glow when there is an electric current in the filament wire? To help answer this question, again consider the analogy of the object sliding over a surface mentioned earlier. When the block slides over a surface, mechanical energy is transformed into thermal energy in the surface and this causes the surface to become warmer. In the case of the electric-circuit, when the charged particles are pushed by the battery through the bulb filament, electrical energy is transformed into thermal energy of the filament material. This causes the filament material to become warmer. When the material warms up sufficiently it will begin to glow, and as it becomes even hotter it will glow more brightly.

Summarizing Questions

S1: Two students both believe there is a flow of electricity in a simple circuit consisting of a battery and bulb. But they differ in thinking about whether the electricity flows one way or two ways.

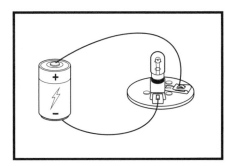

I think electricity flows out of each end of the battery, meets at the bulb, and causes the bulb to light.

I think electricity flows in one direction around the circuit. It comes out of one end of the battery, goes through the bulb, and then into the other end of the battery.

Kristen

Amara

(a) Do you agree with the one-flow, two-flow model, or with both? What is your reasoning?

CHAPTER 5

(b) Do Activities 1, 2 or 3 in this chapter provide any evidence that would support one model over the other? If so, what is the evidence?

S2: How do the length and thickness of the filament wire in a bulb each influence the amount of resistance of the wire? Using the blowing-through-straw analogy, explain why this makes sense.

S3: Two students are discussing what quantity associated with a single battery is the *same* in all circuits.

Student #1: The battery provides the same amount of **voltage** to the circuit, regardless of the number or properties of the bulbs. The battery always provides the same strength push on the electric charges in the circuit, and push is voltage.

Student #2: The battery provides the same amount of **electric current** in the circuit, regardless of the number or properties of the bulbs. The battery always causes the same amount of electric charge to pass by every point in the circuit in one second.

Do you agree with either Student #1 or Student #2? Explain your reasoning.

S4: Compare Newton's Second Law (rate of change of speed = force/mass) with Ohm's Law (current = battery voltage/resistance). In what ways are these two laws similar? What quantities are analogous to each other?

S5: Suppose when you hook up three bulbs in series with a battery and an ammeter, the ammeter reads a value of 16.4 mA. (See circuit below on the left, simulator turned on.) Imagine that you were to add a fourth bulb in series. (Circuit below to the right, simulator turned off.) **Do you predict the ammeter reading to increase, decrease or remain the same? Using Ohm's law as your basis, write a *scientific explanation* to justify your prediction.**

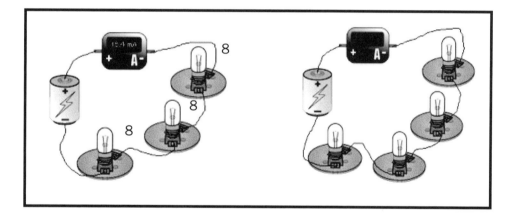

 Participate in a whole-class discussion.

Name:_____ Date:_____ Group: _____

Purpose

In activity 3 you analyzed a simple circuit with one battery and one bulb in terms of battery voltage, electric current and resistance. These three quantities are connected through Ohm's Law: Current = Battery Voltage/ Resistance. You also used the blowing-through-straw analogy to help you make sense of how the current depends both on battery voltage and resistance. In Chapter 5 Activity 2 Homework you analyzed series and parallel circuits in terms of energy. In this homework you will analyze the same circuits, but this time in terms of battery voltage, current and resistance.

Initial Ideas

Below, to the left, is a simple one-battery, ammeter, and one-bulb circuit. We will refer to this as Circuit A. In the middle is a series circuit consisting of one battery, an ammeter, and three bulbs. Call this circuit B. Finally, to the right is a parallel circuit consisting of one battery, an ammeter, and three bulbs. This is circuit C. All the batteries are 1.5 volts, and all bulbs are identical (same resistance).

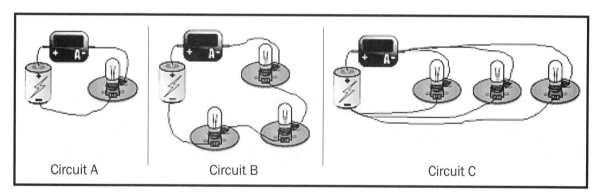

Circuit A   Circuit B   Circuit C

 How do you think the ammeter reading in Circuit B would compare with the ammeter reading in Circuit A? Why do you think so?

CHAPTER 5

How do you think the ammeter reading in Circuit C would compare with the ammeter reading in Circuit A? Why do you think so?

 How do you think the ammeter reading in Circuit C would compare with the ammeter reading in Circuit B? Why do you think so?

Collecting and Interpreting Evidence

 SIMULATOR EXPLORATION #1: How does the electric current compare in series and parallel circuits?

To check your predictions, open *Chapter 5 Activity 3 Homework Setup*. Construct Circuit A, turn on the simulator and record the ammeter reading in the Table below. Repeat with Circuit B, then with Circuit C. Record all ammeter readings in the Table. Keep the simulator open, as you will use it again later in the homework.

Values of Electric Current in Different Circuits

(Battery Voltage = 1.5 volts, all bulbs identical)		
Circuit	**Description**	**Ammeter Reading (mA)**
A	Simple one battery and one bulb	
B	One battery and three bulbs in **series**	
C	One battery and three bulbs in **parallel**	

 Which circuit has the largest value of the current?

Which circuit has the smallest value of the current?

 How does the data compare with your predictions in the Initial Ideas section?

Let's try to make sense of these results in terms of the blowing-through-straw analogy. In activity 3 you compared blowing with the **same strength** through a double-length stirrer and a single stirrer.

 Was the resistance of the double-length stirrer larger than, or smaller than, the resistance of the single stirrer?

 Was the air current in the double-length stirrer larger than, or smaller than, the air current in the single stirrer?

Now imagine that you taped three stirrers together, end-to-end, and blew through them with the same strength that you did with the single or double-length stirrer. Below is a side-view diagram of the stirrers.

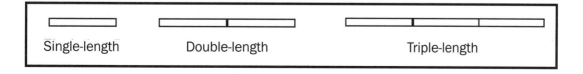

CHAPTER 5

Do you think the triple-length stirrer would have more or less resistance than the double-length stirrer? Why does that make sense?

 Do you think the air current in the triple-length stirrer would be larger or smaller than the air current in the double-length stirrer (assuming you blew with the same strength)? Why does that make sense?

Since the wire filaments of the bulb have much more resistance than any other part of the circuit, when thinking about the resistance of the whole circuit we need only consider the filament(s) of the bulb(s). The resistance offered by three bulbs in series would then be like the resistance offered by a single bulb with a filament three times as long.

 Is the resistance of three bulbs in series greater than or less than the resistance of a single bulb?

The resistance term in Ohm's Law refers to the resistance of the entire circuit—the total resistance of all the bulb filaments.

 Using Ohm's law, explain why the electric current in a three-bulb series circuit is smaller than the electric current in a one-bulb circuit. (Assume the battery voltage is the same for both circuits.)

In Activity 3 you compared blowing with the same strength through a straw and a single stirrer. The straw had a much larger diameter opening than the stirrer.

 Was the resistance offered by the straw larger than, or smaller than, the resistance offered by the stirrer?

 Was the air current in the straw larger than, or smaller than, the air current in the stirrer?

Now imagine that you bundled three stirrers together, side-by-side. The total opening in the three bundled stirrers has approximately the same diameter as the straw. (The walls of the stirrers are much thinner than their openings, so you can ignore the effects of the stirrer walls that touch each other, and consider just the openings.)

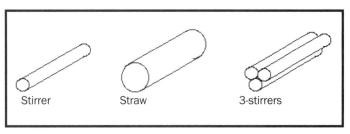

Stirrer   Straw   3-stirrers

CHAPTER 5

Do you think the 3-bundled stirrers would offer more or less resistance than the single-length stirrer? Why does that make sense?

 Do you think the air current in the 3-bundled stirrers would be larger or smaller than the air current in the single-length stirrer (assuming you blew with the same strength)? Why does that make sense?

You can think of each of the stirrers in the bundled combination as providing its own pathway for the flow of air from your mouth out the other end to the palm of your hand. In a similar way, in the three-bulb parallel circuit, each bulb is in its own pathway with the battery. Thus, three bulbs in a parallel circuit would be analogous to three straws bundled together.

 Is the resistance of three bulbs in parallel greater than or less than the resistance of a single bulb?

 Using Ohm's law, explain why the electric current in a three-bulb parallel circuit is greater than the electric current in a one-bulb circuit.

SIMULATOR EXPLORATION #2: How does the electric current compare in the different loops of a parallel circuit?

In Exploration #1 you used the simulator to determine the total electric current in the three-bulb parallel circuit. The ammeter alongside the battery measured the total electric current in the circuit: electric charges flowed through that ammeter before dividing up between the three separate loops, and

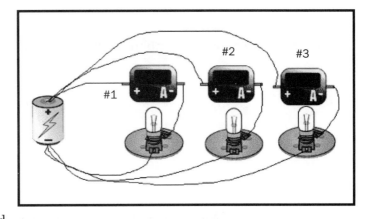

then combining again at the other end of the battery. Imagine that you connected an ammeter next to each of the three bulbs in the circuit, as shown above.

How do you think the three ammeter readings would compare with each other? Explain your reasoning.

If you sum the readings of the three ammeters, how would the sum compare with the value of the electric current measured with the single ammeter next to the battery (in circuit C) that you measured in Exploration #1? Why do you think so?

To test your ideas, return to the simulator. Set up the circuit shown above, and then turn on the simulator.

CHAPTER 5

Record below the values of the three ammeter readings.

Ammeter #1 = _____ ; Ammeter #2 = _____ ; Ammeter #3 = _____

How do the three readings compare with each other?

 How does the sum of the three ammeter readings compare with the single ammeter reading you recorded in the table in Exploration #1? Is it essentially the same, or different? (Essentially the same means that the sum is within 0.8 mA of the ammeter value from Exploration #1. This is because we can assume that each ammeter reading is accurate to 0.1 mA.)

 Why might these last two results make sense? (Think about the blowing-through-straw analogy. Would you expect the air current in each of the three straws to be the same or different? Would the sum of the air currents in each of the three straws be the same as the total air current from your mouth through all the straws?)

Summarizing Questions

S1: As you add more bulbs in series with a battery, does the resistance of the circuit increase, decrease or remain the same? Cite evidence from this homework to support your answer.

S2: As you add more bulbs in parallel with a battery, does the resistance of the circuit increase, decrease or remain the same? Cite evidence from this homework to support your answer.

S3: As you add more bulbs in series with a battery, does the electric current in the circuit increase, decrease or remain the same? Why does this make sense?

S4: As you add more bulbs in parallel with a battery, does the electric current in the circuit (as measured by an ammeter alongside the battery) increase, decrease or remain the same? Why does this make sense?

Purpose

In the previous two activities you learned how to describe an electric-circuit interaction either in terms of either energy or current. In either case you studied circuits consisting of a battery connected to one or more bulbs. There is a special situation, however, where a wire directly connects each end of a battery without a bulb being in that loop. This situation is known as a short circuit. In this activity you will explore short circuits and try to explain what happens in these circuits in terms of both energy and current.

 How can we explain what happens in a short circuit in terms of energy and current?

Initial Ideas

Consider the two circuits, A and B, shown at right. Circuit A is a simple battery-and-bulb circuit, while Circuit B is an example of a short circuit.

 During a certain time period (say 10 seconds), how does the energy transferred out from the battery in Circuit A compare with the energy transferred out from the battery in Circuit B? Why do you think so?

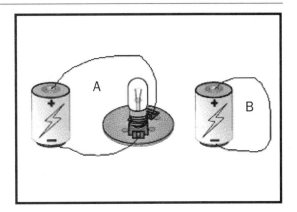

 If you were to measure the electric current in each circuit, how would they compare? Why do you think so?

 Participate in a whole-class discussion.

CHAPTER 5

Collecting and Interpreting Evidence

 EXPERIMENT #1: What happens in a short circuit?

EACH STUDENT WILL NEED:

■ Two batteries

■ One bulb

■ Three bare copper wires

■ One bulb in socket

■ Two hook-up wires

As mentioned in the Purpose section, a *short circuit* is a situation when a wire directly connects the positive and negative ends of a battery without a bulb being in that pathway. (One or more bulbs can still be connected to the battery in different pathways. Also, an ammeter can be connected in the same pathway without changing the status of the circuit as a short circuit.) Below are four examples of short circuits. Notice that the wire directly connecting the two ends of the battery can be short or long; its length does not matter. It can also be in two or more segments, as long as these segments are connected together.

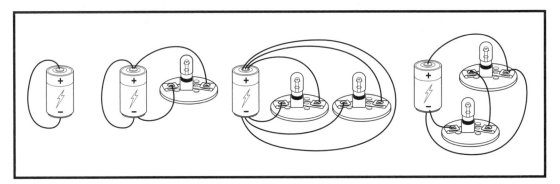

 Mark an X over the wire or wires that are causing the short circuit in each of the above four cases.

STEP 1: Touch a bare copper wire across the two terminals of the battery, as shown in the first example above. Hold it there several seconds.

 Does the battery or the wire get warm?

STEP 2: Remove the single wire connecting the two terminals of the battery, and put that battery aside. Use a second battery and connect bare copper wires from each end of the battery to the bulb-in-socket.

 Is the bulb glowing? (It should be.)

 Feel the two copper wires and the battery for several seconds. Do they feel warmer than before they were connected?

STEP 3: Use the third bare copper wire to short the circuit, as shown in the second example on the previous page. Hold the shorting wire in place for several seconds.

 What happens to the bulb?

 Does the battery or the single wire that is connected directly to the two terminals of the battery feel warm?

 Do the two wires connected between the battery and bulb (no longer glowing) feel as warm as the battery or the shorting wire?

CHAPTER 5

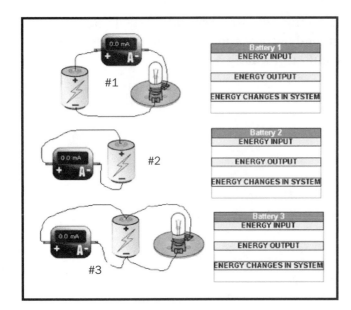

STEP 4: Open *Chapter 5 Activity 4 Setup*. Set up the three circuits shown at left. Circuit #1 is similar to Circuit A from the Initial Ideas section, and Circuit #2 is similar to Circuit B. (The circuits in the simulator, however, include ammeters so you can measure the current. Circuits #2 and #3 are short circuits.)

Run the simulator for 10 seconds, pause the simulator, and then record the values from the ammeters and the three Energy bar graphs in the following tables. You may need to rearrange the positions of the ammeters so they don't overlap.

Values of Electric Current in the Three Circuits

Circuit	Electric Current (mA)
#1 (Regular Circuit)	
#2 (Short Circuit, no bulb)	
#3 (Short Circuit, with bulb)	

Circuit 1 Battery (Regular circuit, one bulb–10 seconds)	
ENERGY INPUT	
Type of Energy =	Amount =
ENERGY OUTPUT	
Type of Energy =	Amount =
Type of Energy =	Amount =
ENERGY CHANGES IN SYSTEM	
Type of Energy =	Amount =
Type of Energy =	Amount =

Circuit 2 Battery (Short circuit, no bulb–10 seconds)	
ENERGY INPUT	
Type of Energy =	Amount =
ENERGY OUTPUT	
Type of Energy =	Amount =
Type of Energy =	Amount =
ENERGY CHANGES IN SYSTEM	
Type of Energy =	Amount =
Type of Energy =	Amount =

Circuit 3 Battery (Short circuit with bulb–10 seconds)	
ENERGY INPUT	
Type of Energy =	Amount =
ENERGY OUTPUT	
Type of Energy =	Amount =
Type of Energy =	Amount =
ENERGY CHANGES IN SYSTEM	
Type of Energy =	Amount =
Type of Energy =	Amount =

 By looking at the brightness numbers on the simulator, how does the brightness of the bulb in the regular circuit #1 compare with the brightness of the bulb in the shorted Circuit #3? Is this consistent with your observations?

CHAPTER 5

We will first analyze the circuits in terms of energy, and then in terms of current.

 How does the electrical energy transferred out from the battery in Circuit #2 compare to the electrical energy transferred out from the battery in Circuit #3? Are they about the same, or very different? (Both are short circuits.)

 How does the electrical energy transferred out from the battery in Circuit #3 (short circuit) compare to the electrical energy transferred out from the battery in Circuit #1 (regular circuit)? Are they about the same, or very different?

 Where does most of electrical energy transferred out from the battery in Circuit #3 go—to the bulb or to the shorting wire? How do you know?

You can check your answer to the previous question by returning to the simulator and adding an energy bar graph for the bulb in Circuit #3. Run the simulator for 10 seconds.

 What is the value of the electrical energy input to the bulb during these 10 seconds? How does that compare to the electrical-energy output from the battery during the same 10 seconds?

 Do the results from the simulator suggest that most of the electrical energy output from the battery goes to the bulb in Circuit #3 or to the shorting wire? How do you know? (The simulator cannot directly measure the electrical energy transferred to the shorting wire. Instead, you need to make an inference from the data you observe.)

 How does the increase in thermal energy and heat energy output in both the short circuits compare with the same quantities in the regular circuit?

CHAPTER 5

Is this consistent with the observation that a battery gets warmer when it is shorted compared to how warm it gets when it is connected in a regular, non-shorted, circuit?

 How does the decrease in chemical potential energy in the battery in both the short circuits compare with the same quantity in the regular circuit?

 Based on that comparison, which battery would you expect to die sooner, the one in a short circuit or the one in a regular (not shorted) circuit?

Now let's consider the electric current measurements.

 How does the electric current in the short circuits (#2 and #3) compare with the electric current in the regular circuit (#1)?

Although you did not measure the electric current in the loop containing the bulb in Circuit #3, if you did measure it, how would the electric current in the bulb loop compare with the electric current in the shorted wire loop? Why do you think so?

You can check your answer with the simulator. Because the simulator only provides three ammeters at a time, you need to use the ammeter from Circuit #2. Delete the battery and wires from Circuit #2 and add the ammeter to the bulb loop in Circuit #3, as shown here.

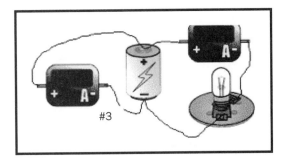

 Turn on the simulator. How does the electric current in the bulb loop compare to the electric current in the shorted loop?

CHAPTER 5

Let's see if we can make sense of the electric current results. Why would we expect the electric current in a shorted loop to be much greater than the electric current in a loop with a bulb? Recall from Activity 3 that the value of the electric current depends on both the battery voltage and the resistance. The exact relationship is given by Ohm's Law: Current = Battery Voltage/Resistance. When we use this law, the value of the resistance refers to the resistance of all the objects in a loop connected to the battery. We can assume the ammeter and the connecting wires have very low resistance. The bulb (mainly its filament) has a much higher resistance.

 Using Ohm's Law, explain why is the electric current in a shorting wire much greater than the electric current in a loop with a bulb?

Most connecting wires in a circuit are made of copper, which has a low resistance. In a short circuit, however, the copper wire can get very hot because the value of the electric current in that wire gets very high. Short circuits in household wiring and appliances can be very dangerous. The wires can get hot enough to set fire to surrounding materials. The function of fuses and circuit breakers is to break a connection in the circuit if the value of the electric current gets too high.

Summarizing Questions

S1: In terms of Ohm's Law, why does the electric current reach a very high value when a circuit is shorted? (You can draw on your answer to the last question in the previous section.)

S2: Below, to the left is a parallel circuit consisting of a battery and two bulbs. When a third wire is added as shown, the two bulbs both go out and the battery and the third wire become very warm. **Write a scientific explanation for why the battery becomes very warm.**

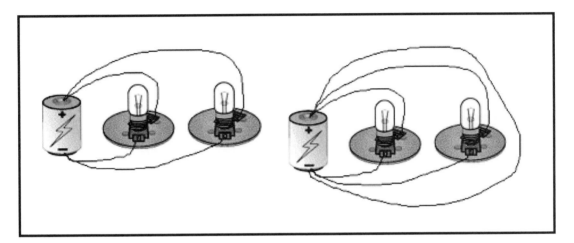

 Participate in a whole-class discussion about answers to the above questions.

CHAPTER 5

Activity 4 Homework—Children's Ideas about Electricity
Learning about Learning

Name:_____ Date:_____ Group:_____

Purpose

Throughout Chapter 5, you developed and tested ideas about electric energy and electric current. The purpose of this activity is to observe how competing models of the flow of electricity can emerge in the elementary science classroom and to discuss the sophistication of elementary students thinking.

  How do elementary students engage in scientific thinking about electricity?

Initial Ideas

 Up to now, you have had several opportunities to recognize your own initial and changing ideas and the ideas of elementary students. Based on your experiences in *PET*, what types of ideas do you think children will have about how electricity flows through a complete circuit to light a bulb?

Collecting and Interpreting Evidence

Movies for this activity can be found on your *PET Student Resources DVD*.

> **Use headphones when viewing videos and make certain that the volume on your computer is at its maximum setting.**

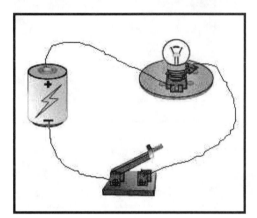

Second and third grade students were given a small light bulb, a battery and wires and were asked to figure out how to light the bulb. When they were successful, the teacher gave them battery and bulb holders, more wires and a switch. Finally, groups of students were asked to use words and pictures to draw their ideas on presentation boards that each group would present at the end of the activity.

Video Clip 1: How can you make a light bulb light?

 Open *C5Act4_HW_Circuits.mpg* and watch the movie.

 1. At time 00:02:10 Kevin starts to explain to the teacher how electricity is flowing through his circuit. How do you think Kevin is thinking about the direction in which electricity flows through his circuit (what is his model)? Use evidence from the movie and cut and paste statements from the transcript to support your claim about how Kevin is thinking.

Video Clip 2: Class Discussion: What did you discover about electricity?

In *C5Act4_HW_Elec_Models.mpg* the teacher asked the class what they discovered about electricity. Students had just finished lighting the bulb with one wire and a battery and they had connected circuits using holders and switches. In this section you will describe some of the different arguments made by Charlie, Harley, and Jacqueline. These students are identified by name in the picture on the right.

For the following questions, use evidence from the movie (such as gestures) and cut and paste statements from the electronic transcript to support your ideas about how students are thinking.

2. **Charlie's versus Harley's model:** What is Charlie's model (how does he think electricity flows through a circuit?)? What is Harley's model? How do you think Charlie's model is different from Harley's?

CHAPTER 5

3. What argument(s) does Charlie use to *support* his model? What argument(s) did Charlie use to *refute* Harley's model?

 4. What argument(s) does Harley use to *support* his model and *refute* Charlie's model?

 5. Jacqueline's model: What is Jacqueline's model? What argument(s) does she use to *support* her model and *refute* Charlie's model?

Summarizing Questions

 The following questions will be discussed in class. Take a moment to prepare your own reflections on these questions to share with your group.

S1: In *C5Act4_HW_Circuits.mpg* at time 02:44, Kevin and Skyler made a drawing of their circuit. Figure (a) shows them drawing the switch. The circuit in figure (a) is a complete circuit with a battery, switch, and bulb. By the time they finished, they had added an extra wire as shown in Figure (b). However, as you can see in Figure (c) the students correctly drew the configuration that would light the bulb with just a battery, a wire, and a bulb.

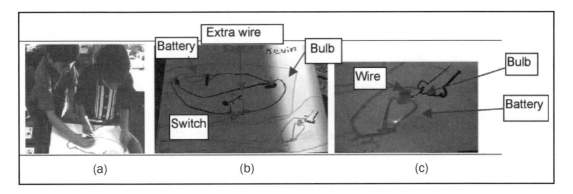

(a) (b) (c)

 Do you think the drawing of the extra wire in (b) was a mistake by the students or do you think they were intending to show something? If you think they were intending to show something, what do you think they were intending to show?

Do you think Skyler and Kevin's thinking is sophisticated or simplistic? Why?

S2: Consider Harley, Charlie, and Jacqueline's statements in the movie and in the transcript. Were these students thinking about electricity more in terms of energy, more in terms of current, or both? Provide evidence from the movie and the transcript to support your claims.

 Participate in a whole-class discussion. If you finish early, discuss anything that you found particularly interesting or troubling.

Name:_____ Date:_____ Group: _____

C5Act4_HW_Circuits.mpg

00:07:14	Jacqueline	'kay, give me that thing.
00:09:28	Georgina	But how do we do, put the little ball?
00:19:03	Georgina	Wait it gets hot, the wire gets hotter and hotter when we each put it on something.
00:28:10	Jacqueline	I think we, cause we put this one together with the metal.
00:33:09	Georgina	Jacqueline! Can't you see, watch come here. Could you see like a little wire?
00:44:28	Georgina	Put it, put it.
00:46:10	Jacqueline	Which one? This one?
00:47:09	Georgina	Yeah.
00:47:24	Jacqueline	Up here?
00:48:24	Georgina	Yeah. However you want it.
00:58:27	Jacqueline	Like that?
01:00:12	Georgina	Ah!
01:06:05	Jacqueline	There! There! It's gonna get hot.
01:10:18	Georgina	Hurry before it gets hot.
01:12:28	Jacqueline	What? Then what should we ...and then you see we connect it.
01:18:16	Georgina	And then right here connect it.
01:30:10	Georgina	We did it!!
01:34:04	Katlin	Can you get it? Well if it's hot that means it's, it's kind of working.
01:41:23	Katie	It works because you're touching the bottom so when you take it, you just take that wire and put it to the side of the light bulb and hook it up and maybe the wire from right there might be traveling over here and might be traveling over here and might be going to the wire and making it light up and maybe going to the bottom of the light bulb.

02:06:17	Ms. Harber	Alright, it sounds like you have a good idea of what's happening, I'm gonna give you some new materials.
02:10:16	Kevin	And these, these take the power from the battery.
02:14:11	Ms. Douglas	Okay and where does it go?
02:15:10	Kevin	It goes all the way until here to the light.
02:17:27	Ms. Douglas	Does it just stop there?
02:19:02	Kevin	No.
02:20:09	Ms. Douglas	Where does it go then?
02:21:18	Kevin	It goes to the light bulb.
02:22:21	Ms. Douglas	But then once it's in the light what happens?
02:23:22	Silvester	Yeah, it goes down here and then it goes right here.
02:25:09	Ms. Douglas	And then what does it do?
02:26:25	Kevin	It lights up.
02:27:24	Ms. Douglas	And it stays right in the light?
02:29:05	Silvester	Oh, let's try to put it right here.
02:31:10	Ms. Douglas	Okay, try some other things.
02:31:21	Silvester	Look at the light! (Having just connected the switch so it turns the bulb on and off.)
02:33:21	Kevin	We did it!
02:35:08	Ms. Douglas	So what's happening now?
02:36:12	Silvester	C'mon, put it on! See look at it.
02:38:24	Ms. Douglas	So it's a big circle still isn't it?
02:40:12	Silvester	Yeah!! We did it!
02:41:07	Kevin	We did it!
02:43:02	Silvester	No, it's okay, see look at (beginning diagram on presentation board).

02:46:10	Kevin	Okay, then this too.
02:50:23	Silvester	Oh, yeah.
02:54:30	Kevin	Oh then, then we have the thing to hold it. Don't we have that thing to hold it?
03:05:02	Silvester	Then what about this part?
03:09:19	Kevin	What part?
03:12:05	Silvester	(Erases a line representing a wire on discussion board.)
03:14:03	Kevin	No, that part's okay!
03:15:23	Silvester	I know, I was just...Where's the purple?
03:28:18	Kevin	And then, where's the ball, and then..
03:36:04	Silvester	You holded the wire right there (they decided to also draw a picture of how they lit the bulb with one wire and one battery).
03:38:18	Kevin	Put the wire down there.
03:41:10	Silvester	And the light bulb.
03:43:11	Kevin	The light bulb.
03:44:21	Silvester	Oh, we need a yellow!
03:54:04	Silvester	Yeah. That's how we did it.
03:55:24	Kevin	We did the one that has um um, before.
04:00:07	Ms. Douglas	Before, without the switch or with the switch?
04:02:09	Kevin	Without.
04:02:25	Ms. Douglas	Without?
04:03:17	Kevin	When, when, that's how we got here.
04:04:30	Ms. Douglas	Oh, to show..

CHAPTER 5

04:05:21	Kevin	Yeah.
04:07:02	Ms. Douglas	That's fine.
04:11:01	Diagrams	(Diagrams that each group completed at the end of the activity.)

C5Act4_HW_Elect_Models.mpg

00:05:05	Ms. Harber	So who can raise your hand and tell me some things you've discovered about electricity so far?
00:11:10	Charlie	That it travels through a wire but like um, it travels through any, um most stuff that's made out of metal and like wires, it's actually like little streaks made out of metal from the inside. So that's why it travels through.
00:29:23	Ms. Harber	So are there some things that electricity doesn't travel through?
00:32:02	Charlie	Um.
00:34:16	Lupe	Paper.
00:35:12	Charlie	Paper?
00:38:14	Harley	Um, electricity needs to travel through metal.
00:43:06	Harley	The battery's right here and then the wire and then more wires and that makes the circle.
00:49:01	Ms. Douglas	Okay, so electricity goes in a circle. Can we agree on that, can we say that, electricity goes...
00:54:10	Charlie	I don't really think it goes in a circle.
00:56:20	Ms. Douglas	You don't?
00:57:14	Charlie	Well, I mean I think it's supposed to go in a circle but like I don't think it travels like only one way.
01:04:07	Ms. Douglas	So it might be going.

01:05:26	Charlie	Yeah because maybe, because—
01:06:29	Harley	Yeah, but it still forms a circle.
01:09:04	Charlie	Yeah, I mean it forms a circle but the electricity but it does—the electricity doesn't go only one way. I mean like it goes two sides and then and so that, so that
01:17:28	Harley	But it still forms a circle.
01:19:06	Charlie	Yeah, so that they meet at the end and then they even give even more power (moving two fists up toward each other in a circle)
01:25:05	Ms. Douglas	So you think it goes like this...
01:25:26	Charlie	Yeah, and they give even more power.
01:26:06	Harley	Yeah, but it's still, it still makes a circle.
01:28:20	Charlie	That's what I'm saying, it is a circle but electricity doesn't go in one way, I mean...
01:36:18	Valerie	Some people are convinced that it goes both directions and I was just wondering if we had any observations that could support that idea.
01:44:22	Felix	Draw a picture maybe?
01:47:20	Charlie	I, I but like so if you only use one side and don't connect the other side um, it will only give power from one side and it won't have enough power so you need to connect the other side so it'll make double the power and then the light bulb can get enough energy to light, to light up.
02:13:23	Valerie	Katie was showing me (earlier) that electricity comes like this and goes drrrrrrvvv and goes in one, one direction and Charlie is saying it goes drrrrvvv in two directions.
02:22:20	Harley	But how could it do that cause, it, if it doesn't—then how could the powers combine?
02:29:12	Charlie	It's like the same power.
02:34:14	Jacqueline	Um, there's only one way um that the, the atoms from inside could go around and not two sides.
02:46:09	Harley	Atoms?
02:47:10	Jacqueline	Because, because they, when they touch together they can't keep going so they have to go only one side and keep going.
02:55:13	Harley	If it goes through two ways then it will just get stuck right there and then it will just go and then it will just go, it would just go off. But if you do it one way it would just keep going in a circle but if you go two ways it would just get, they'd crash into each other.

CHAPTER 5

03:13:14	Kevin	And stop?
03:14:07	Harley	Yes, and then the light bulb would just die.
03:17:29	Charlie	Um, um can I say something?
03:21:12	Ms. Douglas	Sure.
03:22:11	Charlie	Um, I think like if you do it one way, I think that the electricity stays in the light bulb because it uses it. And then like if you only do it one way, like it will use it and it won't go all the way—like I think it goes both ways because if it only went one way uh, I don't think it goes, I don't think it goes in a circle—I mean like one way because like, I think that the electricity that goes to a light bulb stays there and, and, and cause a light bulb uses it, uses the electricity.

Purpose

As you saw in Activity 2 in this Chapter, energy is conserved for each of the electrical devices you studied. That means that the total amount of energy that is input to each device can be accounted for either by being transformed to one or more types of energy output, or by **changes** (increases or decreases) in one or more types of energy within the device itself. (The case of the battery may look a little different at first because there is no input. However, you have seen that the energy output in this case can be accounted for by a **decrease** in chemical energy.) The equation form of the Law of Conservation of Energy is particularly useful when you know all but one of the values for the energy inputs, changes or outputs, and you can use the equation to calculate the unknown energy value. One purpose of this activity is to give you practice using the Law of Conservation of Energy to calculate unknown energy values.

Although the Law of Conservation of Energy accounts for all the types of energy outputs from a device, there is also the issue about whether the energy outputs are useful. (By "useful" we mean an output that corresponds to the intended function of the device.) Does all the energy input to a device get transformed into an energy output that is useful, or does only a certain percentage of that input energy get transformed to a useful energy output? A second purpose of this activity is to learn a way of describing how *efficient* a device is in transforming its energy input into a useful energy output.

 How can we use the Law of Conservation of Energy to calculate values of energy for electrical devices? How can we describe the energy efficiency of electrical devices?

Collecting and Interpreting Evidence

 EXPERIMENT #1: Exploring the buzzer

YOU WILL NEED:

- Battery
- Buzzer
- Hook-up wires

> **If your instructor does not have buzzers, then you can skip Step 1 and go right to Step 2.**

STEP 1: Connect the battery to the buzzer and make sure the buzzer works. If you feel the buzzer, you can tell it's vibrating. (Actually, the buzzer may only work if you connect the positive end of the battery to the appropriate wire on the buzzer, and the negative end to the other wire. If the buzzer does not work, try switching the wires connected to the two ends of the battery.)

CHAPTER 5

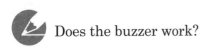 Does the buzzer work?

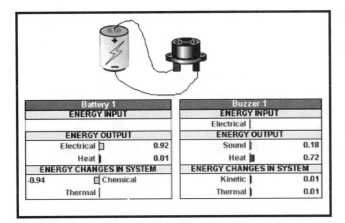

Battery 1		Buzzer 1	
ENERGY INPUT		ENERGY INPUT	
		Electrical	
ENERGY OUTPUT		ENERGY OUTPUT	
Electrical	0.92	Sound	0.18
Heat	0.01	Heat	0.72
ENERGY CHANGES IN SYSTEM		ENERGY CHANGES IN SYSTEM	
-0.94 Chemical		Kinetic	0.01
Thermal		Thermal	0.01

STEP 2: Consider the following battery and buzzer circuit from the simulator. Inside the buzzer is a small metal strip. When the buzzer is connected to the battery, the strip begins moving back and forth (vibrates) many times a second, and emits a "buzzing" sound. Imagine that a group of students in another class used the simulator to analyze the battery-buzzer circuit in terms of energy. They set up the circuit shown at left, and then ran the simulation for 20 seconds. Energy values are in units of joules. There are some energy values that are covered over and are not visible.

 Use the Law of Conservation of Energy to determine the increase in thermal energy in the battery during the 20 seconds. Don't forget to express your answer in units of joules.

 What was the amount of **electrical energy input** to the buzzer? How do you know? (Hint: Think about where this electrical energy came from.)

STEP 3: To check your answers, open *Chapter 5 Activity 5 Setup*. Construct the battery-buzzer circuit as already shown, and include the Energy bar graphs. Run the simulator for 20 seconds.

Record the missing energy values in the Energy bar graphs on the previous page.

How did the actual values compare with your predictions?

During the remainder of this activity we will look at the relationship between heat energy, useful energy, and efficiency.

STEP 4: In Activity 2 you studied energy transfers and changes in the following electric circuits:

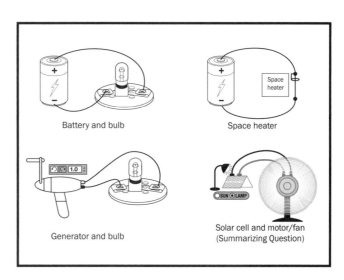

Battery and bulb

Space heater

Generator and bulb

Solar cell and motor/fan
(Summarizing Question)

CHAPTER 5

In answering the following questions you should refer to the Energy bar graphs that you filled in for each of these four circuits in Activity 2. If you do not have access to the information from Activity 2, you can use *Chapter 5 Activity 5 Setup* to construct each circuit, add energy bars, and run the simulator for 10 seconds. Then copy the energy values on a separate sheet of paper. (The space heater is called the *Nichrome Wire tool* in the tools palette of the simulator.) You can also use information from the battery and buzzer circuit you already explored.

 What type of energy output is common for **all** the devices when they operate?

 Why do you think this is?

STEP 5: It turns out that essentially all devices will become warmer as they function, and consequently will transfer heat energy to the surroundings. With a space heater, that's desirable, since the purpose of the space heater is to provide warmth. But the purpose of many other devices is to provide some other type of energy (e.g., light, electrical, mechanical), not heat energy. For example, when we use a battery to push electric charges around a circuit the useful type of output is electrical energy. The type of energy output that corresponds to the intended purpose of a device is called the "useful energy" output.

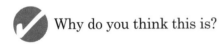 Consider the various devices that have been included in electric circuits that you have studied. In the second column of the Table on the next page, indicate the *useful* type of energy **output** for that device. (For the moment, ignore the other columns in the Table.)

The purpose of most devices is to transform one type of energy into another, usually from a type of energy input into a *useful* type of energy output. (In the case of the battery, use the decrease in chemical potential energy in place of an energy input.)

 Fill in the third column of the Table with the type of energy input (or chemical potential energy for the case of the battery).

Useful types of Energy and Efficiencies for Electrical Devices

Device	Useful type of energy output	Type of energy input	Amount of useful energy output during a certain time (joules)	Amount of energy input during a certain time (joules)	Efficiency of device (%)
Battery					
Generator					
Space Heater					
Bulb					
Motor (fan)					
Buzzer					

STEP 6: Go over the data you collected from the simulator Energy bar graphs and record values (in joules) for the energy inputs and useful energy outputs in the fourth and fifth column of the Table. (It doesn't make a difference whether the simulator is run for 10 seconds or 20 seconds, so long as the input and output energies for each device refer to the same time period.)

CHAPTER 5

For each device, is the amount of useful energy output less than, equal to, or greater than the amount of energy input? Why do you think this is?

 Do you think it would ever be possible, in any device, for the amount of **useful** energy output to be greater than the amount of energy input (or decrease in chemical energy)? Explain your thinking.

STEP 7: Scientists have a measure of how efficient a device is at converting its energy input (or decrease in chemical energy) to useful energy output. This measure expresses the amount of useful energy output as a percentage of the energy input and is called the **efficiency** of the device.

For example, suppose a device has an energy input, over a certain period of time, of 200 J, but over that same time period has a useful energy output of 150 J. In this case only three-fourths of the input is transformed to useful output, so the device is said to be 75% efficient.

In general, efficiency can be calculated from the following formula:

$$\text{Efficiency (in \%)} = \frac{\text{Useful Energy Output}}{\text{Energy Input}} \times 100$$

 Calculate the efficiencies of the devices in the previous Table and record those values in the last column.

 Which is the most efficient device (according to the simulator)?

 Which is the least efficient device?

CHAPTER 5

STEP 8: You may have been surprised at how low the efficiencies of some of the devices were.

 Do you think it is possible for a device that has *moving* parts (like the motor/fan and the buzzer) to have an efficiency of 100% (meaning **all** of its energy input is converted to useful energy output)? Why, or why not?

 The bulb does not have any moving parts, so you might think that its efficiency would be higher than that of the motor/fan and the buzzer, but it is not. Why do you think this is? (Think about why the filament glows.)

 In fact, regular (incandescent) light bulbs (that produce light by heating a filament with an electric current), like those that most people use in their homes, have efficiencies of only about 5% to 8%. Most of the energy output is in the form of heat energy, since the filament has to be at a very high temperature (greater than 4000 °F) to glow brightly and produce a reasonable amount of light energy as an output.

This means that a 100-W bulb has an input of 100 J of electrical energy every second but an output of, at best, only, 8 J of light energy per second. So for every 8 J of light energy you must pay the power company for 100 J of electrical energy.

Fluorescent bulbs, on the other hand, work in a different way. They use electrical energy to excite individual gas atoms inside them; these atoms then emit ultraviolet radiation that is converted to visible light by the white coating on the inside surface of the fluorescent bulb. In theory this process does not produce any heat energy output, but in practice the electrical components inside the bulb do warm slightly.

Nevertheless, the efficiency of a fluorescent bulb is about 25% (approximately four times greater than a regular bulb).

Suppose you wanted a fluorescent bulb to produce the same 8 J of light energy output per second as the regular 100-W bulb discussed above. How much electrical energy input would be needed per second? Why does this make fluorescent bulbs cheaper to run than regular bulbs?

Though fluorescent bulbs are more expensive to buy than regular bulbs, it can be shown that their much better energy efficiency and longer lifetime make them much more cost-efficient to use in the long run.

Summarizing Questions

S1: A group of students are using the simulator to analyze a circuit consisting of a bulb and a buzzer connected in parallel to a battery. They ran the simulator for 20 seconds. On the next page is the circuit, including the Energy bar graphs. As you can see, some of the energy values are missing from the Energy bar graphs.

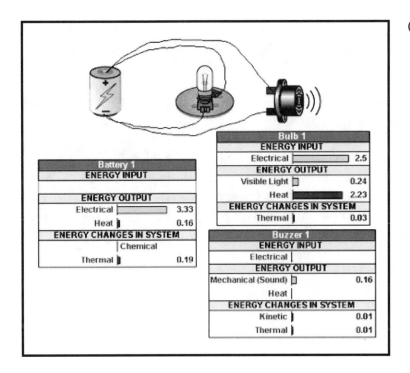

Battery 1		
ENERGY INPUT		
ENERGY OUTPUT		
Electrical		3.33
Heat		0.16
ENERGY CHANGES IN SYSTEM		
	Chemical	
Thermal		0.19

Bulb 1		
ENERGY INPUT		
Electrical		2.5
ENERGY OUTPUT		
Visible Light		0.24
Heat		2.23
ENERGY CHANGES IN SYSTEM		
Thermal		0.03

Buzzer 1		
ENERGY INPUT		
Electrical		
ENERGY OUTPUT		
Mechanical (Sound)		0.16
Heat		
ENERGY CHANGES IN SYSTEM		
Kinetic		0.01
Thermal		0.01

(a) Determine the change in chemical energy in the battery during the 20 seconds. Is this an increase or decrease in energy? Show all your work and express your answer in units of joules.

(b) How much electrical energy was transferred to the buzzer in 20 seconds? How do you know?

(c) How much heat energy did the buzzer transfer to the surroundings in 20 seconds? How do you know?

S2: Halogen bulbs are more efficient and last longer than incandescent bulbs. Suppose a particular halogen bulb has an efficiency of 30%. If, over a certain period of time, the bulb uses 160 joules of electrical energy to operate, how much light energy is transferred from the bulb during this same period of time? How do you know?

S3: After thinking about the ideas of energy conservation and efficiency, two students made the following statements:

I don't understand all this fuss about making sure the light bulbs we use have a high efficiency. Since we know energy is conserved, no energy gets destroyed, so why worry?

Amara

I'm not sure energy really is conserved. The heat energy output from a bulb just disappears, so it can never be used again. If we use more efficient light bulbs at least we lose less energy.

Kristen

CHAPTER 5

Discuss Amara's and Kristen's statements with your group and comment on them below.

 Participate in a whole-class discussion about answers to the questions.

Explaining Electric-Circuit Phenomena

As mentioned earlier in this chapter, you can describe the electric-circuit interaction either in terms of energy or in terms of electric current. This implies that you can also explain or make predictions about electric-circuit phenomena in terms of energy and/or electric current. When using an energy approach you apply the Law of Conservation of Energy, and you should also draw the appropriate I/O energy diagrams. When using an electric-current approach, you generally use Ohm's Law. (In that case, you do not need to draw an energy diagram, but only a diagram of the electric-circuit, if appropriate.)

Your instructor will distribute a copy of *Scientists' Ideas: Electric-circuit Interaction.* This provides a summary of the important ideas you developed in the cycle, and you should use these ideas to support the narrative part of your explanations. As always, you should evaluate explanations based on the criteria of accuracy, completeness and logical reasoning and clarity.

How does the Wake-up Machine Work?

Otis, a 12-year-old middle school student, has a problem. He is finding it more and more difficult to get up in the morning. A normal alarm clock just doesn't seem to be enough. He needs something better. He dreams of a device that can wake him up by blowing air on him, shining lights into his eyes and making a clanging or buzzing sound. He needs a wake-up machine.

You will first use the computer simulator to design the wake-up machine and see if it works. (If your instructor has fan/motors and buzzers, you can carry out Steps 1, 2 and 3 on the next page first with the actual apparatus, and then use the computer

CHAPTER 5

STEP 1: From the Simulator Index page, open *Chapter 5 Activity 6 Setup*. In the setup window place a battery, bulb, buzzer and fan.

STEP 2: Connect everything together so that when you run the simulator the bulb glows (with a brightness number of at least 50), the fan rotates, and the buzzer buzzes. Remember that the buzzer only works when its two terminals are connected in the correct way in the circuit. You can tell the buzzer is working when it looks like this picture.

STEP 3: Figure out how to add a switch to your circuit.

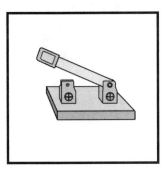

What **should** happen is this: *When you lower the handle of the switch (switch closed), the circuit should be activated: the bulb should go on, the buzzer should begin buzzing, and the fan should begin rotating and blowing air.* When you can make your circuit do that, it will be a prototype of a simple wake-up system. (In an actual device, a clock would activate the switch.)

Sketch a circuit diagram of the arrangement that works (including the switch).

To explain how the wake-up machine works, choose just *one* of the
devices (bulb, buzzer or fan), draw the appropriate I/O energy diagram,
and then in the narrative describe in both words and numbers (joules)
all the energy transfers to/from and changes in the device you chose.
You can obtain energy values from the simulator.

Describe the _____ *using an I/O energy diagram:*

Write the narrative:

 Participate in a whole-class discussion to go over the explanations.

PET

Light Interactions

Purpose

Most people realize that light is necessary to see things. But does that mean that just because there is light around, you will be able to see everything you look at? What you see may depend on what happens when light illuminates the objects you are looking at. In this chapter you will gather evidence to describe various ways that light interacts with objects, and you will describe these interactions in terms of energy transfer. We begin by exploring some simple and familiar things, like what happens when light strikes a mirror.

> **1. How does light interact with a shiny surface?**
> **2. When you look at a light source or a mirror image, does light interact with your eye?**

Initial Ideas

Suppose a piece of white paper with a small Mylar™ square at its center is placed on your table. (Mylar is a mirror-like material.) Three members of your team stand around the table.

Imagine the room lights are turned off. One group member uses a flashlight to illuminate the white paper and Mylar, as suggested in the picture.

Discuss the following questions with your group.

 Many of you are familiar with the observation that mirrors can dazzle you. Which of the three people standing around the table might be dazzled by the Mylar square (which acts like a small mirror)? Why do you think so?

Using lines to represent light, draw a diagram to show how the mirror dazzles a person.

If you thought the mirror would not dazzle one or more of the people standing around the table, what do you think the mirror would look like to them? Would it appear white, gray, black, or something else?

 Participate in a whole-class discussion.

Collecting and Interpreting Evidence

You will perform a series of three experiments to check your predictions and to gather evidence to answer the two key questions for the activity.

 EXPERIMENT #1: What does each person see?

YOU WILL NEED:

- White paper with Mylar™ square
- Flashlight
- Flat mirror
- Protractor (to measure angles)
- Notebook-size sheet of white paper

The room should be darkened while you perform this experiment.

STEP 1: Set up the white paper with the Mylar square on your table. Choose one member to hold the flashlight. The other members should stand around the table, as suggested in the drawing on the previous page. When everyone in the class is ready, the instructor will turn off all the lights to make the room as dark as possible.

STEP 2: The flashlight person should turn on the flashlight and illuminate the entire piece of white paper (with the Mylar square at its center). Each group member should say out loud what he/she sees when looking at the Mylar square, and the white paper. Does each appear dazzling bright, white, gray, black or something else? In particular, pay attention to the face of anyone who says the Mylar appears dazzling bright. Is there any illumination on that person's face? Each person should also move his or her head up and down and back and forth to determine if what is seen depends on the position of the eyes.

STEP 3: Switch positions around the table and repeat. Each team member should try each position, and all members should agree on what is seen.

 Write your observations (*dazzling bright, gray, white* or *black*) in the following Table.

Person	Appearance of Mylar Square to that Person
Flashlight person	
Side person	
Opposite person	

 For people who say they are dazzled, is there illumination on their faces?

 How do your observations compare with your predictions in the Initial Ideas section?

 EXPERIMENT #2: What happens when a beam of light strikes a shiny surface?

The room should be darkened while you perform this experiment.

STEP 1: Hold the front of the flashlight about 30 cm (about 12 inches) above the sheet of white paper and aim the beam onto the paper.

Describe the illumination on the paper: Is the entire paper uniformly illuminated, or is there a circular spot of light on the paper?

STEP 2: Turn the flashlight over and mount it on the right edge of the paper as shown. Hold the flat mirror about 10 cm (4 inches) above the flashlight. Tilt the mirror a little so you can see some illumination on the sheet of paper.

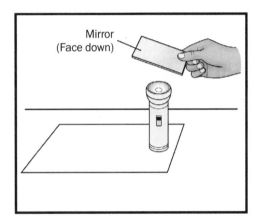

 Describe the illumination on the paper when you use the mirror: Is the entire paper uniformly illuminated, or is there a circular spot of light on the paper?

 Is the size and shape of the pattern of illumination on the paper with the mirror very similar to, or very different from, the pattern without the mirror (Step 1)?

STEP 3: Tilt the mirror more and more and watch what happens to the spot of illumination on the paper.

 Does the spot of illumination stay still, or does it move?

The light is going from the flashlight to the mirror, and then from the mirror to the paper. We say that the light **reflects** from (bounces off) the mirror. When you tilted the mirror you noticed that the spot of illumination also moved. Is the angle at which the light strikes the mirror related to the angle at which the light reflects from the mirror?

Simulator Exploration

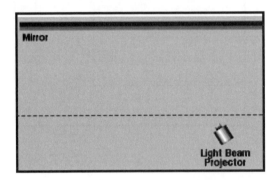

To help answer the question about angles, you can use a special computer simulator that includes a light beam projector and a mirror. The simulator was programmed so that when the beam projector is turned on, the light beam will reflect from the mirror in the same way that an actual light beam would reflect from an actual mirror.

STEP 4. From the computer simulator index page open *Chapter 6 Activity 1 Setup.* The setup area should look similar to the picture above.

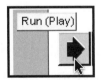

Press the RUN button to turn on the light beam projector. You should see a light beam strike and reflect from the mirror.

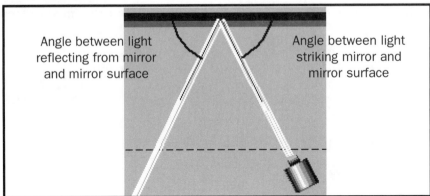

Using the protractor, carefully measure the angle between the middle of the light beam striking the mirror and the surface of the mirror. Record this angle in the left column of the Table below.

 Also measure and record the angle between the middle of the reflected beam and the surface of the mirror.

Comparing the angle at which light strikes a mirror with the angle at which the light reflects from the mirror

Angle between light striking mirror and mirror surface	Angle between light reflecting from mirror and mirror surface

STEP 5: Below we provide instructions on how you can move and rotate the beam projector, so the light beam strikes the mirror at different angles.

 Make observations for several different angles for the beam striking and reflecting from the mirror surface, and record results in the Table above.

Directions for rotating and re-positioning the beam projector

You can keep the simulator running during these changes.

1. When you want to rotate or move the beam projector, make sure the Select button is depressed.

2. Click on the beam projector in the setup window to "select" it.

3. To **move** the projector to a new position, place the cursor on the middle of the projector and click-drag it in any direction you want. To **rotate** the beam projector counter-clockwise, place the cursor on the rotation handle and click-drag the cursor upwards. To rotate the projector clockwise, click-drag the cursor downward.

Look over the data in your Table. What seems to be the relationship between the angle that the light strikes the mirror and the angle that the light reflects from the mirror?

 EXPERIMENT #3: When you look at a light source, or a mirror image of a source, does light interact with your eye?

STEP 1: Hold the flashlight and aim the beam at your face. Move it until the flashlight bulb is *dazzling* bright. Another person should observe where on your face the flashlight beam is striking.

Each person should have a turn at holding the flashlight.

 To the person holding the flashlight, how does it feel when you see the bulb as dazzling bright?

 To the person watching your face, is the area around your eye illuminated when you claim it's dazzling bright?

When you look at a light source, what is the evidence suggesting there is an interaction between the source and your eye, and that light actually enters your eye?

STEP 2: Hold the mirror about 20 cm (8 inches) in front of your face. With the other hand, hold the flashlight very close to your cheek and aim it so the mirror image of the flashlight bulb is *dazzling* bright. Another group member should carefully observe where your face is illuminated when you claim the image is dazzling bright.

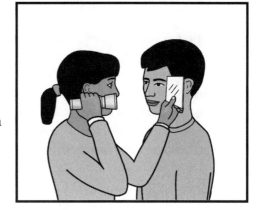

 To the person holding the flashlight, how does it *feel* when you see the mirror image of the bulb as dazzling bright?

 To the person watching your face, is the area around your eye illuminated when you claim the mirror image of the bulb is dazzling bright?

 When you look at a mirror image of the light source, what is the evidence suggesting there is an interaction between the source, mirror and your eye, and that light actually enters your eye?

CHAPTER 6

Light and Energy

The type of interaction occurring when light illuminates objects or your eye
is called a **light interaction**. The type of energy transferred during a light
interaction is called **light energy**. When the interacting objects include the source,
a shiny object, and your eye, it is best to describe the interactions by drawing a
source/receiver energy diagram. Below we consider two cases.

Light interaction between a light source and your eye

In Chapter 5 you studied how a flashlight works. For now, let's just consider
the flashlight as a light source. When it is turned on, the battery decreases in
chemical potential energy. As Experiment #3 suggests, when light enters your eye
something occurs inside your eye-brain system that results in your ability to "see"
the object you are looking at. Although the visual process is complicated, we will
treat the eye as a "black-box" and just assume that when light energy enters the
eye, there is an increase in what we will call "eye-brain system energy."[1]

Complete the following S/R energy diagram to describe the light interaction
between a flashlight and your eye (when you look directly at a flashlight).

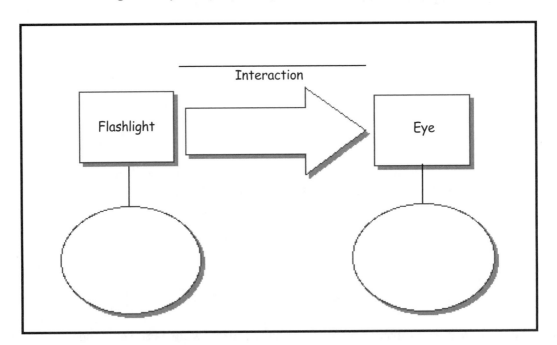

---

[1] The term *eye-brain system energy* is only being defined for the purposes of this *PET* curriculum. It is not a
standard term used in the science community.

If the light source is an electrical source that you plug into a socket, the electricity originates at some distant electric power plant. However, most electric power plants use fossil fuels as energy sources, and when the fossil fuels are consumed there is a decrease in their chemical potential energy. Therefore, whenever we describe the light interaction between an electric light source or a battery-operated light source, we can still describe the energy change in the source as a decrease in chemical potential energy.

Light interaction between a light source, a shiny object, and your eye

As you saw earlier in the activity, when a shiny object is illuminated by light from a source, the light is reflected in a particular direction. If you are positioned so the reflected light enters your eye, there is an interaction between the source and your eye via the shiny object. The shiny object just re-directs the light energy from the source to your eye. Complete the following S/R energy diagram to describe the interactions when you look at a mirror image of a light source.

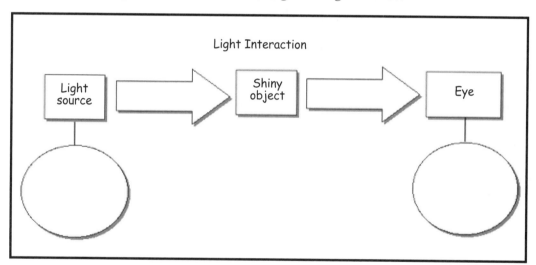

Light Ray Diagrams

An S/R energy diagram describes what types of energy are transferred between objects, and what types of energy changes occur within objects, if any, during interactions. In the case of light, it is also convenient to draw diagrams to show in what direction the light energy travels between objects and what happens to the light when reflecting from the surface of an object. Scientists draw light ray diagrams to show this. A light ray is a straight line with an arrow. The arrow shows the *direction* the light is traveling.

Following are some rules you should follow when drawing light ray diagrams. We illustrate these rules with a light ray diagram describing how light behaves when an observer sees the image of a flashlight in a mirror. (See picture below to the left. The light ray diagram is below the picture.)

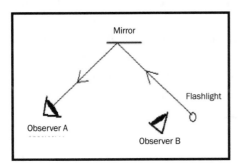

- All light ray diagrams should start with light leaving a light source, interacting with one or more objects, and then ending up in the eye(s) of an observer (or more than one observer). These diagrams are usually drawn from a "side view" or "top view" perspective. Make sure the light ray arrows show the direction that the light travels.

- When a light ray strikes a shiny surface, you should draw the single reflected light ray so that it makes (approximately) the same angle with the surface as the light ray striking the surface.

- When an observer sees an object, you must show a light ray originally from the source (and perhaps reflecting from a mirror) entering the observer's eye.

The light ray diagram above shows how Observer A (the boy in the picture) sees the mirror image of the light source. Another observer, standing to the right of the mirror (but not shown in the picture), would **not** see the mirror image because light from the flashlight, reflecting off the mirror, cannot get into Observer B's eye.

Summarizing Questions

S1: How does light interact with a shiny surface? What evidence from the activity supports your answer?

S2: When you look at a light source or a mirror image of the source, does light interact with your eye? What evidence from the activity supports your answer?

S3: Below is a side-view diagram showing a (light) source, a small mirror, and four observers looking towards the mirror.

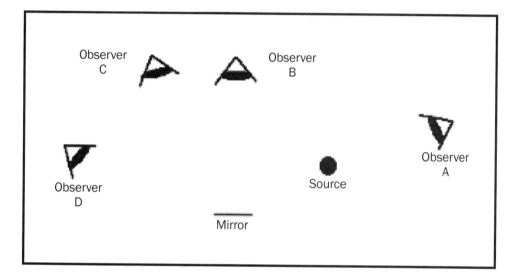

(a) Which of the observers, if any, would see the reflection of the source in the mirror? Support your answer by drawing a light ray diagram above.

(b) What would the other observers see when looking at the mirror? Explain your answer.

S4: Cyclists often wear a special device on their head with a small mirror for safety. The mirror is usually located in front of and to the left of their eyes. The picture shows a cyclist at night looking into her mirror and seeing the headlights of a car behind her. Write a **scientific explanation** for how the cyclist can see the headlight of the car.

Draw a light ray diagram to describe the situation:

Write the narrative: (Tell the story of how light goes from the headlamp to the mirror to the eye.)

 Participate in a whole-class discussion to review your answers to the Summarizing Questions and to the energy and light ray diagrams you have drawn.

Name:_____ Date:_____ Group: _____

1. To the right is a side-view drawing of a room. There is a ceiling lamp, with a card in front of it that blocks light from going straight down to the floor. A small mirror (M1) is stuck to the wall. An observer is looking towards the floor. Show where you should place a second small mirror (M2) flat on the floor, so the person will see the image of the ceiling lamp when looking in M2. Draw a light ray diagram to support your answer. (In this case, the light must reflect from two mirrors.)

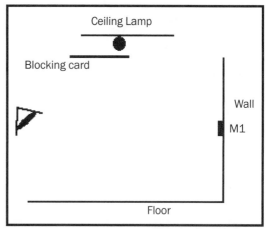

2. A retro-reflector is a device that always reflects light back in the same direction from which it came. (*Retro* comes from a Latin word that means backward or back.)

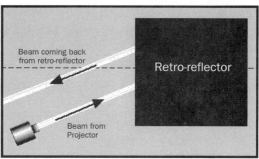

In the picture above right, taken from the reflection simulator, the retro-reflector is hidden behind the black box. Open *Chapter 6 Activity 1 Homework #1 Setup* from the simulator index page. Your task is to construct an arrangement of two mirrors in the Reflection Simulator so that when you aim the beam at the arrangement, it reflects back out in a path parallel (along same direction) to itself—just as shown in the picture above. Directions for how to use the Reflection Simulator are provided at the end of this Homework.

When you have figured it out, draw a picture of the arrangement of mirrors, or print out the arrangement from the simulator and tape it in the space below. Draw your diagram very carefully to show exactly how the mirrors are placed and how the light reflects from them.

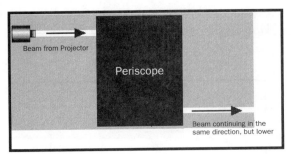

3. A periscope is a device that allows you to view things that are either higher than or lower than your line of sight. For example, you can use a periscope to see what's on the other side of a high wall. In submarines, people use the periscope to see what is above the water.

In the picture above, taken from the simulator, the periscope is hidden behind the black box. Your task is to use the Reflection Simulator and construct an arrangement of two mirrors so that when you aim the beam at the arrangement, it comes out lower on the other side, but traveling in the same direction—just as shown in the picture.

When you have figured it out, draw a picture (or print, cut and paste from the simulator) showing how the mirrors are arranged. Draw your diagram very carefully to show exactly how the mirrors are placed and how the light reflects from them.

How To Use the Reflection Simulator

Open this simulator at *Chapter 6 Activity 1 Homework #1 Setup* on the *PET* Simulator index page.

1. To place the beam projector, click the beam projector tool.

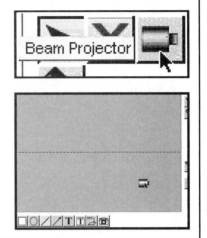

Then click the lower right portion of the setup area. (The entire setup area turns to a gray color.)

2. *Click the RUN button to turn on the beam projector)*

3. You can rotate the beam projector so the beam goes in any direction. To do this, first click the Select button.

Then click the beam projector in the setup area. This will "select" it. You will see four small black squares at the corners of the beam projector, and a small bent double-arrow to the lower right.

4. Click the double arrow and drag it upward or downward until it points in the direction you want. (In this example the beam points straight upward.)

 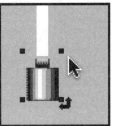

5. To *drag out* a mirror in the setup area, first click the mirror tool in the palette.

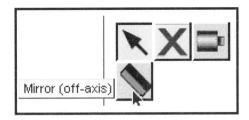

Then **click-drag** out the mirror in the upper right part of the setup area, so the beam strikes the middle of the mirror. (Note: If you just click in the setup area, the mirror will *not* appear. You must click and drag the cursor.)

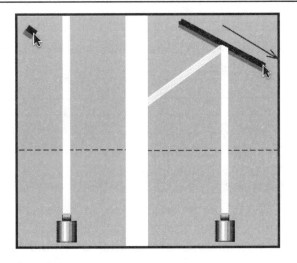

You can drag out as many mirrors as you wish.

6. You can easily change the
mirror's direction so the
beam strikes it at a different
angle. Click the Select
button, and then click the
mirror to select it.

Click-drag the selection
handles (small black square)
to rotate or change the size of
the mirror.

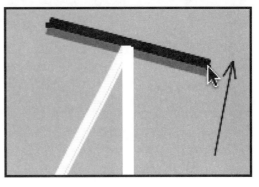

Name:_____ Date:_____ Group: _____

This article provides a broad overview of educational research on student ideas about light. In the educational research literature, student ideas have been referred to as misconceptions, pre-conceptions, naïve conceptions, and intuitive knowledge. Students' ideas are often consistent, reliable, and reasonable to students even though they are not necessarily consistent with scientists' ideas. Because a student's ideas make sense to the student and because teachers can utilize these ideas effectively in instruction, some educational practitioners and researchers are more comfortable using the term "resources" or "common ideas" to refer to students' ideas (Hammer, 2000).

Educational research has revealed that several common ideas about light exist among school-age children. Common ideas that appear in children's written work and in children's talk are discussed below.

Common Idea 1: The Source/Effect Idea

Studies involving large samples of children suggest that 10- and 11-year-old children tend to speak of light in terms of its source or its effects (Guesne, 1985). In a study conducted in a sunny room children were asked "Where is there light in this room?" Many responded by pointing to the light bulb on the ceiling (source) or by pointing to a spot of light on the wall (effect). When asked whether light moves, children responded in terms of the source. For example, children reported that the light on the ceiling

does not move, but a flashlight or the headlights of a car do move. The source/effect idea makes it difficult to explain how we see things or how light is reflected from a mirror into one's eyes.

Another example of the source/effect idea can be found in children's common ideas about shadows. Elementary aged students often view a shadow as an independent entity that actually propagates from the object to the sidewalk or screen. According to this idea, light triggers the movement of a shadow from the object to the sidewalk or screen (Feher and Rice, 1988; Feher, 1990). In this view of shadows, light is only involved to the extent that it triggers the motion of the shadow. In order to develop the scientific idea of a shadow as the blocking of light, the learner must view light as an entity that moves through space and interacts with objects.

Common Idea 2: Light as an Entity Idea

Older children aged 13-14 also speak of light in terms of its source and effects. However, they are more likely than younger children to speak of light as an entity located in space (Guesne, 1985). The idea that light is an entity in space between the source and the effect is consistent with the scientists' idea about light. This idea is useful for explaining shadows, reflection, and the process of seeing, since it allows us to discuss the interaction of light with an object and/or the eye. The notion of light as a source or as an effect does not provide as much versatility.

Common Idea 3: The Mirror Reflects Light in all Directions Idea

Both young and old students conceive of a mirror as a device that reflects. They typically view the reflection of light from a mirror as the scattering of light in all directions. While this idea is consistent with the notion of light as an entity, it is inconsistent with observations. The Mirror Reflects Light in all Directions Idea may be associated with everyday experiences such as getting blinded by sunlight when it is reflected by a car mirror or being able to shine an intense spot of light on the wall using a mirror. This idea is consistent with the notion that light is an entity in space because it describes the behavior of light when it interacts with a shiny surface.

Common Idea 4: The Intrinsic Illumination Idea

Children typically do not believe that non-shiny surfaces such as white paper reflect light. Instead, they describe this interaction in terms of the intrinsic illumination of the paper: When the light shines upon the paper, the paper becomes illuminated and glows like a lantern or a light source.

This view is consistent with the Source/Effect idea where the interaction of light with the white paper is explained not in terms of the behavior of the light, but in terms of the effect of illumination of the paper. Even students who explain light interaction with a flat mirror in terms of light as an entity in space often resort to Source/Effect ideas when explaining why they can see white paper when light shines upon it. In this case, the paper "absorbs" the light.

In the case of the white paper, the paper, not the light, has the property of glowing. Guesne (1985) argues that the conception of light as an effect may be due to children's sensory perceptions. She argues that children view light as an entity in space or as a source such as a flashlight only when the light is intense enough to produce a perceptible effect such as a blinding effect. When light is not seen to impact one's senses in this intense way, it is not seen as a thing, or an entity; it is only seen in terms of its effects.

Common Idea 5: The Vision Idea

When asked how one is able to "see" light or objects, children often associate the process of seeing with an active role of the eye rather than as an interaction of light with the eye. Children of ages 7-12 tend to draw lines of vision between the light source and the eye as shown in the picture below.

In most cases, students do not think that something is actually coming out of the eye, but that the eye is seeing through its active "vision." This is consistent with the Source/Effect idea rather than the Light as an Entity idea because vision is attributed to the active processes associated with the eye rather than the behavior of light as it moves through space and interacts with objects.

It is not clear exactly what children mean by "vision" although it appears that they define vision as the thing or process that allows us to see. The vision idea is incomplete in the sense that it does not involve the interaction of light with the object or the eye. Nevertheless, it can be useful because it does involve both the eye and the object. Some children as young as 10-years-old have built their idea of vision into an idea that also involves the brain.

Common Idea 6: The Brain is Involved in Seeing Things

As shown in the picture above right, to the child, vision appears to be the process by which people see and vision is associated with the brain. It is not clear from the diagram that the light is actually entering or interacting with the eye, but the brain is clearly depicted as associated with the eye and the process of seeing.

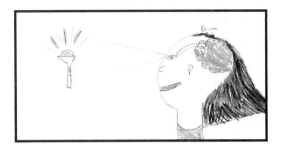

Close inspection of the picture reveals an "image" of the flashlight in the students' brain.

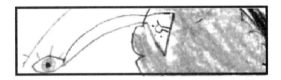

Common Idea 7: In Order For Us to See Things, Light Must Enter the Eye

This scientifically accepted idea is a less common pre-instructional idea than the common ideas about seeing discussed above. This idea requires that students conceive of light as an entity in space that interacts with objects including the eye. As mentioned in Common Idea 1: The Source/Effect idea, young students typically view light as a source (e.g., a flashlight or a lamp) or its effects (e.g., a spot of light on the wall) and rarely conceive of light as an entity that travels through space. An instructional implication of this is that it is important for a teacher to be aware that her students may need to develop ideas about light as an entity that interacts with objects before they can develop a meaningful understanding of how light is involved in how people see things such as the moon, a flashlight, or an apple.

Summary

The development of science knowledge in school is a process of connecting classroom observations and theories with one's own understandings of how the world works. As learners, it is important to keep in mind that we come into the classroom with our own ideas about how the world works. Some of these ideas have proved to work very well in the conditions under which we live. In science, however, we are often asked to imagine a broader range of possible conditions and to extend our explanations to account for them. As learners and teachers, we must become aware of our own ideas and the ideas of others. We must also be aware that our students' *misconceptions* or *pre-conceptions*, as well as our own, are actually resources that can be used toward the development of science ideas that have a broader range of application.

Awareness of children's ideas about various concepts in science has allowed teachers and curriculum developers to design lessons and curricula that can help students build on their own ideas. Our ideas, and our children's ideas, should be respected and valued. Through carefully crafted classroom experiences, children's ideas can be used as resources that actually facilitate, rather than inhibit, further learning about science.

References

Feher, E. (1990). Interactive museum exhibits as tools for learning: Exploration with light. *International Journal of Science Education*, **12**(1), 35-39.

Feher, E., and Rice, K. (1988). Shadows and anti-images: Children's conceptions of light and vision. *Science Education*, **72**(5), 637-649.

Guesne, E. (1985). Light. In *Children's Ideas in Science*, R. Driver, E. Guesne, and A. Tiberghien, Eds. Taylor and Francis Inc. Chapter 5, p. 10-32.

Hammer (2000). Student Resources for Learning Introductory Physics. *American Journal of Physics, Physics Education Research Supplement*, **68** (S1), S52-S59.

Purpose

In this activity you will analyze two different videos involving third and fourth grade students' ideas about vision and reflection. The purpose of this activity is for you to get a sense of the types of pre-instructional ideas children have involving how we see things, and to think about how these ideas might evolve through classroom experimentation.

 What types of ideas do elementary students have about light and how might evidence impact childrens' thinking?

Initial Ideas

 To begin a unit on light with her third grade students, Ms. Jackson showed students a flashlight and asked them to draw pictures representing how they are able to see light. What initial ideas about how we see light do you think third grade students might express?

Early in Chapter 6 you conducted an experiment involving a Mylar™ square and white paper sitting on the center of the table. You were asked to predict what each person standing around the table would see when the lights were turned off and a flashlight directed at the center of table was turned on.

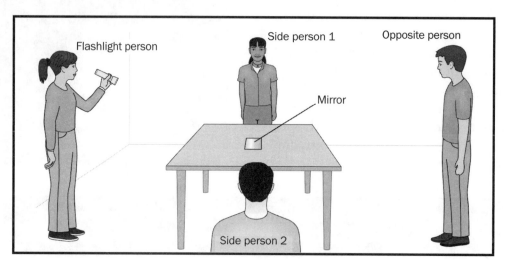

 Imagine that fourth grade students conducted a similar experiment with only a mirror (not the white paper) in the center of the table. Imagine that they were asked to predict which of four students standing around the table would see the light. What types of predictions do you think these students would make? Why do you think so?

Collecting and Interpreting Evidence

Part 1: How do we see the light?

Your instructor will show a movie of third grade students expressing their ideas about how they see light *(Light_Initial)*. The pictures associated with this movie are included at the end of this activity. Keep the pictures handy as you watch the movie. Please take a few minutes to examine the childrens' pictures after you watch the movie.

What key feature(s) relating to how we see things seem to be present in the students' drawings? What key features seem to be missing from many of the students' drawings? Select four or five pictures to evaluate. Use evidence from the transcript and the article *Children's Ideas about Light* to support your claims.

Part 2: Who will see the light?

Your instructor will now show a movie of fourth grade students performing an experiment with mirrors. In the experiment, fourth grade students were asked to predict and observe which student(s) standing around a table would see the light when a flashlight directed at a mirror in the center of the table was turned on.

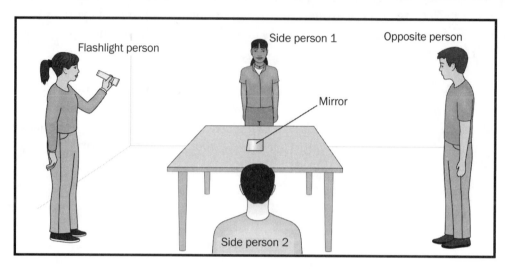

 At video time 01:06:22, a student described his prediction about who would see the light. What idea about light do you think this student was using to guide his prediction? Use the transcript and the article *Children's Ideas about Light*, to support your claim.

What idea or ideas did the fourth grade students construct regarding the behavior of light?

Summarizing Questions

S1: After looking at the children's drawings, Ms. Jones said, "All of my students clearly understand that in order to see a flashlight, light must enter your eye." Do you agree or disagree with Ms. Jones? Use the transcript, the childrens' pictures and the article *Children's Ideas about Light* to support your claim.

S2: In the reflection movie, at the end of the first experiment (video time 6:47:17), Josh stated, "Well we discovered, we thought, we found out that the — we started thinking at the end that the mirror could only reflect the light one way." Do you think students had ownership of this idea or do you think the interviewer played a large role in telling this idea to the students? Support your claims with evidence from the transcript. Follow the transcript from video time 1:31:17 through video time 7:16:10.

S3: In your *PET* class, you or one of your group members might have said at one time or another, "Why doesn't the instructor just tell us the answer?" Why don't we just tell students, "In order for you to see things, light must enter your eye?"

 Participate in a whole-class discussion about your answers to these questions.

Light_Initial

00:05:14	Teacher	But what I want to know is how are you able to see this? How are you able to see this? Now, I want you to discuss that with your partners.
00:28:00	Teacher	What I want you to do, I'm going to give you a sheet of paper and I want you to draw how you are able to see this. And I want you to include the flashlight in your picture and yourself. You can label it, you can use your coloring crayons. Alright. But I want you to show how you're able to see this, as Sarah Beth said, "with vision." Okay? So let's go ahead and pass out our paper.
01:01:05	Daniel	Look at they eye, to look at the light you to use your vision. Use the vision. Use the eye because your brain controls your eye.
01:12:06	Interviewer	So what's the line?
01:14:09	Daniel	That's showing the vision.
01:16:12	Interviewer	Oh, okay. What's this around the flashlight?
01:20:22	Daniel	That's the light.
01:33:21	Interviewer	Lauren, tell me about your picture.
01:37:01	Lauren	Well these are the batteries which provide energy for the light to go up and then you can see the light by vision.
01:43:28	Interviewer	Oh, okay so the light goes up here is that right?
01:45:07	Lauren	Um hum.
01:47:18	Interviewer	Okay. Is there anything between you and the flashlight?
01:50:26	Lauren	No.
01:52:01	Interviewer	No? Okay. So the light comes up out of the flashlight and you look at it and you see it?
01:57:24	Lauren	Um hum.
01:58:22	Interviewer	Okay, thank you.
02:00:17	Interviewer	Hi Laykelin.
02:02:09	Laykelin	Hello.
02:02:27	Interviewer	How are you?
02:03:20	Laykelin	Pretty good.
02:04:24	Interviewer	Good? Okay. Can you tell me a little bit about your picture?
02:07:20	Laykelin	Well it sort of makes like that and when you see it just sends a message to your brain and the brain tells the eye what you're seeing. So that's pretty much it.
02:21:24	Interviewer	So, this is, what's this right here?
02:23:15	Laykelin	It's supposed to be a light bulb.
02:25:16	Interviewer	That's a picture in your brain!
02:27:06	Laykelin	Yeah.
02:28:22	Interviewer	And what are these lines here?

02:30:16	Laykelin	Well it's just sort of like, I don't know, I mean seeing something.
02:34:16	Interviewer	Oh okay, I see. And what about these lines here?
02:37:12	Laykelin	It's just showing the light coming off it.
02:41:09	Interviewer	Oh, okay I see. Very nice.
02:46:14	Interviewer	Hi Jared.
02:47:16	Jared	How do you know all our names?
02:49:30	Interviewer	Because you've got them written on the table. (laugh) Can you tell me a little bit about your picture?
02:57:07	Jared	It's about the eye feels the light. The light is reflecting off the iris of people and then it's sending the message to the brain which is, "that's light."
03:08:16	Interviewer	Oh, I see. So what are these yellow lines here?
03:12:17	Jared	They're like little, I don't know, like waves, I don't know.
03:16:06	Interviewer	Light waves okay. And where are they going?
03:18:15	Jared	To the eye.
03:19:06	Interviewer	To the eye okay.
03:20:05	Jared	And then it travels through the veins and then sends the message, "that's light."
03:28:09	Interviewer	Okay I see. Thank you very much.
03:34:10	Interviewer	Donald, can you tell me what you're drawing?
03:37:17	Donald	Um, the flashlight here (inaudible) and it's showing that you're seeing the flashlight.
03:49:25	Interviewer	So what are the lines?
03:52:22	Donald	It's your vision.

Mirrors

00:09:06	Teacher	Now do we have somebody on all four sides? Now, this is what I want you to do. You think about where you're standing and where the persons around your table are standing, and when your flashlight holder turns the flashlight on, who do you think is going to be able to look in that mirror and see the picture? What I want you to do is to kind of draw on your paper who's going to be able to see that, that — Predict and show me what you think, how you think the person or people that you think is going to see that light.
01:06:22	Student	Well the flashlight person is going to shine it at the mirror, and I think from our last thing we've been doing, it's going to go back to her, to the side person, to that side person and to the opposite person — cause the mirror has it all the way around.
01:19:10	Interviewer	So it's going to go all the way around?
01:20:20	Student	Um hum.
01:21:04	Interviewer	What if these people moved around? Say this person moved over here?
01:25:02	Student	I'd say he'd still see it.
01:26:02	Interviewer	He'd still see it so anywhere around the table, he'd still see it.
01:27:28	Student	Um hum.
01:28:24	Interviewer	Okay, let's have a look at—
01:31:17	Comment	(groups begin the experiment)
01:37:16	Interviewer	Can you see it now?
01:38:03	Light holder	Yes.
01:38:18	Interviewer	Can you tell that you can see it?
01:40:26	Flashlight holder 1	Yeah, cause it's got the reflection on—
01:44:08	Interviewer	Now can you really see the flashlight on the mirror, the picture of the flashlight?
01:48:10	Student across from light 1	Yes, I can. Like where the light's coming.
02:03:28	Interviewer	Well, why don't you change places. Okay, everybody go around. Could you see it?
02:11:23	Student on the right of holder	Hum?
02:12:10	Interviewer	Could you see it in the mirror?
02:14:02	Student on the right of holder	No.
02:14:20	Interviewer	No? Okay. Now give her the flashlight.

02:18:06	Flashlight holder	Oh, okay.
02:21:28	Interviewer	Can you see it over there?
02:23:24	Student across from the holder 2	Yes.
02:24:18	Interviewer	Can you see it?
02:25:08	Student to the left of holder	No.
02:26:04	Interviewer	Can you see it?
02:27:10	Student to the right of holder	No. So the opposite person can see it.
02:32:05	Student to left of holder	Yeah, only the opposite person can see it.
02:33:08	Flashlight holder 2	That makes sense.
02:34:06	Interviewer	Okay, let's make sure everybody gets a turn, move around again.
02:40:04	Student across from the holder 3	Oh, I can see it big time! Yeah, I can see it. I can see the reflection from all sides.
02:52:24	Student to the left of holder	Like the finger (inaudible) smudged it, that's where I can see it reflecting.
02:59:18	Student	Should we switch?
03:01:16	Student	Okay, switch. JR, JR, JR. (students move around the table)
03:08:22	Student across from holder 4	Oh my goodness! I can so see it now!
03:11:26	Student to right of holder	I, I can't see, I can see Josh's face but I can't see it.
03:15:10	Josh — the left of holder	I can see your face.
03:19:08	Student across from the holder	It's turning around a little bit - like
03:22:13	Flashlight holder	I almost had it.
03:23:16	Discussion	(inaudible)
03:42:16	Student to left of holder	So it's just the opposite person because it goes like this and it bounces off.

03:47:05	Student to right of holder	Yeah! That's what I thought but - Some people can't even see it.
03:54:02	Student across from holder	Yeah, could you see it? Try and look around a little bit like scoot —
03:58:00	Student to left of holder	No, it's just the opposite person. It's like hitting here (motions her hand from the flashlight to the mirror.)
04:02:02	Student across from holder	(pointing to student to left of holder) Over there I could sort of see it.
04:04:10	Student to right of holder	(moving toward the person across from the light) I could see it when I was like right here.
04:05:28	Student to left of holder	I can't see it at all.
04:05:24	Interviewer	So what do you think is happening here?
04:08:16	Student to left of holder	I think the opposite person can see it.
04:10:14	Group	Yeah!
04:11:10	Interviewer	Only the opposite person could see it. Why do think that is?
04:12:25	Student to left of the holder	Well it bounces down hits the mirror and kind of goes like that (moves her hand from the light to the mirror and back up toward the face of the student across from the holder).
04:18:06	Interviewer	So what does it have to do when it gets over here, can you see it right now?
04:21:02	Student across from holder	Yeah, I can see it in the mirror.
04:23:25	Interviewer	Okay but right now? Okay. Duck down a little bit. Now what about now?
04:29:24	Student across from holder	Yes, I can see it.
04:32:00	Interviewer	Really bright now?
04:33:12	Student across from holder	Yeah.
04:33:29	Interviewer	Why do you think she can really see it well right now?
04:36:08	Student to right of holder	Because from what I see, it has to do with hitting her right there in the eye.
04:39:24	Interviewer	Okay so what is that?

04:41:05	Student to left of holder	It's like where the light is bouncing off the mirror and hitting her in her —
04:44:11	Interviewer	In her face? Alright, okay. Did everybody get a turn?
04:47:07	Group	Yes.
04:50:16	Interviewer	So why do you think you can't see it right now and you can't see it right now?
04:58:24	Student across from holder	Well, it's kind of like it's angled down so it would be like that, so it's hitting it at an angle, sort of —
05:06:12	Student to right of holder	If you could move it, it would be like going like that.
05:10:06	Student across from holder	—but if JR's (the one holding the light) right there and she's right there (pointing to the position to the left of the holder) it would be hitting it like, it would be hitting it at an angle and it would go into an angle to her.
05:18:02	Interviewer	Okay, so is there something special about the way the light behaves?
05:23:02	Student to left of the holder	Well, it's kind of like when, we had the pinhole and the light goes the light goes through the pinhole, it goes up. I bet if we moved it down and we moved the mirror up, it would probably kind of go down.
05:35:23	Interviewer	Okay.
05:38:25	Student to left of holder	(flashlight holder moves flashlight and image on student moves upward) See it's going up!
05:42:02	Interviewer	Oh okay. So, so do you think there's kind of a pattern there, in the light?
05:49:14	Student across from holder	Well, it's shining sort of that way but the mostly directly going right there.
05:55:04	Student to right of holder	You can see it, you can see it right there.
05:56:06	Interviewer	Okay, where's it going from there?
05:57:16	Student across from holder	It's hitting and then it's going back to my face.
06:00:12	Interviewer	Okay, okay, I see, alright, thank you.
06:05:18	Teacher	I need to know at your group, Beth what did you guys discover at that group?
06:11:10	Beth	Um, you shine the flashlight on the mirror and it reflects off and (?) on the other person's eye, but the people across cannot see it because you're pointing it —

06:24:28	Teacher	You mean of all of these four people at your table only one person could see it?
06:28:25	Student	Um hum. Because it would bounce off and hit her it would go in her eyes.
06:34:18	Beth	And if you turned this way, it would do the same that way.
06:38:25	Teacher	So only one person at a time could see it, not all four of you, not even three of you.
06:43:30	Student	Right.
06:45:07	Teacher	'kay. What did you discover Josh at your group?
06:47:17	Josh	Well we discovered, we thought, we found out that the — we started thinking at the end that the mirror could only reflect the light one way.
06:59:08	JR	Yeah, one way.
07:00:04	Teacher	So what does that mean?
07:02:10	Josh	That means that the light can only go in one direction.
07:07:08	Teacher	'kay.
07:08:28	JR	We're shining it —
07:10:23	Teacher	So just one person at a time saw it at your table?
07:12:30	Josh	Yeah, right.
07:13:28	Teacher	And who was that, when you were holding it Josh that would have been?
07:16:10	Josh	Mary Beth

Activity 2 Homework—Ideas about Learning Science
Learning About Learning

Name:_____ Date:_____ Group: _____

Purpose

For *Chapter 1 Activity 1 Homework* you filled out a table, similar to the one below, where you agreed or disagreed with various claims about your learning, and provided a reason for your response. We are interested in how your responses to the same questions, and/or your reasons, may have changed as a result of your experiences in this course. First, copy your agree/disagree responses from the original *Chapter 1 Activity 1 Homework*

in the Table below. Then respond to the same claims based on your views at the present time, by circling either *agree* or *disagree*. In the last column, please compare your initial and current responses. If they are the same, indicate how your experiences in this course further supported your initial view. If your response is different, indicate how your experiences in this course caused you to change your view.

Your Ideas about learning science

Learning Science	Chapter 1 Activity 1 Agree/ Disagree	Chapter 6 Activity 2 Agree/ Disagree	Reason for change or further justification for the same response
When learning a science concept, I usually either get it or I don't.	Agree Disagree		
Learning science is more a matter of following specific procedures than it is a matter of being creative.	Agree Disagree		
When I learn science, I find that being confused can be useful.	Agree Disagree		

Learning Science	Chapter 1 Activity 1 Agree/ Disagree	Chapter 6 Activity 2 Agree/ Disagree	Reason for change or further justification for the same response
If my own science ideas turn out to be different from the ideas of others, I find it hard to change my ideas.	Agree Disagree		
In order for me to learn science, I need to spend time listening to the thinking of other students.	Agree Disagree		
In order for me to learn science, I need to spend time describing my current thinking out loud to other students.	Agree Disagree		
I am a science person.	Agree Disagree		

Activity 3–Non-Shiny White and Black Surfaces
Developing Ideas

Purpose

In the first activity of this Chapter you observed how light interacts with shiny surfaces. You also gathered evidence for the idea that for you to see a light source or its mirror image, light must enter your eye. But most objects around us are non-shiny. What happens then?

 1. How does light interact with non-shiny white and black surfaces?

2. When you look at white or black surfaces, does light interact with your eye?

Initial Ideas

Three members of the class were having a discussion about whether light reflects off white paper. The conversation went something like this:

> Light does not reflect from the paper because it just shines on the paper and illuminates it.

> Light must reflect from the paper because otherwise how could you see the paper?

> Light does not reflect from the paper because if it did the paper would be like a mirror, and obviously it is not.

Amara   **Daryl**   **Samantha**

 Do you agree with Amara, Daryl or Samantha, or with none of them? What **evidence** do you have from prior experience that supports your answer?

 Participate in a whole-class discussion.

Collecting and Interpreting Evidence

YOU WILL NEED:

- Flashlight (bright one with good batteries)
- Tubular bulb in socket
- White card
- Gray card
- Black card
- Flat mirror
- Piece of white paper (notebook size)
- Card with crinkled aluminum foil wrapped around it.

 EXPERIMENT #1: What happens when light strikes white, gray and black surfaces?

The room should be darkened for this experiment.

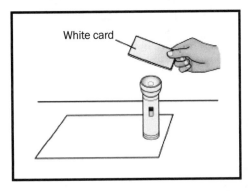

White card

STEP 1: Turn on the flashlight and stand it upright at one end of the paper.

STEP 2: Hold the white card as shown in the picture, so the flashlight beam strikes the card. Move the card in and out of the beam of light and observe what happens on the sheet of paper.

 Describe the illumination on the paper: Is the entire paper uniformly illuminated, or is there a circular spot of light on the paper?

STEP 3: Tilt the white card in different directions, but make sure the flashlight beam still strikes it. Observe what happens on the paper.

Does the illumination on the paper change significantly when you tilt the white card in different directions?

 STEP 4: Replace the white card with the small mirror, and repeat Steps 2 and 3.

How are your observations with the white card **different** from your observations with the mirror?

 At right is part of a light ray diagram showing light from the flashlight striking the white card. The flashlight sits on a sheet of paper.

From the point where the light ray from the flashlight strikes the card, draw several light rays to show how the reflected light illuminates the entire sheet of paper.

STEP 5: Replace the mirror with the crinkled aluminum foil card. Repeat Steps 2 and 3 above.

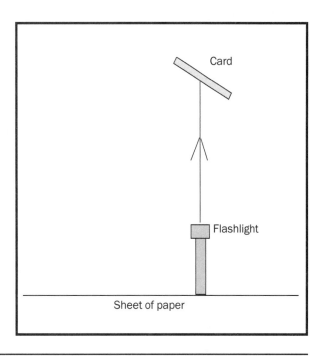

CHAPTER 6

Describe the illumination on the white paper. Is the entire paper uniformly illuminated, or is there mainly a circular pattern of light on the paper?

 Is the illumination on the paper from the crinkled foil more similar to that from a mirror or from a white card?

STEP 6: Replace the crinkled aluminum foil card with the gray card. Move the gray card in an out of the flashlight beam and observe what happens on the sheet of paper.

 Does the white paper appear to be illuminated by light from the gray card?

 How does this compare to what happens when the flashlight beam strikes a white card?

STEP 7: Replace the gray card with the black card. Move the black card in and out of the flashlight beam and observe what happens on the sheet of paper.

Does the white paper appear to be illuminated by light from the black card?

 How does this compare to what happens when the flashlight beam strikes a gray card and a white card?

Seeing White and Black Objects

When you *look at* white paper, does light from the paper come into your eye? Two other members of the class offered their own answers:

No, because when I look at white paper my eyes are not dazzled like they are when I look directly at a bright light source or its image in a mirror. That means that light is not coming into my eyes.

Luisa

Yes, I think so. Although I agree that my eyes are not dazzled when normally looking at a piece of white paper, I do squint my eyes when reading outside on a sunny day if I'm not wearing sunglasses. That means light is coming into my eyes.

Dave

Do you agree with Luisa, with Dave, or with neither? What additional evidence (from your own experiences) can you provide to support your answer?

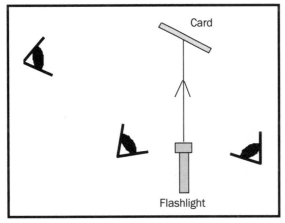

Imagine that three students are looking at the **white card** illuminated directly by the flashlight. They all see a spot of illumination on the card. To the left is part of a light ray diagram for this situation.

 From the point where the light ray from the flashlight strikes the card, draw several light rays to show how each of the three students can see the illuminated card.

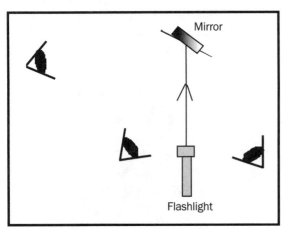

To help compare the behavior of a mirror with a white card, imagine that the three students are looking at a **mirror** illuminated directly by the flashlight. To the left is part of a light ray diagram for this situation.

 Complete the light ray diagram to show which of the students, if any, can see the dazzling bright mirror image of the flashlight.

To the right is (part of) a light ray diagram showing a flashlight illuminating a perfectly **black card**. Three students are looking at the black card (which we assume is pure black).

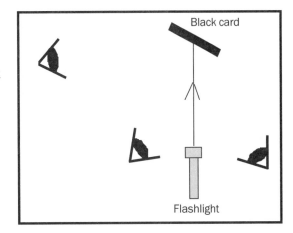

 Based on the evidence you gathered from the experiment, will light be reflected from the black card?

 As each of the three students looks at the black card, is light from the card going into their eyes?

If essentially no light reflects from a black object, then when you look at a black object no light comes into your eye. This is puzzling, because how then do you see the object as black? The answer has to do with how our eye-brain system works.

Imagine a piece of black paper in the center of a larger piece of white paper. When you look at the paper, light comes into your eye from the white part, but not from the black part. Your eye-brain system then does two things:

(1) It *processes* the light coming from the white region surrounding the black part, enabling you to "see" the white paper.

(2) Since no light comes into your eye from the black region, your eye-brain system assumes there is something there, and *interprets* that area as black.

Thus, *perceiving an object as black* is your eye-brain system's response to looking at an object from which no light comes into your eye, while *at the same time* looking at surrounding objects from which light does come into your eye. Without light also coming into your eye from surrounding objects, would you have the same perception of blackness? Think about walking into a room at night with no lights turned on. What is your first impression: that the room is *black*, or that the room is *dark*?

In addition to drawing light ray diagrams to show how light interacts with objects, we can draw energy diagrams to describe how energy is involved in the interaction. We first consider the white card. (You will think about the black and gray cards after you perform Experiment #2.) Complete the energy diagram to describe the light interaction involved in seeing the white card illuminated with light from the flashlight.

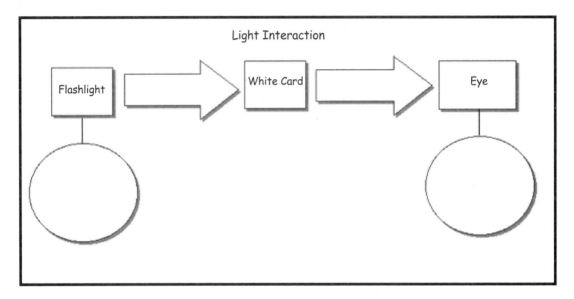

As you saw in Activity 1, if the light source was an electric light, then the energy diagram would be similar.

EXPERIMENT #2: What happens to black and white objects that are illuminated with light?

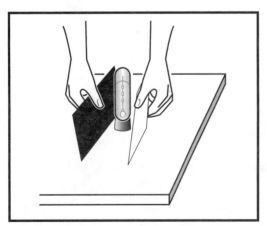

STEP 1: Turn on the tubular bulb. Hold the black and white cards 3 cm from opposite sides of the bulb, as suggested in the picture. Keep them there for about 30 seconds.

STEP 2: Remove them from the bulb and place each card against one of your cheeks to feel how warm it is.

Which of the two cards feels warmer?

Why do you think that happens?

In Chapter 1 you learned that when the temperature of an object increases there is an increase in **thermal energy** inside the object.

 Based on the evidence from Experiment #2, complete the following energy diagram to describe what happens when light from a flashlight illuminates a pure black card.[2]

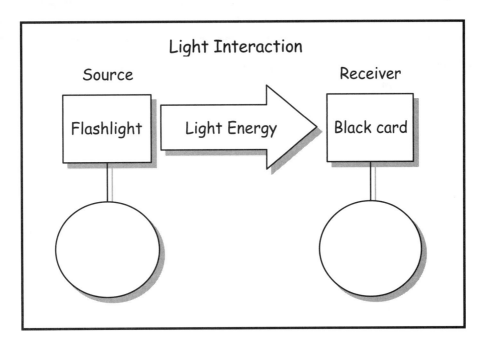

Summarizing Questions

S1: What is the difference between how light interacts with shiny surfaces and white non-shiny surfaces?

---

[2]As you learned in Chapter 1, when an object warms up more than its surroundings, it transfers heat energy to the surroundings. In this source/receiver energy diagram, we are only considering the interactions between the flashlight and card, and ignoring the interactions between the warmed card and the surroundings.

S2: Consider the following picture from Activity 1.

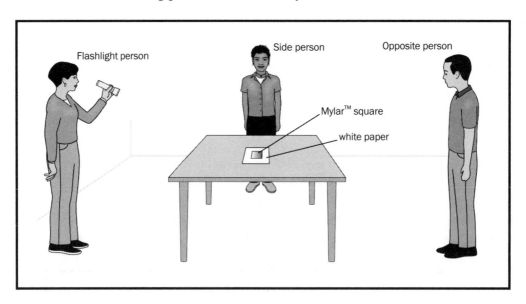

Draw a light ray diagram showing how the flashlight person can see the illuminated white paper surrounding the Mylar™ square.

S3: In Activity 1 you observed that the Mylar™ square appeared black to the side person. Write a few sentences to explain this observation.

S4. Draw three different energy diagrams describing the interactions involved when you look at a **white** card, a **gray** card, and a **black** card, all illuminated with light from a flashlight. Since the three cards are different, you should expect some differences in the three diagrams.

S5: Below is a rough diagram of a "person" standing in front of a fully mirrored wall. A ceiling lamp hangs above. The person is wearing white shoes. Write a scientific explanation for why the person can see the image of her shoe in the mirrored wall.

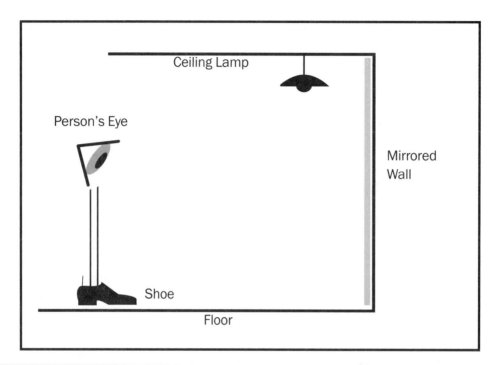

Draw a light ray diagram on the picture above: (Remember that the shoe is first illuminated by light from the lamp, and then some of the reflected light must enter the person's eye.)

Write the narrative: (Use your light ray diagram as a guide, telling in words what happens to the light as it starts at the lamp and ends up in her eye.)

S6: Write a scientific explanation for why, on a hot summer day, it is more comfortable to wear white (or very light) clothing rather than black (or very dark) clothing.

Using an Analogy to Help Understand the Non-Shiny White Surface

In this and in the previous activity you gathered evidence to support the following two ideas:

• *When light strikes a shiny surface (mirror), it reflects off in just **one** direction from the surface (at the same angle that it struck the surface).*

• *When light strikes a non-shiny surface (white card or paper), it reflects off in **all** directions (at all angles) away from the surface.*

You may be wondering what is really **different** about shiny and non-shiny surfaces. Why doesn't a white card behave like a mirror? After all, to the touch a white card feels smooth like a mirror. To help us understand the difference between a mirror and a white surface we will use an analogy.

(You have already used analogies earlier in this course to think about different phenomena. For example, you used a sequence of sticky-notes as an analogy to help think about friction, you used a test-tube filled with iron filings as an analogy to help think about the inside of magnetized materials, and you blew through straws as an analogy to help you think about electric circuits.)

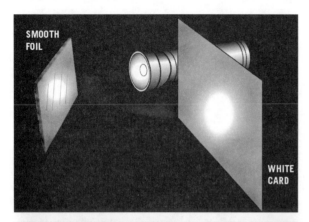

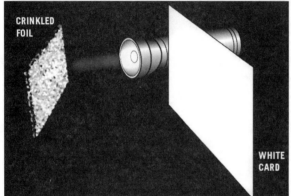

Imagine that you did the following experiment, which is only a little different from what you did in Experiment #1. You have a card with aluminum foil wrapped around it. The foil is very smooth, so there are no crinkles in it. You aim a flashlight beam at the *smooth foil*, and observe the reflected light on another white card. Since the *smooth foil* surface behaves like a mirror, it reflects the incoming beam in one direction, as suggested in the drawing above left.

Now suppose you remove the foil, crinkle it, and wrap it around the card again. This time when you shine the flashlight beam onto the *crinkled foil* surface, the reflected light illuminates the entire white card. See drawing at left.

As you saw in your own experiment earlier in this activity, the crinkled foil reflects light in the same way that a white card reflects light — in all directions. Thinking about how the surface of the crinkled foil causes light to reflect in all directions may help us think about how the surface of a white card causes light to reflect in all directions. The crinkled foil serves as an analogy for the white card.

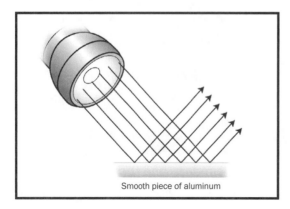

Smooth piece of aluminum

To the left is a picture of a flashlight shining its light on a smooth foil surface. We've drawn several light rays to show how the light travels from the flashlight to the smooth foil surface, and then how light interacts with the surface.

Now consider a flashlight shining its light on a *crinkled foil* surface.

Draw a flashlight aimed at a crinkled foil surface. Then draw light rays to show how the light travels from the flashlight to the crinkled foil surface, and then how light interacts with the surface of the crinkled foil. (Remember that the light reflecting from the surface of the crinkled foil needs to go in all directions in order to illuminate the entire surface of the nearby white card or paper.)

If you were able to look at the surface of a white card up close through a microscope, would you expect the surface to be perfectly smooth, like a mirror, or like something else?

We observed that light behaves similarly when reflecting from a white card and from crinkled foil. The crinkled foil serves as an analogy for the surface of the white card. Although we cannot see "crinkles" in the white card, we can imagine there is something similar to crinkles at the microscopic level. The analogy helps us understand why light reflects from the white card in all directions.

Participate in a whole class discussion to go over your answers to some of the experiment questions, the Summarizing Questions and your drawings for the crinkled foil analogy.

Activity 3 Homework—Refraction of Light
Developing Ideas

Name:_____ Date:_____ Group: _____

Purpose

Did you ever put a stick in a glass of water and notice that it appeared bent? Did you ever stand in a swimming pool, look down at your feet, and wonder why they appeared to be much closer than they actually are? Did you ever look through a magnifier and wonder how it makes things appear larger than they actually are? The explanation for these, and other similar phenomena, involves what happens to light when it travels through transparent material (like water or glass).

In this homework activity you will investigate what happens to light when it goes into or out of a transparent material. You will then apply what you learn from your observations to explain an interesting phenomenon.

 How does light behave when it travels between air and other transparent materials?

Collecting and Interpreting Evidence

 SIMULATOR EXPERIMENT #1:
What happens to the direction that light travels when going between air and another transparent material?

The computer simulator was programmed to simulate a beam of light passing between air and a transparent surface like water or glass.

Open *Chapter 6 Activity 3 Homework Setup.*

STEP 1: In the setup area you will see a rectangular container. The area in the top part is *air*, and the bluish area in the bottom represents *water*. A beam projector has already been placed inside the air.

When you turn on the simulator (run button), a simulated beam of light is projected straight outward from the beam projector.

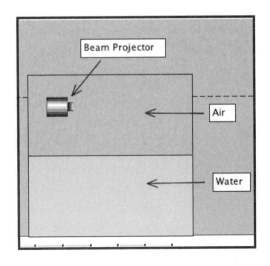

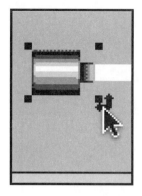 

STEP 2: If you click on the beam projector to select it, you can then click-drag the double-headed arrow down and to the left to rotate the projector until the projector aims the beam **straight down** into the water.

 When the light beam heads **straight down** into the water (so the light makes a 90 degrees angle with the surface), does the light continue in a straight line or does the light beam change direction?

Rotate the beam projector so the light beam strikes the water at an angle, as shown on the left.

 According to the simulator, when the light beam strikes the water at an angle, does it continue in a straight line, or does the light beam change direction?

 Rotate the beam projector so the light enters the water at different angles, and observe what happens to the simulated light beam in each case. On the next page we define the angles that the light and the transmitted light make with the water surface.

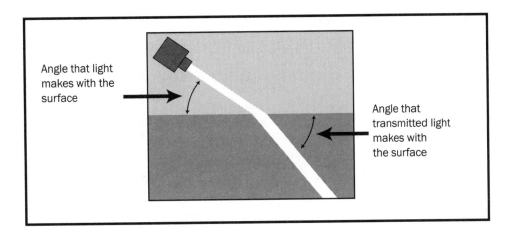

 Complete the following statements based on your observations with the simulator:

When light enters water at an angle other than 90 degrees, the angle that the light

makes with the surface is _____ (less than, equal to,

greater than) the angle that the transmitted light makes with the surface.

When light enters water at an angle of exactly 90 degrees, the angle that the light

makes with the surface is _____ (less than, equal to,

greater than) the angle that the transmitted light makes with the surface.

Draw three sketches from the simulator that support your statements.

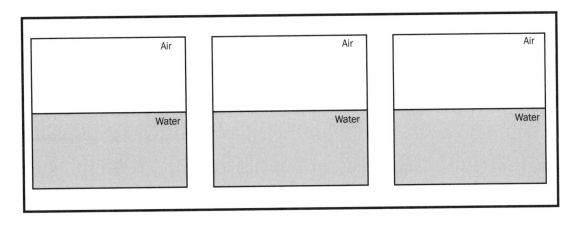

STEP 3: Turn the simulator off. Drag the beam projector into the water at the bottom left. Rotate it so it points straight upward.

STEP 4: Turn on the simulator.

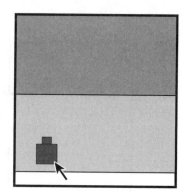

 Assuming the light is going straight upward (striking the surface at 90 degrees), what happens to its direction when it passes from the water into the air?

Rotate the beam projector so the simulated light beam strikes the surface at an angle of about 30 degrees or so.

 What happens to the direction of the light that passes into the air?

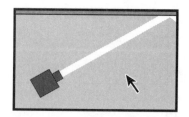

 Continue rotating the beam projector so the angle the light beam makes with the surface becomes greater and greater. Observe what happens to the light beam. Eventually, something unusual happens. What happens?

Complete the following statement based on your observations with the simulator.

When light goes from water into air (striking the surface at an angle less than

90 degrees, and before something unusual happens), the angle that the light makes

with the surface is _____ (less than, equal to,

greater than) the angle that the transmitted light makes with the surface.

Draw three sketches from the simulator that support your statement.

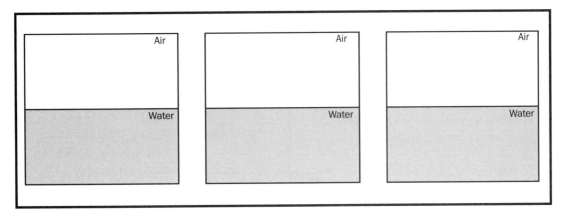

The change in direction of light when it goes between air and a transparent material, like water, is called **refraction**. In the next experiment, you will observe an interesting phenomenon that can be explained in terms of the refraction of light.

 EXPERIMENT #2: Where is the coin?

YOU WILL NEED:

- 1 Styrofoam® (or other opaque) cup and a second cup (or drinking glass)
- Coin
- Access to water
- Preferably another person to assist you

STEP 1: Fill the second cup about $\frac{3}{4}$ full with water. Put that cup aside for the moment. Place your coin at the bottom of the opaque cup, with one edge of the coin touching the side of the cup. Look into the cup from above one of its edges at the coin.

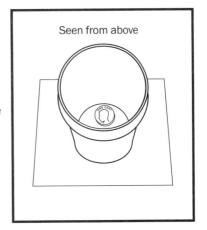

Seen from above

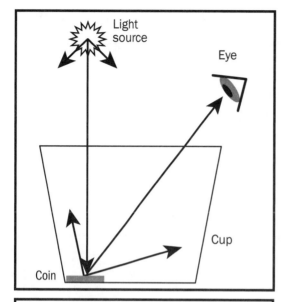

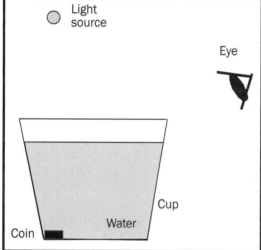

STEP 2: To the left is a light ray diagram showing a person (eye) looking at the coin from above the edge of the cup, and **how** he sees the coin. This is drawn from a side-view perspective and it is assumed that light originates from a source above the cup.

STEP 3: Put your eye in the position described in Step 2. You should just be able to see the coin above the edge of the cup. Next, lower your head down until the coin just disappears behind the edge of the cup. Keep your position fixed while you (or preferably another person) carefully and slowly pour water from the other cup into your empty cup. You should observe that the coin again comes into view!

To the left is part of a light ray diagram showing a person (eye) looking at the coin through the water. The same light source is above the cup (on the ceiling).

 Complete the light ray diagram to show how the person can now see the coin in the water. (Remember, the cup is opaque—light cannot pass through it!)

 Write a few sentences to explain how the person can now see the coin, even though the side of the cup blocks his straight-line view of the coin.

Summarizing Question

S1: Suppose you wanted to describe to someone else what happens to light when it travels between air and water, or between water and air (from either direction). Below, write some sentences that correctly describe what happens to the light. (Make sure your comments are supported by the evidence gathered in this experiment.)

Purpose

The Sun, and most light sources we are familiar with in everyday life, produce white light. Yet, we also see colored lights, for example, in fountains, at dances, in theaters, etc. Is colored light completely different from white light, or are they connected in some way?

Many interesting color lighting effects, especially those in live theatrical productions, depend on the use of transparent colored plastic materials called **gels**. Stained glass windows use

transparent colored glass to produce their visual effects.

How do gels and stained glass cause the colors that they do?

Most colored objects we see around us, however, are opaque, not transparent. How do we see them?

In this activity you will learn about the relationship between light and color, and will investigate how color gels work and how we see colored objects.

 How does a color gel work? How do you see colored objects?

Initial Ideas

You should have red, green and blue color gels at your table, along with a tubular-shaped white light source. Turn on the source and look through each color gel at the light source.

Looking through a gel should make the source appear colored. Why does this happen? What does the color gel do to the light?

Consider the following conversation between three students who are trying to explain what the red gel is doing to the light.

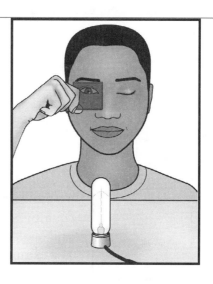

The gel is adding its color to the white light, making it red.

Kristen

No, the red gel is taking away some color from the white light, leaving it red.

Victor

I think you are both right! The gel is both adding color to the light and also taking something away.

Daryl

Do you agree with Kristen, Victor or Daryl, or do you have a different idea? Why?

 Participate in a whole-class discussion.

Gathering and Collecting Evidence

 EXPERIMENT #1: Does a gel add its color to the light, take away some of the color, or both add and take away?

YOU WILL NEED:

- Spectral glasses (one pair per person)
- Set of colored gels: red, green and dark blue
- Tubular white light source in socket (one per group)

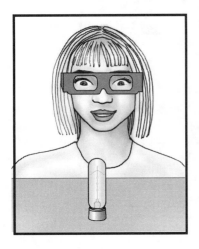

STEP 1: Look at the white light source through your *spectral* glasses. You should see many bands of colors. Concentrate on the band that spreads out to the **left** from the light source. The range of colors that you see is called the color **spectrum** of the white light source.

To make things simple, we can label the major color bands: **R**ed, **O**range, **Y**ellow, **G**reen, **B**lue and **V**iolet. These bands are not of equal width. For example, the red band is about the same width as the green band, but each is much wider than

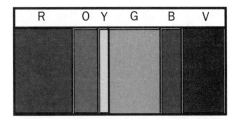

the yellow band. (Check to make sure this is what *you* observe.) At right is an approximate sketch of the different colored bands. The colors of the spectrum are sometimes simply referred to as **ROYGBV**.

Some of you may have seen pictures showing a beam of white light passing through a prism and creating a spectrum. The range of colors in this spectrum is the same as you can see with your special spectral glasses, namely ROYGBV.

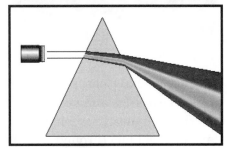

STEP 2: Close one eye and hold the red gel in front of the other eye. By moving the gel down so that it covers only the lower half of the frame in the spectral glasses, you should be able to see the full spectrum at the top, and the spectrum seen through the red gel at the bottom. This should help you compare what happens to the light with and without the gel.

Shade in the color bands that you can observe through the red gel. For example, if you see mainly the red and orange bands, then just shade those in.

 Spectrum seen through *red* gel

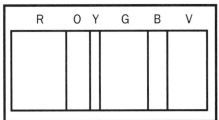

STEP 3: Repeat step 2 for the green and blue gels.

 Spectrum seen through *green* gel

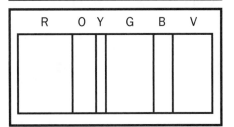

 Spectrum seen through *blue* gel

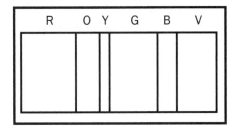

Does a gel seem to *add* its color to the light, *take away* some of the color, or both add and take away? What is your evidence?

Most people have observed that the red gel lets through mainly red light, but also some orange and yellow (and perhaps even a little bit of blue), the green gel lets through mostly green, but also some orange, yellow, blue and violet, and the dark blue gel lets through mainly blue and violet, but also a significant amount of green, and perhaps a little red. To make our discussion and analysis of gels simpler, let us assume we have *ideal gels*. An *ideal red gel* lets through only red light, an *ideal green gel* lets through only green light, and an *ideal blue gel* lets through only blue light.

 EXPERIMENT #2: How does white light interact with a colored object?

YOU WILL NEED:

- Flashlight
- Sheet of white paper
- Red, green and white pieces of cardboard

The room should be darkened for this part of this experiment. In an earlier activity you held a white card over a flashlight and observed white illumination on a white sheet of paper underneath the flashlight. That observation supported the idea that a white card reflects white light in all directions away from its surface.

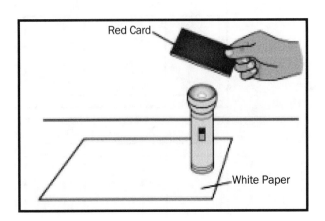

For this experiment you will use a similar setup, but will use colored cards instead of a white card.

STEP 1: Stand the flashlight upright on one edge of the white paper, and hold the red card as shown. While looking at the white paper, move the red card in and out of the flashlight beam.

Describe what you see on the white paper. Does the illumination have a particular hue?

STEP 2: Replace the red card with the green card and repeat the procedure described in Step 1.

 Describe what you see on the white paper.

 What seems to be the pattern here? When white light illuminates a colored object, what can you say about the light reflected from that object?

STEP 3: Replace the green card with the white card and repeat the procedure described in Step 1.

 Describe what you see on the white paper. How does the **brightness** of the illumination compare with the brightness of the illumination in Steps 1 and 2?

Since the light reflected from a colored piece of paper seems to be less bright than the light reflecting from white paper, what do you think happened to the rest of the white light that was not reflected from the colored paper?

STEP 4: In an earlier activity you observed that a black card warms up much more than a white card when each is illuminated with white light. We accounted for

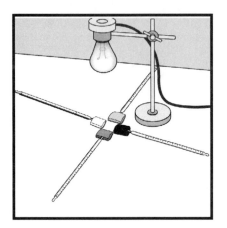 that observation by assuming that the black card absorbed the light energy transferred from the light source and transformed it into thermal energy. The increase in thermal energy caused the black card to increase its temperature. What about when light illuminates a colored card? Does the colored card also absorb the light energy and increase in temperature?

To help answer these questions, students in another class performed the following experiment. Thermometers were inserted into small pockets of white, green, red and black felt material. These were all placed the same distance beneath a bulb, as shown in the figure. The four pockets were all made of the same felt material, and differed only in color. After the temperatures of the four thermometers were recorded, the bulb was turned on for five minutes. Then the temperatures of the four thermometers were recorded again. The data shown in the table below represents the class averages.

Increase in Temperature versus Color of Material

Color of pocket	Initial temperature (°C)	Final temperature (°C) after 5 minutes	Increase in temperature (°C)
White	23	25	
Green	23	32	
Red	23	33	
Black	23	36	

Fill in the last column of the table.

How do the increases in temperature of the red and green materials compare with the increases in temperature of the white and black materials?

 If we assume that the black material absorbs essentially all of the white light energy reaching it from the light bulb, what might you conclude about the red and green materials? Would you infer that they also absorb all of the white light energy reaching them, some of the energy, or none of the energy? Why do you think so?

 If you thought that the colored material absorbed just some of the light energy, what happened to the rest of the light energy that was transferred to it from the source?

 The data in the table shows that that the white material also increased in temperature. Does this suggest that the white material also absorbed some energy from the source?

 In Activity 2 we had assumed that white paper reflects *all* the light that strikes it. Does the data in the table suggest this is a good assumption? Explain.

We could have done a different experiment other than the one described above. Instead of using white, red, green and black *felt pads*, we could have used clear, red, green and dark gray *transparent plastic gels*. The results of the experiment would have been similar: the increase in temperature of the red and green gels would have been in between the small increase in temperature of the clear gel and the much higher increase in temperature of the dark gray gel.

Light, Energy and Color

In Activity 1 you learned that when you look at a light source, light energy is transferred from the source to your eye. Scientists have found out that the light energy that is transferred actually consists of a range of energy values. **Your eye-brain system perceives these different energies as different colors. From lowest to highest values, the different light energies are perceived as red, orange, yellow, green, blue and violet.**

Most sources of visible light, like the Sun, a flashlight, or the electric bulb you used in the experiment, emit a whole range of different energies. **When the entire range of energies enters your eye, your eye-brain system perceives that mixture as white.**

Special devices, like a prism, or the spectral glasses you used in the first experiment, are able to separate the different energies present in the light by causing them to travel through the device in slightly different directions. This is why you were able to perceive the different color components of the white light (ROYGBV) as distinct bands that were spread out.

To help us keep track of the different energies present in the light, we can modify the S/R energy diagram that we drew in Activity 1, as follows. We call this a *color energy diagram*. Assume you are looking directly at a flashlight.

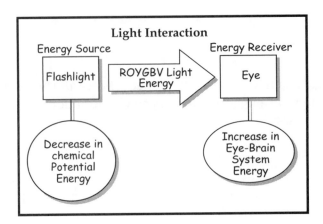

By labeling the energy transferred from the source to the eye as "ROYGBV Light Energy," we are suggesting that the source is emitting white light, and the eye would perceive it as white light. If, instead, the source were emitting red light only, we would label the transfer arrow as "R Light Energy."

We can also modify the light ray diagrams we drew in Activity 1. To include information about color we can label each light ray with the colors that correspond to the different energies in the light. For example, the following diagram represents a person looking at a white light source and seeing the source as white.

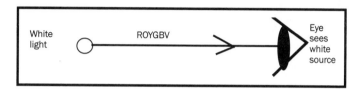

If the person were looking directly at a reddish-orange source, the diagram would be drawn as follows:

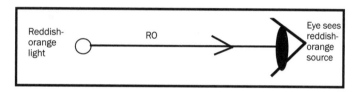

To distinguish these types of ray diagrams from the ones we drew in Activity 1, we will call these *color light ray diagrams*.

Summarizing Questions

S1: Imagine you illuminate a green piece of paper with white light from a flashlight and you look at the green paper. Complete the following color energy diagram to describe this situation.

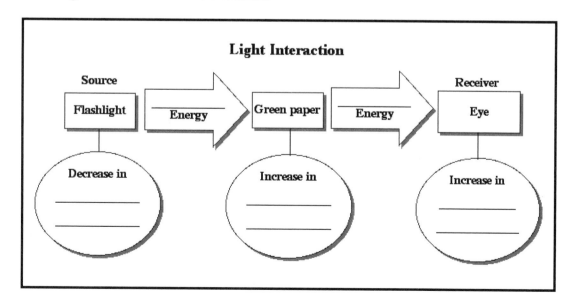

S2: Complete the following color light ray diagram for the same situation described in S1.

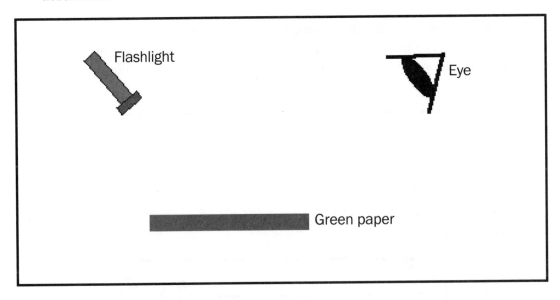

S3: In the **Initial Ideas** section you considered what happened when you looked through a red gel at a white light source. Draw a color energy diagram describing this situation.

S4: Draw a color light ray diagram describing the situation in S3.

S5: In the data table from Experiment 2 you noticed that the red material warmed up slightly more than the green material. Why might this make sense?[1]

 Participate in a whole-class discussion to review the Summarizing Questions.

[1] Actually, the situation is not quite as simple as implied here. An incandescent light bulb, or a flashlight bulb, emits more light at the red end of the spectrum than at the blue end of the spectrum.

Name:_____ Date:_____ Group: _____

Purpose

Throughout *PET* you have completed several in-class and homework activities that have focused on learning about learning. This activity is intended to bring together the ideas you have developed about your own learning, scientists' learning, and the learning of others, specifically children. First read through the historical perspective on social scientists' ideas about learning. Then, below each Social Scientists' Idea, circle the type of learner to whom you think each idea applies.

Historical Perspective

Since the beginning of the 20th century, researchers have been studying how people learn. Researchers studied how and what people learn in and out of school and other formal settings. Psychologists Jean Piaget (1896-1980) from Switzerland and Lev Vygotsky (1896-1934) from Russia generated evidence-based theories of learning that are still used today.

It wasn't until the mid 1970s that linguists, psychologists, philosophers, neuroscientists, anthropologists, and those who study artificial intelligence got together and formed a new discipline now known as "cognitive science," or the study of cognition and learning. By the late 1980s, these theories had been transformed by others into what is called cognitive and socio-cultural "constructivism," ways of viewing learning as the individual and social active construction of knowledge. American philosopher Thomas Kuhn also studied how people learn, except he studied how a community constructed knowledge, specifically the scientific community. Science education researchers have found his work valuable for understanding how people learn science both individually and socially.

While there are many subtle differences between Kuhn's, Piaget's and Vygotsky's theories, there are also many similarities. Some general aspects of these theories were used in the development of the *PET* curriculum and were practiced by you in the *PET* classroom environment. Some of these are:

Social Scientists' Ideas 1 — Learning takes time

At a given point in time, learners have some sense of how things work although their understanding might not be aligned with evidence or the ideas of others. Learning is much more than "getting it" or "not getting it." Usually a learner "kind of gets it" and works with data and with others to further refine that understanding. This takes place over extended periods of time.

This idea applies to the following types of learners (circle all that apply):

Myself   Young Children   Scientists

Social Scientists' Ideas 2 — Both creativity and procedure play large roles in the generation of science knowledge

In order to create explanations of what is going on, learners have to be creative. In order to have confidence in what they are trying to explain, they need to have followed careful, precise procedures.

This idea applies to the following types of learners (circle all that apply):

Myself   Young Children   Scientists

Social Scientists' Ideas 3 — Science knowledge is tentative

It is natural for learners to have ideas that fit available evidence, but these ideas are subject to change as soon as more evidence becomes available. Confusion happens when ideas are not consistent with all available evidence, and this leads to further learning. Confusion is a natural and important part of the learning process.

This idea applies to the following types of learners (circle all that apply):

Myself   Young Children   Scientists

Social Scientists' Ideas 4 — All learners have prior knowledge

Learners interpret events through the lens of this prior knowledge and it therefore greatly influences their learning. Prior knowledge and experiences can serve as valuable resources for further learning.

This idea applies to the following types of learners (circle all that apply):

Myself   Young Children   Scientists

Social Scientists' Ideas 5 — Sometimes a learner's ideas are very resistant to change — even in the face of confounding evidence

This idea applies to the following types of learners (circle all that apply):

Myself   Young Children   Scientists

Social Scientists' Ideas 6 — Science knowledge is generated through agreements and disagreements among people

Typically, learners have to run their ideas by others in order to fully appreciate and become aware of subtle aspects of their own thinking. They also need to hear the thinking of others as well as others' reactions to their own ideas in order for their knowledge to continue to change.

This idea applies to the following types of learners (circle all that apply):

Myself   Young Children   Scientists

Social Scientists' Ideas 7 — Good learners reflect on their own learning

The process of "thinking about one's own thinking" is called metacognition. Expert learners such as scientists spend time considering what they understand at a given point in time and what they do not understand.

This idea applies to the following types of learners (circle all that apply):

Myself   Young Children   Scientists

Comparing Scientists' Ideas and Class Ideas

Your instructor will distribute copies of *Scientists' Ideas: Light Interactions.* Read through these to ensure that the ideas make sense and are consistent with what your group and the class had developed. Where appropriate, summarize the evidence or examples relevant to each idea.

Explanations Involving the Light Interaction

EXPLANATION #1: Explain how you can see the white markers on the road ahead of you when you are driving at night.

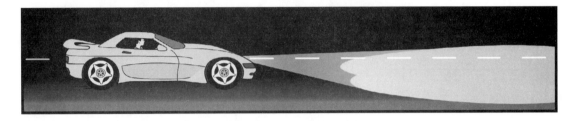

Following is an explanation constructed by another person. Determine whether this explanation is good or poor by applying the criteria of accuracy, completeness, and logical reasoning and clarity. If it is poor, state what is wrong and correct it.

Light Ray Diagram

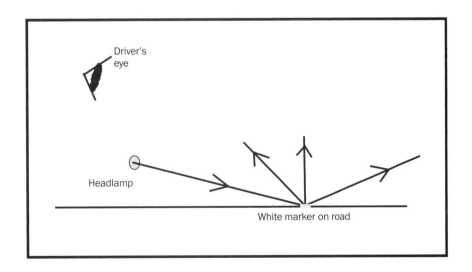

Write the narrative:

The driver can see the markers on the road ahead because light from the headlamp goes to the marker. Since the marker is a white, non-shiny surface, the light reflects in all directions. Because the driver is looking at the marker where the light is reflecting, he can see the marker.

Your evaluation:

 EXPLANATION #2: Explain why it is difficult to see the road markers ahead of you when you are driving at night after it rains, and the road is very wet.[1]

Draw the light ray diagram:

---

[1] The point is that you can still see the markers, just not nearly as well as you can see them when the road is dry.

Write the narrative:

 EXPLANATION #3: Explain why green grapes appear dull gray or black when looked at through red-colored glasses.

Imagine it's a sunny day at the beach. You are sitting on the warm, white sand with your red-tinted sunglasses, ready to eat a bunch of delicious green grapes. As you hold them in your hand, you notice the grapes look an unappetizing dark gray (almost black). How can this be explained?

Before trying to explain why this happens you should try to observe a similar phenomenon. We can't take you to the beach, but we can provide you with a similar experience.

YOU WILL NEED:

■ Small piece of green paper

■ Larger piece of white paper

■ Small red gel

STEP 1: Place the green paper in the middle of the white paper.

STEP 2: Close one eye, hold the red gel in front of the other eye, and look at the green and white pieces of paper together.

What color does the green piece of paper appear to be?

Returning now to the beach, we can assume the red gel is like the red sunglasses, and the green paper is like the green grapes. You should have observed something similar to what you would have experienced at the beach. **Your task now is to explain why the green grapes appear dull gray or black.**

Draw the color light ray diagram:

Write the narrative:

 Participate in a whole-class discussion to go over all the explanations.

Purpose

The *Student Resources DVD* is included with the *Physics & Everyday Thinking* curriculum text. The DVD contains Microsoft® Word electronic versions of all the homework activities in the curriculum, plus several movies.

Some of the movies are in QuickTime™ format. If your computer does not already have a QuickTime player installed, you will need to install one to view the movies. To do this, go to apple.com and select the QuickTime tab. (Web pages often change so we cannot guarantee that these instructions will continue to be accurate, but they are at the time of writing.) If you use a PC, select *Get QuickTime for Windows*. If you use a Mac, select *Free Download Now*. Follow the installation instructions.

There are two types of movies present on the DVD. One type consists of demonstrations of physics phenomena that you will need to view in order to answer some of the homework questions. The other type consists of video from elementary classrooms where the children are engaged in physics experiments or are being interviewed about their physics ideas. The elementary children videos provide support for homework activities where you need to answer questions about the children's ideas. Each of these homework activities also includes full transcripts of the movies, and in some cases copies of pictures the children drew while answering questions.

To answer the questions in a homework activity electronically:

- Copy the appropriate homework document from the DVD to your computer
- Open the document and type in your text
- Save and print it using your normal computer functions

For those activities involving children's ideas, you can copy and paste excerpts from the transcript or pictures (located at the end of the document) into the document to support your answers to questions.

Start-Up Procedure

If you are using the Data Studio software, your Motion Sensor should be connected to a small PASPort™ interface module that is, in turn, connected to a USB port on a computer (see right).

To start the Data Studio software, double-click on the setup file for your experiment. (Your instructor will give you directions on how to access these in your particular classroom setup.) Data Studio files always have the extension *.ds*. After a second or so, the program should start up normally showing a blank speed-time graph for the experiment.

Data Studio files look like this

Collecting Data

Your computer screen should now look something like this. (The example shown is from *Chapter 1 Activity 1* – graphs for other activities may look slightly different.)

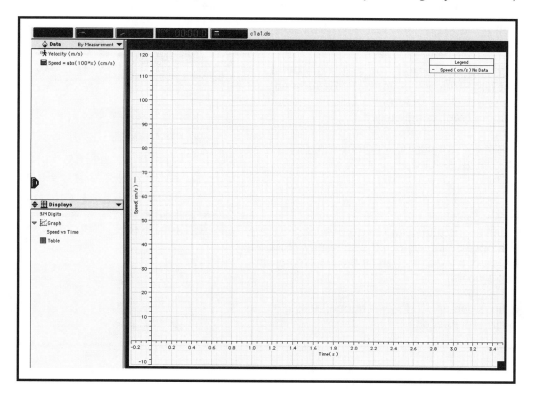

There are two ways to collect data:

■ Click on the **Start** button at the top center of the screen.

■ Select **Start Data** from under the **Experiment** menu at the top left of the screen.

Data collection will usually stop on its own after a preset time, but if you want to stop it before this you can:

■ Click on the **Stop** button at the top center of the screen, or

■ Select **Stop Data** under the **Experiment** menu.

Storing and Deleting Data

Each time you collect data the Data Studio program automatically saves the previous graph and draws a new line on the same set of axes. This can be useful if you want to compare different runs. However, sometimes you may want to delete one or more of the previous graphs.

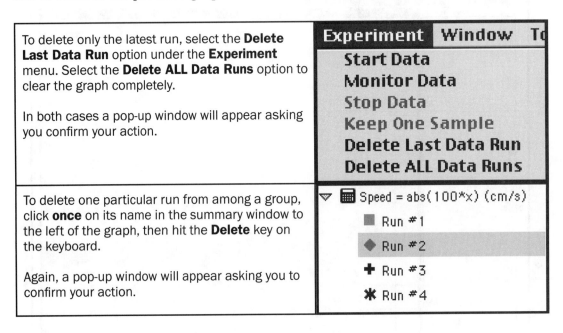

To delete only the latest run, select the **Delete Last Data Run** option under the **Experiment** menu. Select the **Delete ALL Data Runs** option to clear the graph completely.

In both cases a pop-up window will appear asking you confirm your action.

To delete one particular run from among a group, click **once** on its name in the summary window to the left of the graph, then hit the **Delete** key on the keyboard.

Again, a pop-up window will appear asking you to confirm your action.

Changing the Graph Scales

You may need to change the scaling of the graph, depending on how the data you have recorded looks. To do this, first double-click anywhere in the graph window to open the Graph settings window.

Click on the Axis Scaling tab in this window.

In the window that appears next, you can set minimum and maximum display settings for both the speed (*y*-axis) and time (*x*-axis) by typing values into the appropriate boxes.

Click the OK button at the bottom of the window to close it and apply your new settings.

There is also an option available to adjust the scaling automatically to fit the data. However, care should be taken when selecting this option because an inappropriate scaling can obscure the important features of a graph.

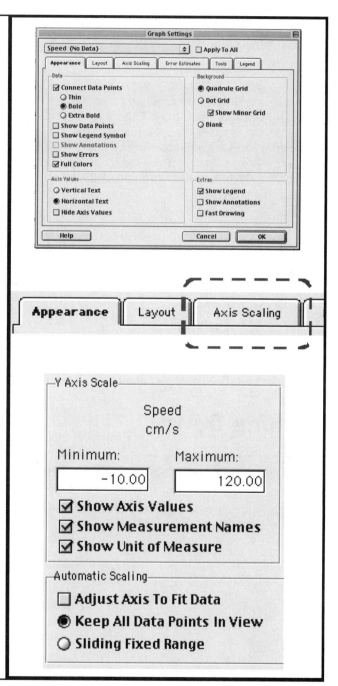

Changing the Experiment Time

Though the files for each activity have been set up to measure for a fixed length of time that should be suitable for the experiment in question, you may want to measure for a longer (or shorter) time period.

To change the experiment time, first select **Set Sampling Options**... under the **Experiment** menu. When the window appears, select the **Automatic Stop** tab and enter the desired time in the box next to the **Time** radio button. Click on the **OK** button at the bottom of the box to enter the new time.

Experiment	Window	To‹
Start Data		
Monitor Data		
Stop Data		
Keep One Sample		
Delete Last Data Run		
Delete ALL Data Runs		
Change Interface		
Connect to Interface...		
Disconnect for Data logg		
Set Sampling Options...		

Manual Sampling	Delayed Start	**Automatic Stop**

○ None
● Time   3.000 seconds
○ Data Measurement

Printing Graphs

To print copies of your graph select Print under the File menu. In the Print Options box make sure you select the correct number of copies.

Shutting Down

When you have finished using the Data Studio program, you can shut it down by selecting the **Exit** option under the **File** menu. A pop-up window may appear asking if you want to save any changes to the setup file. Please click on the **No** button!

Start-Up Procedure

If you are using the Logger Lite software then it is likely you are using a Vernier Go!™ Motion sensor (see right). The sensor should be connected to a USB port on your computer before beginning.

To start the Logger Lite software, double-click on the setup file for your experiment. (Your instructor will give you directions on how to access these in your particular classroom setup.) Logger Lite files always have the extension *.gmbl*. After a second or so the program should start up normally, showing a blank speed-time graph for the experiment.

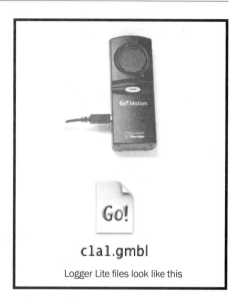

clal.gmbl

Logger Lite files look like this

Collecting Data

Your computer screen should now look something like this. (The example shown is from *Chapter 1 Activity 1* – graphs for other activities may look slightly different.)

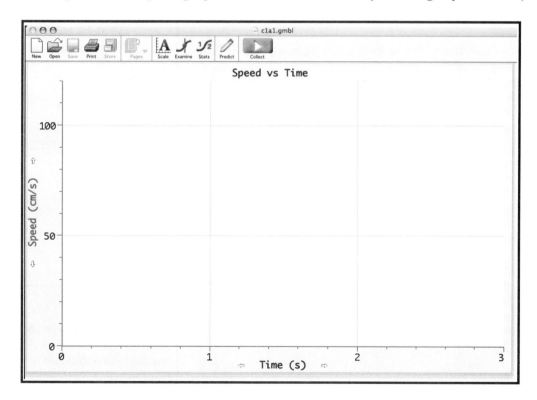

There are three possible ways to collect data: ■ Click on the **Collect** button at the top of the screen. ■ Hit the **F11** key on the keyboard. (May not work on Macintosh computers.) ■ Select **Start Collection** from under the **Experiment** menu at the top left of the screen.	
Data collection will usually stop on its own after a preset time, but if you want to stop it before this you can: ■ Click on the **Stop** button at the top center of the screen. ■ Hit the **F11** key on the keyboard. (May not work on Macintosh computers.) ■ Select **Stop Collection** under the **Experiment** menu.	

Changing the Graph Scales

You may need to change the scaling of the graph, depending on how the data you have recorded looks. ■ Clicking on the small arrows on either side of the axis labels on the graph moves the vertical or horizontal scales up or down, without actually changing the scaling. (For example, to display a range of 2 to 7 seconds, instead of 0 to 5 seconds.) ■ To change only the maximum (or minimum) values on an axis, move the cursor to the top (or bottom) of an axis. A text box should appear showing the current maximum (or minimum) for this axis. Type in the new maximum (or minimum) value you want displayed and hit the **Enter** key. ■ To have the computer automatically select the scaling on an axis for you, double-click somewhere on the main body of the graph and the **Graph Options** window will appear. In this window select the *Axis Options* button at the top. In the window you can now choose four options for the scaling of the *x* (time) and *y* (speed) axes: **1.** Autoscale — the computer will automatically choose maximum and minimum axis limits to fit your data. (Be careful — if you have data that is essentially flat, this option will blow up even the smallest fluctuations into "mountains".)	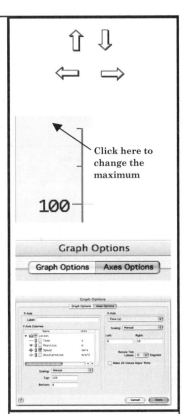 *The Axis Options window* *Note: Use care when changing the graph scales as almost any reasonable data can be made to look 'weird' with inappropriate scaling choices.*

2. Autoscale from 0 — the computer will automatically choose the maximum axis limit, but keep the minimum at zero. (This is often the best choice, except when you have faulty data that has very large spurious "spikes" in it.)

3. Manual scaling — you can enter your own maximum and minimum values in the boxes.

4. Autoscale larger — the computer will scale the graph such that it won't get smaller when new points are added. If a new point is off the graph, then the graph will be enlarged to include it.

When you have chosen your preferred option and entered any required values, click on the **Done** button.

Storing and Deleting Data

When you begin collecting data the Logger Lite program automatically erases the previous run from the graph. Sometimes it is useful to store the old data so that you can compare it with a new run.

To store the most recent data set, select **Store Latest Run**, under the **Experiment** menu, before collecting a new data set. Other options, available under the **Data** menu, allow you to delete particular runs you have previously stored; simply hide those runs (they are saved, but not displayed), or delete all previous data.

Changing the Experiment Time

Though the files for the activity have been set up to measure for a fixed length of time that should be suitable for the experiment in question, you may want to measure for a longer (or shorter) time period.

Select the **Data Collection...** option under the **Experiment** menu and enter the desired collection time in the window. Click on the **Done** button at the bottom of the box to enter the new time.

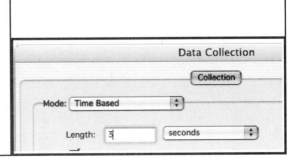

Printing Graphs

To print copies of your graph select **Print** under the **File** menu. In the Print Options box make sure you select the correct number of copies.

Shutting Down

When you have finished using the Logger Lite program, you can shut it down by either:

■ Clicking on the program exit button at the top right corner of the screen. (PCs only.)

■ Select the **Exit** option under the **File** menu. (PCs only.)

■ Select the **Quit** option under the **Logger Lite** menu. (Macintoshes only.)

A box may appear asking if you want to save any changes to the setup file. Please click on the **No** button!

Start-Up Procedure

The Motion Sensor should be connected to an interface box that is, in turn, connected to a computer. This interface box will typically either be a ULI (see right) or a LabPro (see below right).	
Before proceeding any further make sure the interface box has power. *For the ULI there is a red switch on the back that turns the ULI on and off. The green light on the front indicates when the ULI is turned on.* *For the LabPro, simply make sure it is connected to the power "brick".*	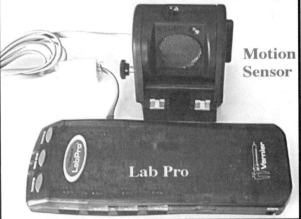
To start the Logger Pro 2 software, double-click on the set-up file for your experiment. (Your instructor will give you directions on how to access these in your particular classroom setup.) Logger Pro 2 files always have the extension *.mbl*. When the program first starts up it checks to see whether an interface box is connected to the computer. Depending on the state of the computer, the Setup Interface box may appear. If so, make sure the COM1 Port is selected. Then click on the **Scan** button.	 C1A1.mbl *Logger Pro 2 files look like this* **Setup Interface** ☒ From the pull-down menu, choose the port (COM 1, 2, 3, 4, or USB) to which your lab interface is connected, then click on the Scan button. When the interface is found, you will be ready to collect data. Port: COM1 ▼ Interface: Select port to scan. Scan Cancel *This button should change to* **OK** *after clicking on it.*
After a second or so, the **Scan** button should change to an **OK** button. Click on this button and the program should start up normally, showing a blank speed-time graph for the experiment.	*Note: If you are using a Lab Pro interface a box may appear telling you there is already data in the Lab Pro. Click on the button indicating that this data is to be ignored.*

Collecting Data

Your computer screen should now look something like this. (The example shown is from *Chapter 1 Activity 1* — graphs for other activities may look slightly different.)

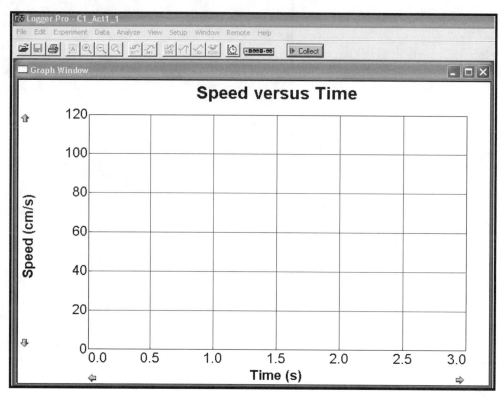

There are three ways to collect data: ■ Click on the **Collect** button at the top center of the screen. ■ Hit the **Enter** key on the keyboard. ■ Select **Collect** from under the **Experiment** menu at the top left of the screen.	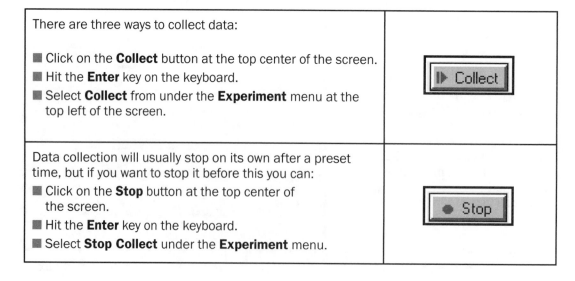
Data collection will usually stop on its own after a preset time, but if you want to stop it before this you can: ■ Click on the **Stop** button at the top center of the screen. ■ Hit the **Enter** key on the keyboard. ■ Select **Stop Collect** under the **Experiment** menu.	

Changing the Graph Scales

You may need to change the scaling of the graph, depending on how the data you have recorded looks.

■ Clicking on the small grey arrows on the graph moves the vertical or horizontal scales up or down, without actually changing the scaling. (For example, to display a range of 2 to 7 seconds, instead of 0 to 5 seconds.)

■ To change only the maximum (or minimum) values on an axis, click once on the highest (or lowest) number and a box will appear. Type in the new value you want displayed and hit the **Enter** key.

■ To have the computer automatically select the scaling on an axis for you, click on one of the numbers (except the highest or lowest) and an axis scale box will appear. In the box you can choose three options:

1. Autoscale — The computer will automatically choose maximum and minimum axis limits to fit your data. (Be careful — if you have data that is essentially flat, this option will blow up even the smallest fluctuations into "mountains".)

2. Autoscale from 0 — The computer will automatically choose the maximum axis limit, but keep the minimum at zero. (This is often the best choice, except when you have faulty data that has very large spurious "spikes" in it.)

3. Manual scaling — You can enter your own maximum and minimum values in the boxes.

When you have chosen your preferred option, click on the **OK** button.

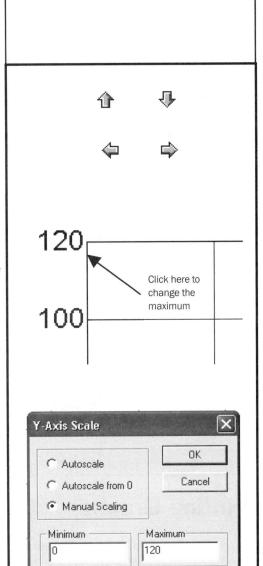

Click here to change the maximum

Note: Use care when changing the graph scales as almost any reasonable data can be made to look "weird" with inappropriate scaling choices.

Storing and Deleting Data

When you begin collecting data, the Logger Pro 2 program automatically erases the previous run from the graph. Sometimes it is useful to store the old data so that you can compare it with a new run.

To save the most recent data set, select **Store Latest Run**, under the **Data** menu, before collecting a new data set. Other options under the **Data** menu allow you to delete particular runs you have previously stored; simply hide those runs (they are saved, but not displayed), or delete all previous data.

Changing the Experiment Time

Though the files for the activity have been set up to measure for a fixed length of time that should be suitable for the experiment in question, you may want to measure for a longer (or shorter) time period. There are two ways to change the experiment time.

1. Click once on the maximum value displayed on the horizontal (time) axis on the graph and a text box will appear. Type in the new measuring time you want and hit the **Enter** key.

2. Select the **Sampling** option under the **Experiment** menu and enter the desired time. Click on the **OK** button at the bottom of the box to enter the new time.

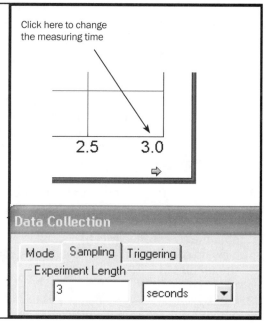

Printing Graphs

To print copies of your graph, select **Print** under the **File** menu. In the Print Options box make sure you select the correct number of copies.

Shutting Down

When you have finished using Logger Pro 2 program, you can shut it down by either:
- Clicking on the program exit button at the top right corner of the screen.
- Select the **Exit** option under the **File** menu.

A box may appear asking if you want to save any changes to the set up file. Please click the **No** button!

Start Up Procedure

The Motion Sensor should be connected to a Lab Pro interface that is, in turn, connected to a computer (see right).

Before proceeding any further make sure the Lab Pro interface has power, by making sure it is connected to the power "brick".

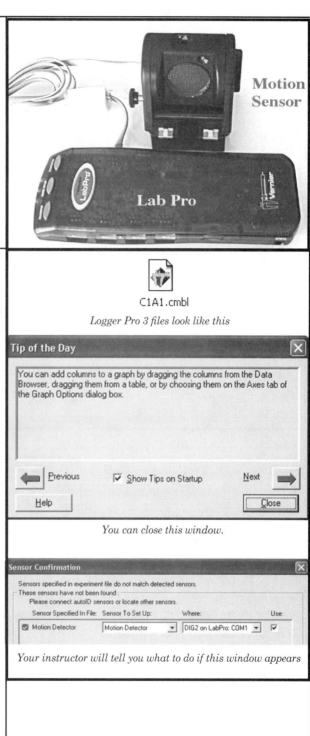

To start the Logger Pro 3 software, double-click on the setup file for your experiment. (Your instructor will give you directions on how to access these in your particular classroom setup.) Logger Pro 3
files always have the extension *.cmbl*. When the program first starts up it may present you with a "Tip of the Day" window — you can simply close this.

Depending on the state of the computer, interface, and motion sensor, the Sensor Confirmation window may appear. If so, your instructor will tell you how to proceed.

C1A1.cmbl

Logger Pro 3 files look like this

Tip of the Day

You can add columns to a graph by dragging the columns from the Data Browser, dragging them from a table, or by choosing them on the Axes tab of the Graph Options dialog box.

Previous ☑ Show Tips on Startup Next

Help Close

You can close this window.

Sensor Confirmation

Sensors specified in experiment file do not match detected sensors. These sensors have not been found :
Please connect autoID sensors or locate other sensors.

Sensor Specified In File:	Sensor To Set Up:	Where:	Use:
☑ Motion Detector	Motion Detector	DIG2 on LabPro: COM1	☑

Your instructor will tell you what to do if this window appears

Collecting Data

Your computer screen should now look something like this. (The example shown is from *Chapter 1 Activity 1* — graphs for other activities may look slightly different.)

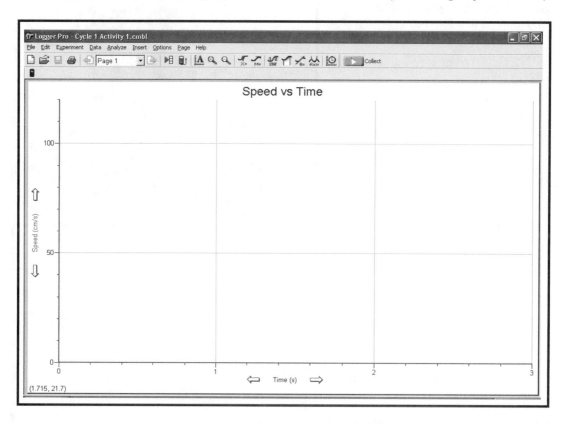

There are three ways to collect data: ■ Click on the **Collect** button at the top of the screen. ■ Hit the **F11** key on the keyboard. ■ Select **Start Collection** from under the **Experiment** menu at the top left of the screen.	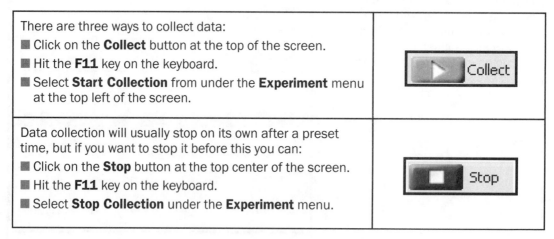
Data collection will usually stop on its own after a preset time, but if you want to stop it before this you can: ■ Click on the **Stop** button at the top center of the screen. ■ Hit the **F11** key on the keyboard. ■ Select **Stop Collection** under the **Experiment** menu.	

Changing the Graph Scales

You may need to change the scaling of the graph, depending on how the data you have recorded looks.

■ Clicking on the small arrows on either side of the axis labels on the graph moves the vertical or horizontal scales up or down, without actually changing the scaling. (For example, to display a range of 2 to 7 seconds, instead of 0 to 5 seconds.)

■ To change only the maximum (or minimum) values on an axis, click once on the highest (or lowest) number and a box will appear. Type in the new maximum (or minimum) value you want displayed and hit the **Enter** key.

■ To have the computer automatically select the scaling on an axis for you, double-click somewhere on the axis (except on the highest or lowest values) and the Graph Options window will appear. In the window you can choose four options:

1. Autoscale — The computer will automatically choose maximum and minimum axis limits to fit your data. (Be careful — If you have data that is essentially flat, this option will blow up even the smallest fluctuations into "mountains".)

2. Autoscale from 0 — The computer will automatically choose the maximum axis limit, but keep the minimum at zero. (This is often the best choice, except when you have faulty data that has very large spurious "spikes" in it.)

3. Manual scaling — You can enter your own maximum and minimum values in the boxes.

4. Autoscale larger — The computer will scale the graph such that it won't get smaller when new points are added. If a new point is off the graph, then the graph will be enlarged to include it.

When you have chosen your preferred option, click on the **OK** button.

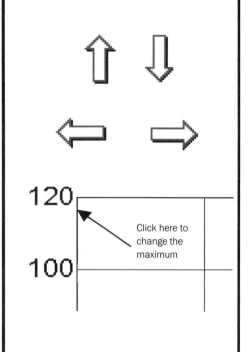

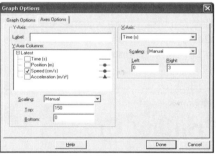

The Graph Options window

Note: Use care when changing the graph scales as almost any reasonable data can be made to look "weird" with inappropriate scaling choices.

Storing and Deleting Data

When you begin collecting data the Logger Pro program automatically erases the previous run from the graph. Sometimes it is useful to store the old data so that you can compare it with a new run.

To store the most recent data set, select **Store Latest Run**, under the **Experiment** menu, before collecting a new data set. Other options, available under the **Data** menu, allow you to delete particular runs you have previously stored; simply hide those runs (they are saved, but not displayed), or delete all previous data.

Changing the Experiment Time

Though the files for the activity have been set up to measure for a fixed length of time that should be suitable for the experiment in question, you may want to measure for a longer (or shorter) time period.

Select the **Data Collection...** option under the **Experiment** menu and enter the desired time in the window. Click on the **Done** button at the bottom of the box to enter the new time.

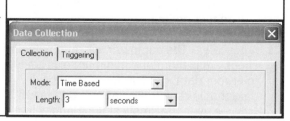

Printing Graphs

To print copies of your graph select **Print** under the **File** menu. In the Print Options box make sure you select the correct number of copies.

Shutting Down

When you have finished using the Logger Pro program, you can shut it down by either:

■ Clicking on the program exit button at the top right corner of the screen.

■ Select the **Exit** option under the **File** menu.

A box may appear asking if you want to save any changes to the setup file. Please click on the **No** button!

Important: See the notes at the end of this appendix regarding compatible operating systems and browsers.

Use a computer connected to the Internet. After starting up your web browser you can access the simulators at:

http://cpucips.sdsu.edu/petsims

(You should check with your instructor to determine if the *url* for the simulator has changed.) When you go to this page you will see two lists of links, one for the simulator setups for in-class activities, the other for setups to be used in homework assignments. (The top of the page and the first few links should be similar to those shown below.)

PET ACTIVITY AND HOMEWORK SETUPS

PET

ACTIVITY SETUPS

Chapter 1 Activity 4 Setup

HOMEWORK SETUPS

Chapter 2 Activity 2 HW Setup
Chapter 2 Activity 3 HW Setup 1

To access one of these setups simply click on the relevant link.

Note that, depending on the speed of your Internet connection, it may take up to several minutes for the setup to fully load. Do not attempt to use your computer until the loading process is complete or it may interrupt the download and you will have to start all over again!

Once the setup is fully loaded you can run the simulator. The simulators are Java applets; on some of the latest versions of web browsers, you may need to click once on the simulator to activate the Java program.

1. To run the simulator click on the "**Run**" button.	Run (Play)
2. Usually the simulator will stop by itself, but you can also stop it by clicking the "**Stop**" button.	Stop
3. You can reset the simulator back to its original starting setup by clicking the "**Rewind**" button. *Note: This must always be done before changing anything in the setup.*	Rewind
4. While the simulation is running you can also click the "**Pause**" button to stop the action.	Pause
5. When you want to change anything in the setup, first rewind the simulator to its original configuration. Then make sure the **Selection Tool** is active (the **Select** button will appear pushed in.). *Instructions for changing individual elements in simulator setups are given in the relevant PET activities.*	Select

Troubleshooting

If a simulator setup does not seem to be working properly (and you are sure you are using a compatible browser setup), the simplest solution is usually to quit your web browser and start again!

Recommended Browsers and Java Virtual Machines

Java: *InterActions Simulators* work with both Java VM 1.5 (the latest version from Sun Microsystems), also called Java Runtime Environment Version 5.0, and Java 1.4.2. Update to Java 1.5 at **http://java.com**. Update Java 1.4.2 for **PCs** at **http://java.sun.com/j2se/1.4.2/download.html**. Update Java for **Mac OS X** at **http://apple.com/java** (only the latest versions of Mac OS X are likely to use Java 1.5).

NOTE: On both PCs and Macintoshes, conflicts between different versions of Java **MAY** reduce the performance of the simulators. If you have recurring problems running the simulators, you may want to uninstall older versions of Java.

PCs: Use Microsoft Internet Explorer 5+ or Netscape Navigator 7+.

Best bets:

Internet Explorer 6.0+ **(http://www.microsoft.com/windows/ie/)**

Mozilla Firefox 1.0+ **(http://www.mozilla.com/)**

Netscape Navigator 7.2 **(http://channels.netscape.com/ns/browsers/ download.jsp)**

Macs (OS X): Use Mozilla Firefox 1.0+ or Netscape Navigator 7+. Use Safari **ONLY** if you have **OS 10.3** or later.

Best bets:

Safari 1.2 **(http://www.apple.com/safari)** if you are using **Mac OS 10.3** or later.

Mozilla Firefox 1.0+ **(http://www.mozilla.com/)**

Netscape Navigator 7.2 **(http://www.apple.com/downloads/macosx/internet_ utilities/netscape.html)**

Using Simulators with Internet Explorer on PCs

■ From the *Start* menu, select *Control Panel*. If *Control Panel* doesn't show, open *My Computer* and double-click *Control Panel*.

■ In *Control Panel*, double-click on the icon that says *Java* or *Java Plug-in*. If you don't see this icon, you need to install Sun's Java Virtual Machine **(http://java.com)**.

Java Plug-in

■ In the *Java* or *Java Plug-in* window:

— If there is a *Browser* tab, click on it. Under *Settings*, check the box next to the name of the browser(s) you use. Click *Apply* and then close the *Java Plug-in*.

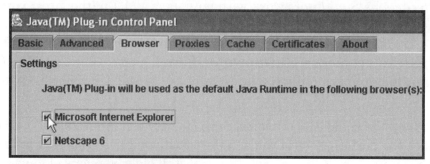

— If there is no Browser tab, click on the *Advanced* tab. Then click on the plus sign next to *<APPLET> tag support*, and check the box for *Internet Explorer*. Click Apply, and then click OK.

■ If you use Internet Explorer, open the *Internet Options* control panel. Alternatively, you may open an Internet Explorer window and from the *Tools* menu, select *Internet Options*.

— Click on the *Advanced* tab.

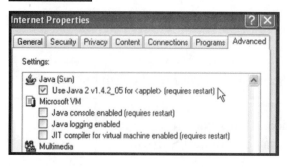

— Scroll down until you find the *Microsoft VM* heading. **Uncheck** every box under *Microsoft VM*.

— Scroll up slightly to see if you have a *Java (Sun)* heading. If you do, check the box under it. If you don't, the changes you made in the Java plug-in should be enough to guarantee that the simulators work under Sun's Java Virtual Machine.

— Click OK.

— Close all Internet Explorer windows (if any are open) before trying to use the simulators.

Notes

Notes

Notes